W9-BMF-416

DE1-12

DE1-13

**E1-3**

| | 1 | 2 | 3 |
|---|---|---|---|
| | | | |
| | | | |
| | | | |
| | | | |
| | | | |
| | | | |
| | | | |
| | | | |
| | | | |
| | | | |
| | | | |
| | | | |

**Computations:**

## Analysis of Transsactions

| DATE | | ASSETS | | = | LIABILITIES | + | OWNER'S EQUITY | | TYPE OF OWNER'S EQUITY TRANSACTION |
|------|--|--------|--|---|-------------|---|----------------|--|------------------------------------|
| | | | | | | | | | |
| | | | | | | | | | |
| | | | | | | | | | |
| | | | | | | | | | |
| | | | | | | | | | |
| | | | | | | | | | |
| | | | | | | | | | |
| | | | | | | | | | |
| | | | | | | | | | |
| | | | | | | | | | |
| | | | | | | | | | |
| | | | | | | | | | |
| | | | | | | | | | |
| | | | | | | | | | |

*Req. 1*

*Req. 2*

*Req. 1*

*Req. 2*

## INCOME STATEMENT

## BALANCE SHEET

*Reqs. 1 & 2*

*Req. 1*

*Req. 1*

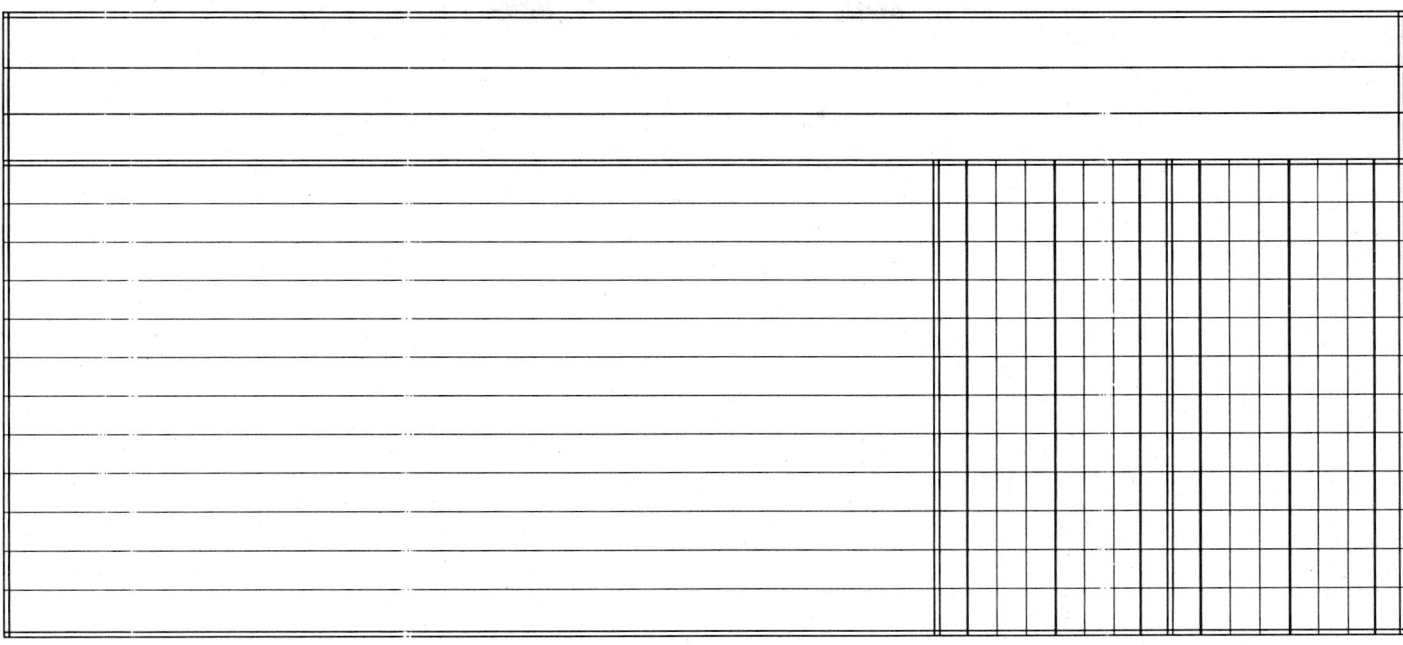

*Req. 2*

*Req. 3*

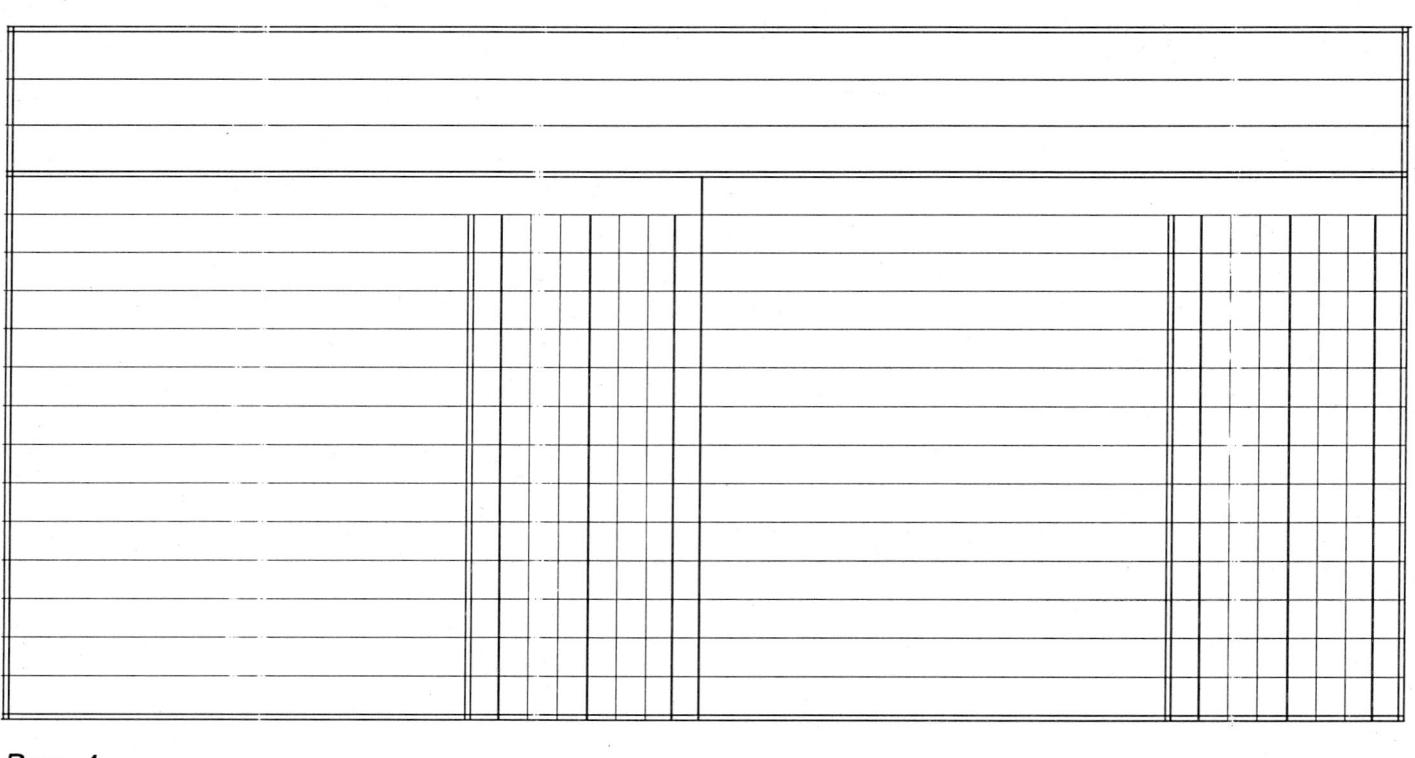

*Req. 4*

Req. 4

*Req. 1*

# P1-1B

NAME
SECTION
DATE
*Req. 2*

| DATE | ASSETS | | | = | LIABILITIES | + | OWNER'S EQUITY | | TYPE OF OWNER'S EQUITY TRANSACTION |
|------|--------|--|--|---|-------------|---|----------------|--|------------------------------------|
|      |        |  |  |   |             |   |                |  |                                    |
|      |        |  |  |   |             |   |                |  |                                    |
|      |        |  |  |   |             |   |                |  |                                    |
|      |        |  |  |   |             |   |                |  |                                    |
|      |        |  |  |   |             |   |                |  |                                    |
|      |        |  |  |   |             |   |                |  |                                    |
|      |        |  |  |   |             |   |                |  |                                    |

*Req. 1*

*Req. 2*

*Req. 1*

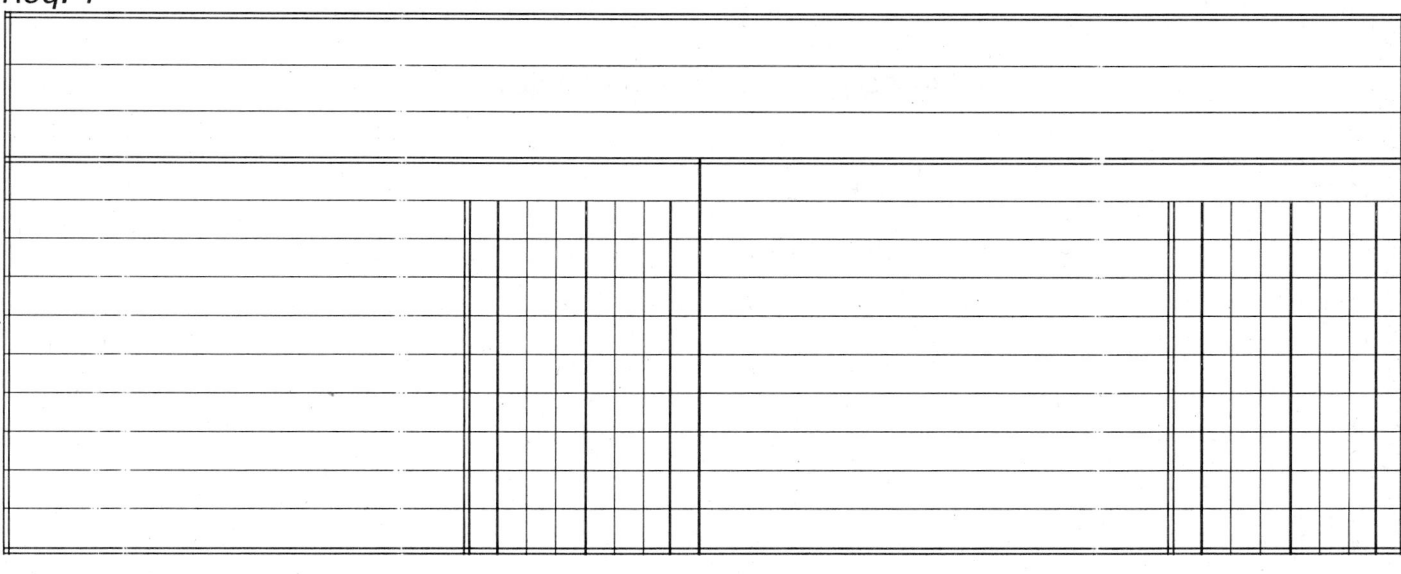

*Req. 2*

*Req. 1*

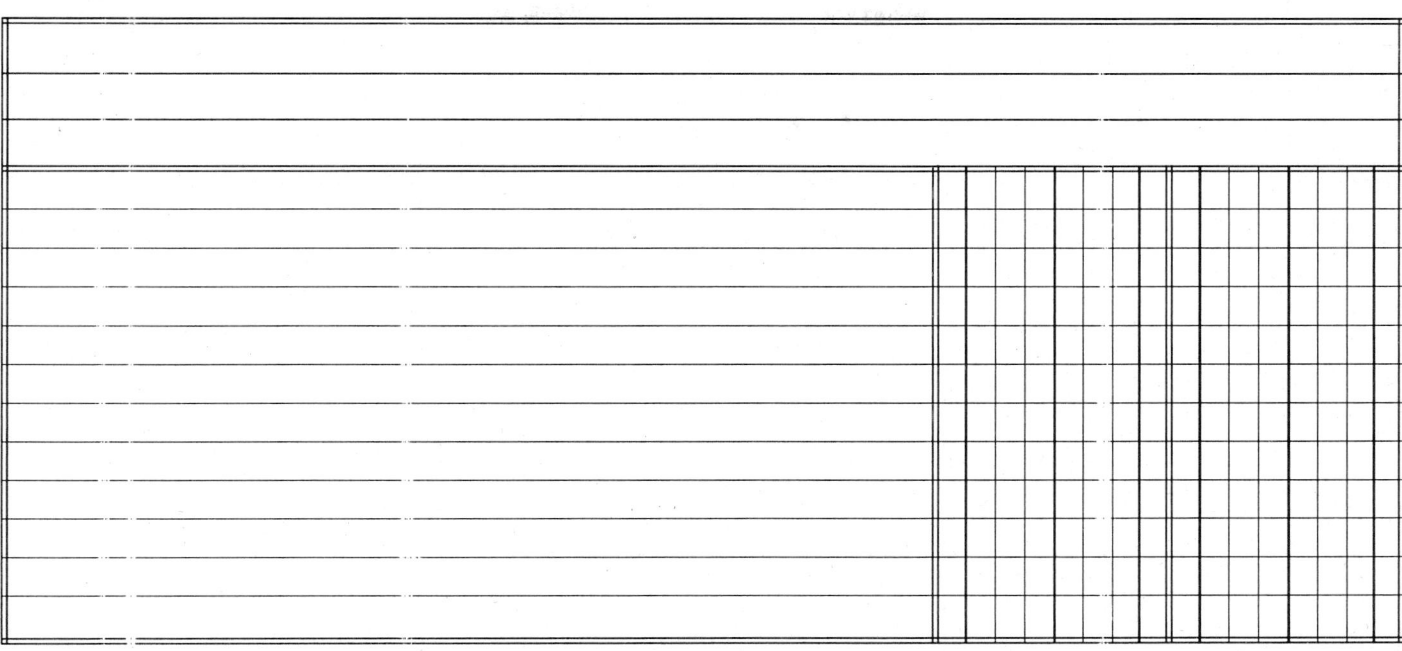

*Req. 2*

*Req. 3*

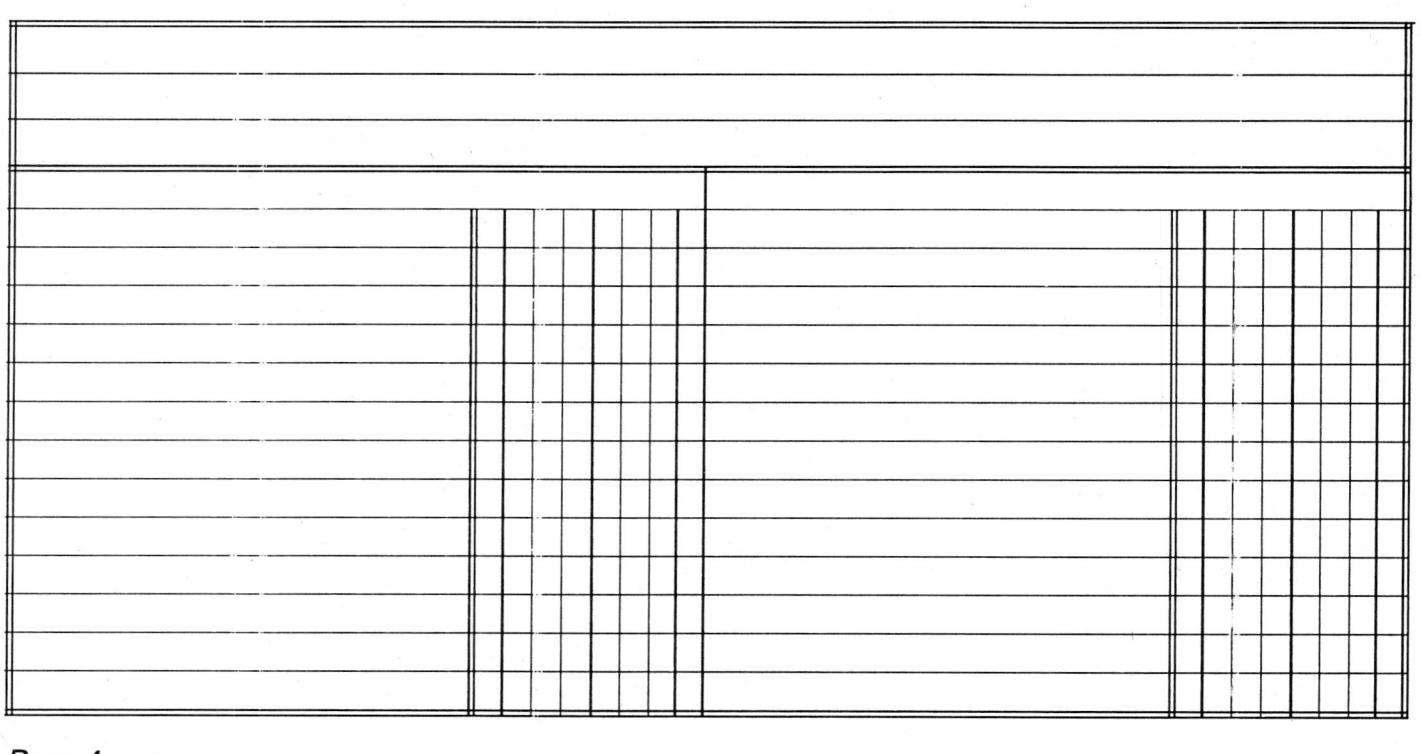

*Req. 4*

NAME
SECTION
DATE
*Req. 1*

| DATE | ASSETS | = | LIABILITIES | + | OWNER'S EQUITY | TYPE OF OWNER'S EQUITY TRANSACTION |
|------|--------|---|-------------|---|----------------|-----------------------------------|
|      |        |   |             |   |                |                                   |
|      |        |   |             |   |                |                                   |
|      |        |   |             |   |                |                                   |
|      |        |   |             |   |                |                                   |
|      |        |   |             |   |                |                                   |
|      |        |   |             |   |                |                                   |
|      |        |   |             |   |                |                                   |
|      |        |   |             |   |                |                                   |
|      |        |   |             |   |                |                                   |
|      |        |   |             |   |                |                                   |
|      |        |   |             |   |                |                                   |
|      |        |   |             |   |                |                                   |
|      |        |   |             |   |                |                                   |

*Req. 2*

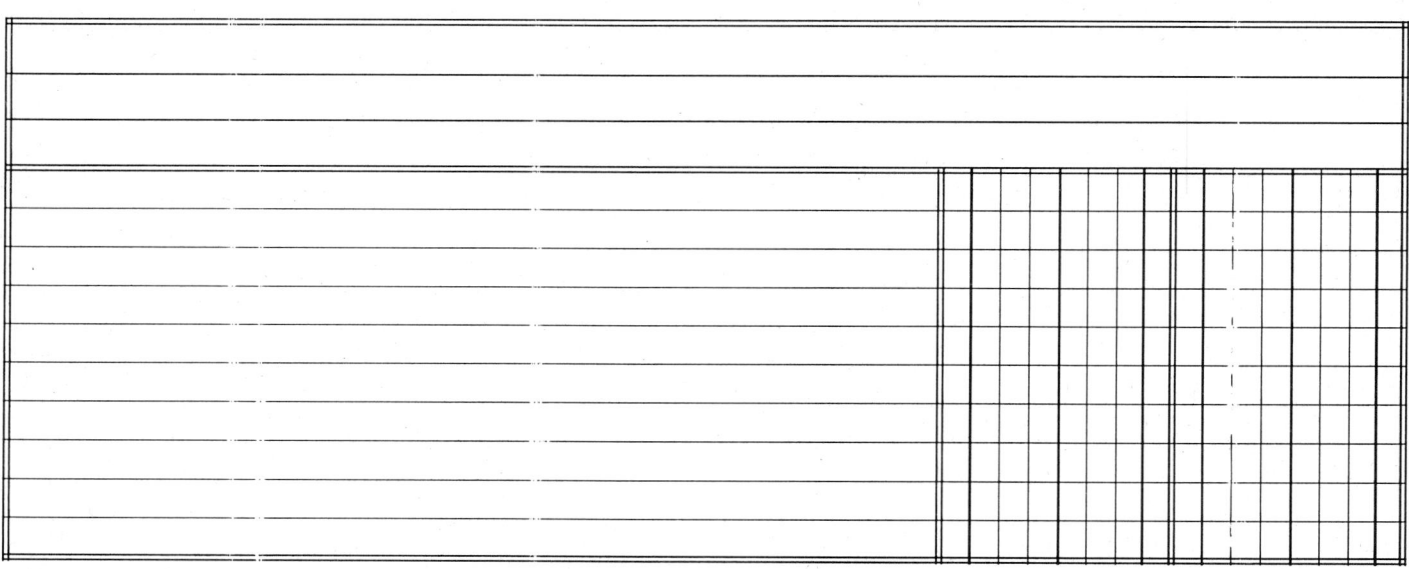

*Req. 3*

Req. 4

|  |  |  |  |
|---|---|---|---|
|  |  |  |  |
|  |  |  |  |
|  |  |  |  |

*Reqs. 1 & 2*

*Reqs. 1 & 2*

*Chapter 1* **Financial Statement
Case 1**

# Financial Statement
# Case 2

# Financial Statement
# Case 2 *(Continued)*

_____

_____

_____

_____

_____

_____

_____

**DE2-4**

_____

_____

_____

_____

_____

_____

_____

_____

_____

_____

_____

_____

**DE2-5**

_____

1. _____    6. _____

2. _____    7. _____

3. _____    8. _____

4. _____    9. _____

5. _____    10. _____

*Req. 1*

| | | Journal | | | | |
|---|---|---|---|---|---|---|
| DATE | | ACCOUNTS AND EXPLANATIONS | POST. REF. | DEBIT | | CREDIT |
| | | | | | | |
| | | | | | | |
| | | | | | | |
| | | | | | | |
| | | | | | | |
| | | | | | | |
| | | | | | | |
| | | | | | | |
| | | | | | | |
| | | | | | | |

*Req. 2*

*Req. 3*

*Req. 1*

| | | Journal | | | |
|---|---|---|---|---|---|
| DATE | | ACCOUNTS AND EXPLANATIONS | POST. REF. | DEBIT | CREDIT |
| | | | | | |
| | | | | | |
| | | | | | |
| | | | | | |
| | | | | | |
| | | | | | |
| | | | | | |
| | | | | | |
| | | | | | |
| | | | | | |
| | | | | | |

*Req. 2*

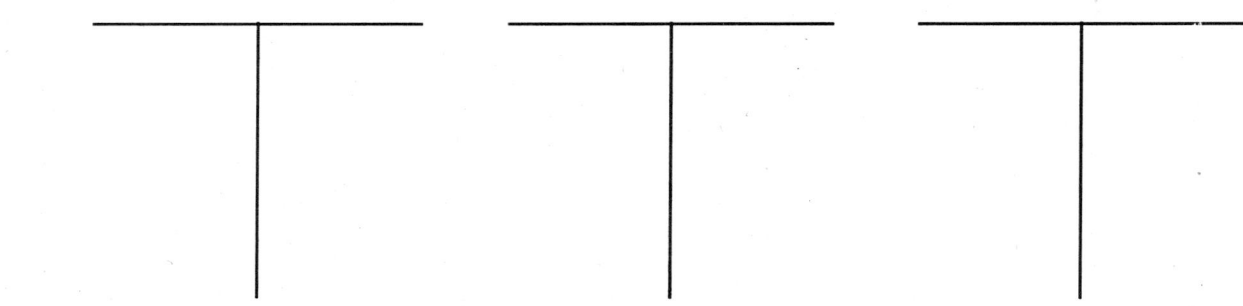

*Req. 3*

*Reqs. 1--4*

Reqs. 1–3

*Reqs. 1 & 3*

*Req. 2*

| | | Journal | | | | | | | |
|---|---|---|---|---|---|---|---|---|---|
| DATE | | ACCOUNTS AND EXPLANATIONS | POST. REF. | | DEBIT | | | CREDIT | |
| | | | | | | | | | |
| | | | | | | | | | |
| | | | | | | | | | |
| | | | | | | | | | |
| | | | | | | | | | |
| | | | | | | | | | |
| | | | | | | | | | |
| | | | | | | | | | |
| | | | | | | | | | |
| | | | | | | | | | |
| | | | | | | | | | |
| | | | | | | | | | |
| | | | | | | | | | |
| | | | | | | | | | |
| | | | | | | | | | |
| | | | | | | | | | |
| | | | | | | | | | |
| | | | | | | | | | |
| | | | | | | | | | |
| | | | | | | | | | |
| | | | | | | | | | |
| | | | | | | | | | |
| | | | | | | | | | |
| | | | | | | | | | |
| | | | | | | | | | |
| | | | | | | | | | |
| | | | | | | | | | |
| | | | | | | | | | |
| | | | | | | | | | |
| | | | | | | | | | |

Req. 4

| ACCOUNT | DEBIT | CREDIT |
|---------|-------|--------|
|         |       |        |
|         |       |        |
|         |       |        |
|         |       |        |
|         |       |        |
|         |       |        |
|         |       |        |
|         |       |        |
|         |       |        |
|         |       |        |
|         |       |        |
|         |       |        |
|         |       |        |
|         |       |        |
|         |       |        |
|         |       |        |
|         |       |        |
|         |       |        |
|         |       |        |
|         |       |        |

a. _____

b. _____

c. _____

d. _____

## EFFECT ON TRIAL BALANCE

## ACCOUNT(S) MISSTATED

*Req. 1*

| | Journal | | | | |
|---|---|---|---|---|---|
| DATE | ACCOUNTS AND EXPLANATIONS | POST. REF. | DEBIT | CREDIT | |
| | | | | | |
| | | | | | |
| | | | | | |
| | | | | | |
| | | | | | |
| | | | | | |
| | | | | | |
| | | | | | |
| | | | | | |
| | | | | | |
| | | | | | |
| | | | | | |
| | | | | | |
| | | | | | |
| | | | | | |
| | | | | | |
| | | | | | |
| | | | | | |
| | | | | | |
| | | | | | |
| | | | | | |
| | | | | | |
| | | | | | |

Req. 2

*Req. 1*

| ACCOUNT | DEBIT | CREDIT |
|---------|-------|--------|
| | | |
| | | |
| | | |
| | | |
| | | |
| | | |
| | | |
| | | |
| | | |
| | | |
| | | |
| | | |
| | | |
| | | |
| | | |
| | | |
| | | |
| | | |

Req. 2

Req. 3

| ACCOUNT | DEBIT | CREDIT |
|---|---|---|
|  |  |  |
|  |  |  |
|  |  |  |
|  |  |  |
|  |  |  |
|  |  |  |
|  |  |  |
|  |  |  |
|  |  |  |
|  |  |  |
|  |  |  |
|  |  |  |
|  |  |  |
|  |  |  |
|  |  |  |
|  |  |  |
|  |  |  |
|  |  |  |
|  |  |  |

*Req. 1*

*Req. 2*

*Req. 3*

*Req. 1*

Req. 1 (Continued)

Req. 1

| | | Journal | | | | |
|---|---|---|---|---|---|---|
| DATE | | ACCOUNTS AND EXPLANATIONS | POST. REF. | DEBIT | | CREDIT |
| | | | | | | |
| | | | | | | |
| | | | | | | |
| | | | | | | |
| | | | | | | |
| | | | | | | |
| | | | | | | |
| | | | | | | |
| | | | | | | |
| | | | | | | |
| | | | | | | |
| | | | | | | |
| | | | | | | |
| | | | | | | |
| | | | | | | |
| | | | | | | |
| | | | | | | |
| | | | | | | |
| | | | | | | |
| | | | | | | |
| | | | | | | |
| | | | | | | |
| | | | | | | |
| | | | | | | |
| | | | | | | |
| | | | | | | |
| | | | | | | |
| | | | | | | |
| | | | | | | |
| | | | | | | |
| | | | | | | |
| | | | | | | |
| | | | | | | |
| | | | | | | |
| | | | | | | |
| | | | | | | |
| | | | | | | |

| ACCOUNT | | | | | ACCOUNT NO. | | | |
|---------|--|--|--|--|--|--|--|--|
| | | JRNL. | | | BALANCE | | | |
| DATE | ITEM | REF. | DEBIT | CREDIT | DEBIT | | CREDIT | |
| | | | | | | | | |
| | | | | | | | | |
| | | | | | | | | |
| | | | | | | | | |
| | | | | | | | | |
| | | | | | | | | |
| | | | | | | | | |
| | | | | | | | | |
| | | | | | | | | |
| | | | | | | | | |

| ACCOUNT | | | | | ACCOUNT NO. | | | |
|---------|--|--|--|--|--|--|--|--|
| | | JRNL. | | | BALANCE | | | |
| DATE | ITEM | REF. | DEBIT | CREDIT | DEBIT | | CREDIT | |
| | | | | | | | | |
| | | | | | | | | |
| | | | | | | | | |
| | | | | | | | | |

*Req. 2 (Continued)*

| ACCOUNT | | | | | ACCOUNT NO. | | |
|---|---|---|---|---|---|---|---|
| | | JRNL. | | | BALANCE | | |
| DATE | ITEM | REF. | DEBIT | CREDIT | DEBIT | CREDIT | |
| | | | | | | | |
| | | | | | | | |
| | | | | | | | |

| ACCOUNT | | | | | ACCOUNT NO. | | |
|---|---|---|---|---|---|---|---|
| | | JRNL. | | | BALANCE | | |
| DATE | ITEM | REF. | DEBIT | CREDIT | DEBIT | CREDIT | |
| | | | | | | | |
| | | | | | | | |
| | | | | | | | |

| ACCOUNT | | | | | ACCOUNT NO. | | |
|---|---|---|---|---|---|---|---|
| | | JRNL. | | | BALANCE | | |
| DATE | ITEM | REF. | DEBIT | CREDIT | DEBIT | CREDIT | |
| | | | | | | | |
| | | | | | | | |
| | | | | | | | |

| ACCOUNT | | | | | ACCOUNT NO. | | |
|---|---|---|---|---|---|---|---|
| | | JRNL. | | | BALANCE | | |
| DATE | ITEM | REF. | DEBIT | CREDIT | DEBIT | CREDIT | |
| | | | | | | | |
| | | | | | | | |
| | | | | | | | |

| ACCOUNT | | | | | ACCOUNT NO. | | |
|---|---|---|---|---|---|---|---|
| | | JRNL. | | | BALANCE | | |
| DATE | ITEM | REF. | DEBIT | CREDIT | DEBIT | CREDIT | |
| | | | | | | | |
| | | | | | | | |
| | | | | | | | |

*Req. 2 (Continued)*

| ACCOUNT | | | | | | ACCOUNT NO. | | | |
|---|---|---|---|---|---|---|---|---|---|
| | | | JRNL. | | | | BALANCE | | |
| DATE | | ITEM | REF. | DEBIT | CREDIT | | DEBIT | | CREDIT |
| | | | | | | | | | |
| | | | | | | | | | |
| | | | | | | | | | |

| ACCOUNT | | | | | | ACCOUNT NO. | | | |
|---|---|---|---|---|---|---|---|---|---|
| | | | JRNL. | | | | BALANCE | | |
| DATE | | ITEM | REF. | DEBIT | CREDIT | | DEBIT | | CREDIT |
| | | | | | | | | | |
| | | | | | | | | | |

| ACCOUNT | | | | | | ACCOUNT NO. | | | |
|---|---|---|---|---|---|---|---|---|---|
| | | | JRNL. | | | | BALANCE | | |
| DATE | | ITEM | REF. | DEBIT | CREDIT | | DEBIT | | CREDIT |
| | | | | | | | | | |
| | | | | | | | | | |

*Req. 3*

| ACCOUNT | DEBIT | CREDIT |
|---------|-------|--------|
|         |       |        |
|         |       |        |
|         |       |        |
|         |       |        |
|         |       |        |
|         |       |        |
|         |       |        |
|         |       |        |
|         |       |        |
|         |       |        |
|         |       |        |
|         |       |        |
|         |       |        |
|         |       |        |
|         |       |        |
|         |       |        |

Req. 1

| ACCOUNT | DEBIT | CREDIT |
|---|---|---|
|  |  |  |
|  |  |  |
|  |  |  |
|  |  |  |
|  |  |  |
|  |  |  |
|  |  |  |
|  |  |  |
|  |  |  |
|  |  |  |
|  |  |  |
|  |  |  |
|  |  |  |
|  |  |  |
|  |  |  |
|  |  |  |
|  |  |  |
|  |  |  |
|  |  |  |
|  |  |  |
|  |  |  |
|  |  |  |

*Req. 2*

*Reqs. 1 & 2*

*Reqs. 1 & 2*

*Req. 3*

| ACCOUNT | DEBIT | CREDIT |
|---|---|---|
| | | |
| | | |
| | | |
| | | |
| | | |
| | | |
| | | |
| | | |
| | | |
| | | |
| | | |
| | | |
| | | |
| | | |
| | | |
| | | |
| | | |
| | | |
| | | |
| | | |
| | | |

Req. 1

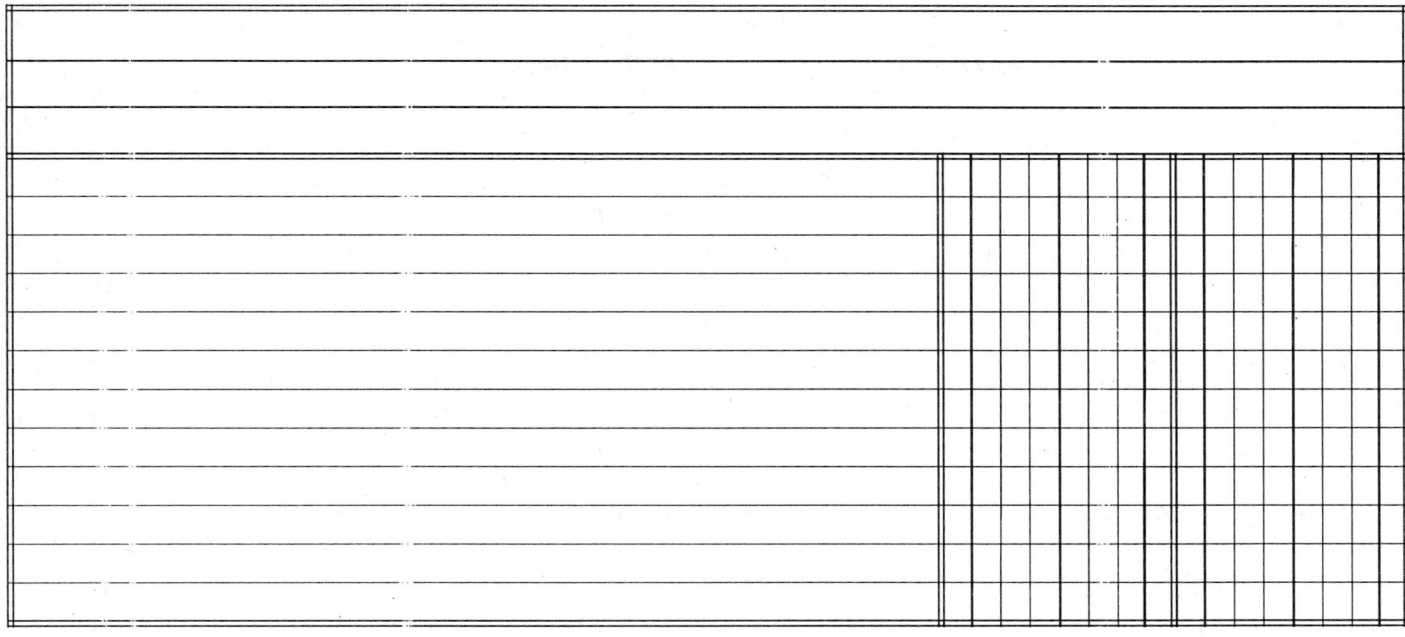

Req. 2

Req. 3

*Reqs. 1 & 2*

NAME
SECTION
DATE

Chapter 2

**Decision Case 1**
*(Continued)*

*Req. 3*

| ACCOUNT | DEBIT | CREDIT |
|---|---|---|
| | | |
| | | |
| | | |
| | | |
| | | |
| | | |
| | | |
| | | |
| | | |
| | | |
| | | |
| | | |
| | | |
| | | |

NAME
SECTION
DATE

Chapter 2

**Decision Case 1**
*(Continued)*

*Req. 4*

NAME
SECTION
DATE

Chapter 2

# Financial Statement
# Case 1

| | | Journal | | | |
|---|---|---|---|---|---|
| DATE | | ACCOUNTS AND EXPLANATIONS | POST. REF. | DEBIT | CREDIT |
| | | | | | |

| | | Journal | | | |
|---|---|---|---|---|---|
| DATE | | ACCOUNT TITLES AND EXPLANATIONS | POST. REF. | DEBIT | CREDIT |
| | | | | | |
| | | | | | |
| | | | | | |
| | | | | | |
| | | | | | |
| | | | | | |
| | | | | | |
| | | | | | |
| | | | | | |
| | | | | | |
| | | | | | |
| | | | | | |
| | | | | | |
| | | | | | |
| | | | | | |
| | | | | | |
| | | | | | |
| | | | | | |
| | | | | | |
| | | | | | |
| | | | | | |
| | | | | | |
| | | | | | |
| | | | | | |
| | | | | | |
| | | | | | |
| | | | | | |
| | | | | | |
| | | | | | |
| | | | | | |
| | | | | | |
| | | | | | |
| | | | | | |
| | | | | | |
| | | | | | |
| | | | | | |
| | | | | | |
| | | | | | |
| | | | | | |
| | | | | | |
| | | | | | |
| | | | | | |

**DE3-1**

**DE3-2**

**DE3-3**

**DE3-4**

**DE3-5**

**DE3-6**

*Req. 1*

| | Journal | | | |
|---|---|---|---|---|
| DATE | ACCOUNTS AND EXPLANATIONS | POST. REF. | DEBIT | CREDIT |
| | | | | |
| | | | | |
| | | | | |
| | | | | |
| | | | | |

*Req. 2*

| | Journal | | | |
|---|---|---|---|---|
| DATE | ACCOUNTS AND EXPLANATIONS | POST. REF. | DEBIT | CREDIT |
| | | | | |
| | | | | |
| | | | | |
| | | | | |

*Req. 1*

## Journal

| DATE | | ACCOUNTS AND EXPLANATIONS | POST. REF. | DEBIT | CREDIT |
|------|--|---------------------------|------------|-------|--------|
| | | | | | |
| | | | | | |
| | | | | | |
| | | | | | |
| | | | | | |
| | | | | | |
| | | | | | |

*Req. 2*

*Reqs. 3 & 4*

*Req. 1*

| | | Journal | | | |
|---|---|---|---|---|---|
| DATE | | ACCOUNTS AND EXPLANATIONS | POST. REF. | DEBIT | CREDIT |
| | | | | | |
| | | | | | |
| | | | | | |
| | | | | | |
| | | | | | |
| | | | | | |
| | | | | | |
| | | | | | |
| | | | | | |
| | | | | | |
| | | | | | |

*Req. 2*

*Reqs. 3 & 4*

*Req. 5*

*Req. 1*

| | | Journal | | | |
|---|---|---|---|---|---|
| DATE | | ACCOUNTS AND EXPLANATIONS | POST. REF. | DEBIT | CREDIT |
| | | | | | |
| | | | | | |
| | | | | | |
| | | | | | |
| | | | | | |
| | | | | | |
| | | | | | |
| | | | | | |
| | | | | | |
| | | | | | |
| | | | | | |
| | | | | | |

*Req. 2*

*Reqs. 3 & 4*

*Req. 5*

**DE3-12**

Req. 1

## Journal

| DATE | | ACCOUNTS AND EXPLANATIONS | POST. REF. | DEBIT | CREDIT |
|------|--|---------------------------|-----------|-------|--------|
| | | | | | |
| | | | | | |
| | | | | | |
| | | | | | |
| | | | | | |
| | | | | | |
| | | | | | |
| | | | | | |
| | | | | | |
| | | | | | |

Req. 2

| | | |
|--|--|--|
| | | |
| | | |
| | | |
| | | |
| | | |
| | | |
| | | |
| | | |
| | | |
| | | |
| | | |
| | | |
| | | |
| | | |
| | | |
| | | |
| | | |
| | | |
| | | |
| | | |

Reqs. 1–3

*Reqs. 1-3*

## Amount of Revenue or Expense for August

| Date | Cash Basis | Accrual Basis |
| --- | --- | --- |
| | | |
| | | |
| | | |
| | | |
| | | |
| | | |
| | | |
| | | |
| | | |
| | | |

**E3-2**

a. Matching concept
b. Time period / Accrual concept
c. No, there has been no services
   preformed. Revenue Concept.
d. Time Period / Accounting Period

**E3-3**

*Req. 2*

## Journal

| DATE | ACCOUNTS AND EXPLANATIONS | POST. REF. | DEBIT | CREDIT |
|------|---------------------------|------------|-------|--------|
|      |                           |            |       |        |
|      |                           |            |       |        |
|      |                           |            |       |        |
|      |                           |            |       |        |
|      |                           |            |       |        |
|      |                           |            |       |        |
|      |                           |            |       |        |
|      |                           |            |       |        |
|      |                           |            |       |        |
|      |                           |            |       |        |
|      |                           |            |       |        |
|      |                           |            |       |        |
|      |                           |            |       |        |
|      |                           |            |       |        |
|      |                           |            |       |        |
|      |                           |            |       |        |
|      |                           |            |       |        |
|      |                           |            |       |        |
|      |                           |            |       |        |
|      |                           |            |       |        |
|      |                           |            |       |        |
|      |                           |            |       |        |
|      |                           |            |       |        |
|      |                           |            |       |        |
|      |                           |            |       |        |
|      |                           |            |       |        |
|      |                           |            |       |        |
|      |                           |            |       |        |
|      |                           |            |       |        |
|      |                           |            |       |        |
|      |                           |            |       |        |

*Req. 2*

| | | Journal | | | |
|---|---|---|---|---|---|
| DATE | | ACCOUNTS AND EXPLANATIONS | POST. REF. | DEBIT | CREDIT |
| | | | | | |
| | | | | | |
| | | | | | |
| | | | | | |
| | | | | | |
| | | | | | |
| | | | | | |
| | | | | | |
| | | | | | |
| | | | | | |
| | | | | | |
| | | | | | |
| | | | | | |
| | | | | | |
| | | | | | |
| | | | | | |
| | | | | | |
| | | | | | |
| | | | | | |
| | | | | | |
| | | | | | |
| | | | | | |
| | | | | | |
| | | | | | |
| | | | | | |
| | | | | | |
| | | | | | |
| | | | | | |
| | | | | | |
| | | | | | |
| | | | | | |
| | | | | | |
| | | | | | |
| | | | | | |
| | | | | | |

*Req. 7*

Req. 7 (Continued)

*Req. 1*

| Date | Cash Basis | Accrual Basis |
|------|-----------|---------------|
|      |           |               |
|      |           |               |
|      |           |               |
|      |           |               |
|      |           |               |
|      |           |               |
|      |           |               |
|      |           |               |
|      |           |               |
|      |           |               |
|      |           |               |
|      |           |               |
|      |           |               |

*Req. 2*

*Req. 3*

Req. 1

*Req. 1 (Continued)*

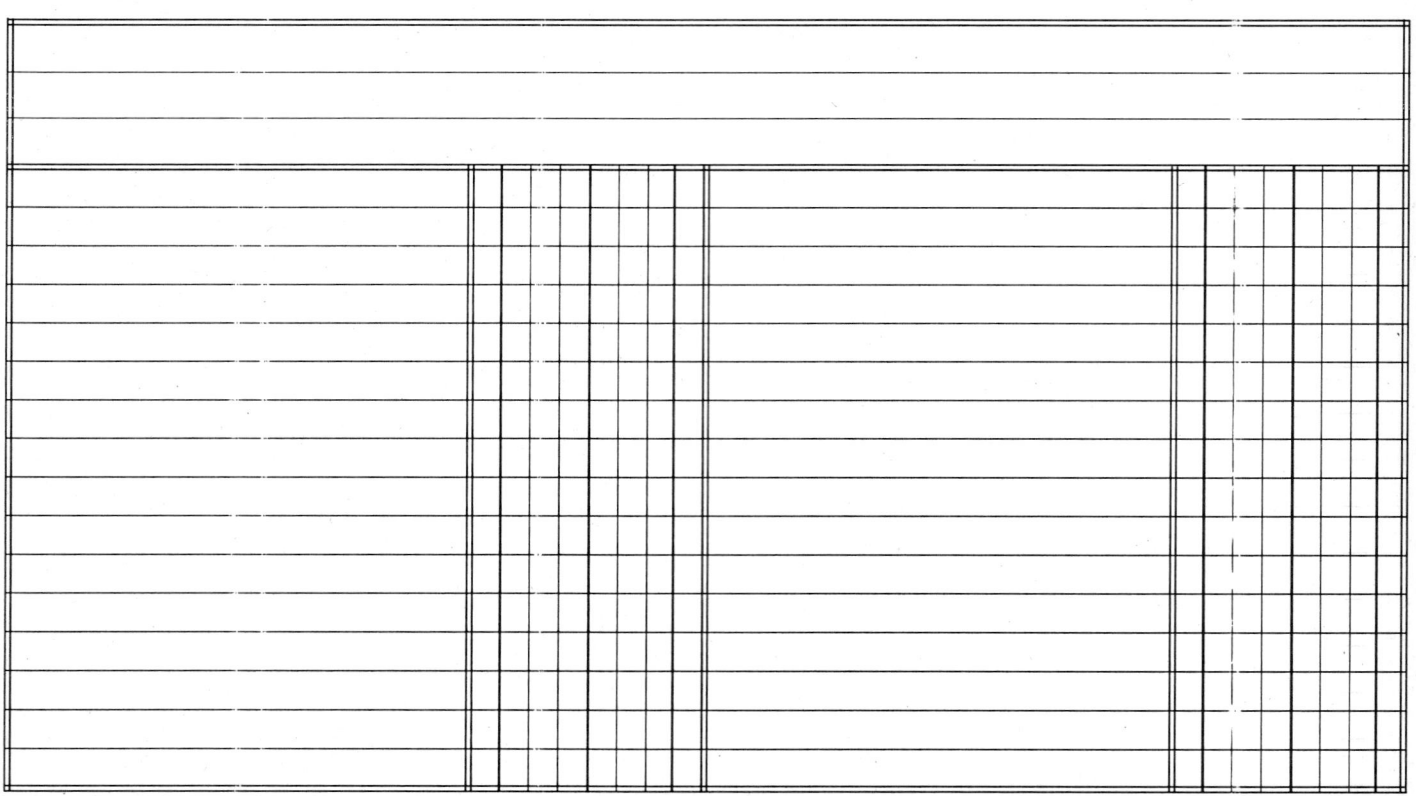

Note: If Needed, Create a Second Dollar-Column for Assets

*Req. 2*

*Req. 1*

| ACCOUNT TITLE | TRIAL BALANCE | | ADJUSTMENTS | | ADJUSTED TRIAL BALANCE | |
|---|---|---|---|---|---|---|
| | DEBIT | CREDIT | DEBIT | CREDIT | DEBIT | CREDIT |
| Cash | | | | | | |
| Accounts receivable | | | | | | |
| Prepaid rent | | | | | | |
| Supplies | | | | | | |
| Furniture | | | | | | |
| Accumulated depreciation | | | | | | |
| Accounts payable | | | | | | |
| Salary payable | | | | | | |
| Jim Panther, Capital | | | | | | |
| Jim Panther, Withdrawals | | | | | | |
| Legal service revenue | | | | | | |
| Salary expense | | | | | | |
| Rent expense | | | | | | |
| Utilities expense | | | | | | |
| Depreciation expense | | | | | | |
| Supplies expense | | | | | | |

*Req. 2*

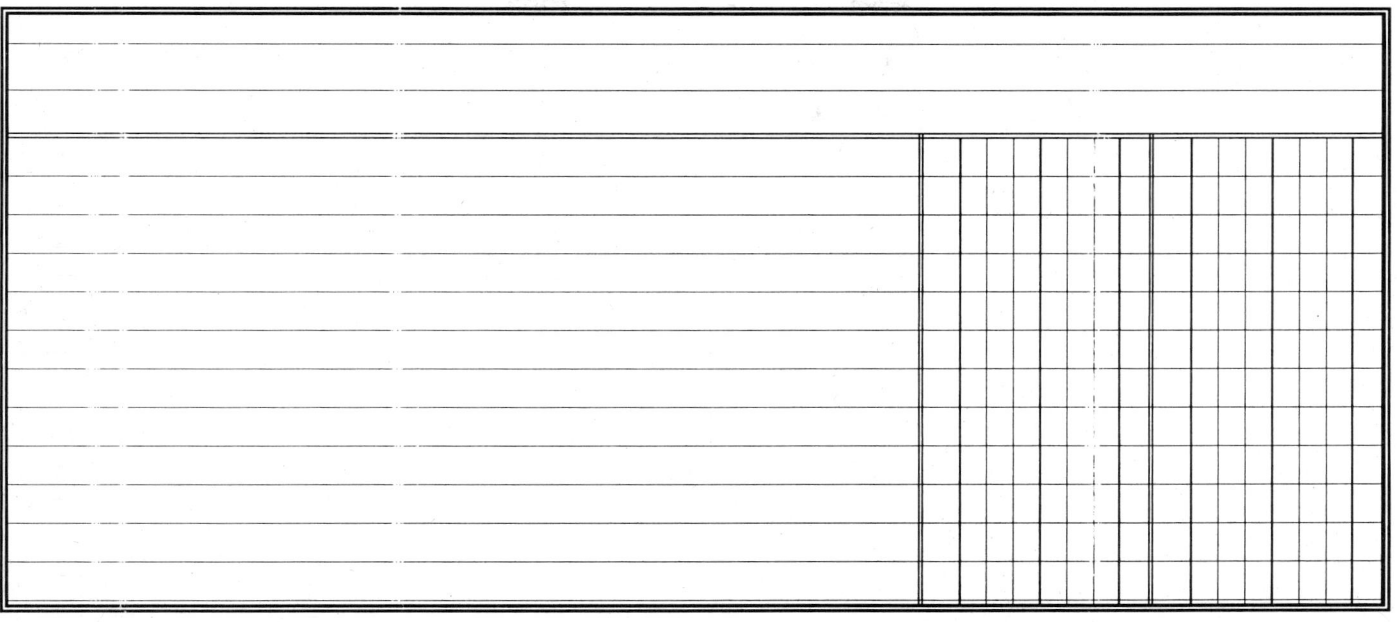

*Req. 2 (Continued)*

Note: If Needed, Create a Second Dollar-Column for Assets

*Req. 1*

| Date | Cash Basis | Accrual Basis |
| --- | --- | --- |
|  |  |  |
|  |  |  |
|  |  |  |
|  |  |  |
|  |  |  |
|  |  |  |
|  |  |  |
|  |  |  |
|  |  |  |
|  |  |  |
|  |  |  |
|  |  |  |
|  |  |  |

*Req. 2*

*Req. 3*

## Journal

| DATE | ACCOUNTS AND EXPLANATIONS | POST. REF. | DEBIT | CREDIT |
|------|---------------------------|------------|-------|--------|
|  |  |  |  |  |
|  |  |  |  |  |
|  |  |  |  |  |
|  |  |  |  |  |
|  |  |  |  |  |
|  |  |  |  |  |
|  |  |  |  |  |
|  |  |  |  |  |
|  |  |  |  |  |
|  |  |  |  |  |
|  |  |  |  |  |
|  |  |  |  |  |
|  |  |  |  |  |
|  |  |  |  |  |
|  |  |  |  |  |
|  |  |  |  |  |
|  |  |  |  |  |
|  |  |  |  |  |
|  |  |  |  |  |
|  |  |  |  |  |
|  |  |  |  |  |
|  |  |  |  |  |
|  |  |  |  |  |
|  |  |  |  |  |
|  |  |  |  |  |
|  |  |  |  |  |
|  |  |  |  |  |
|  |  |  |  |  |
|  |  |  |  |  |

## Journal

| DATE | ACCOUNTS AND EXPLANATIONS | POST. REF. | DEBIT | CREDIT |
|------|---------------------------|------------|-------|--------|
|  |  |  |  |  |
|  |  |  |  |  |
|  |  |  |  |  |
|  |  |  |  |  |
|  |  |  |  |  |
|  |  |  |  |  |
|  |  |  |  |  |
|  |  |  |  |  |
|  |  |  |  |  |
|  |  |  |  |  |
|  |  |  |  |  |
|  |  |  |  |  |
|  |  |  |  |  |
|  |  |  |  |  |
|  |  |  |  |  |
|  |  |  |  |  |
|  |  |  |  |  |
|  |  |  |  |  |
|  |  |  |  |  |
|  |  |  |  |  |
|  |  |  |  |  |
|  |  |  |  |  |
|  |  |  |  |  |
|  |  |  |  |  |
|  |  |  |  |  |
|  |  |  |  |  |
|  |  |  |  |  |
|  |  |  |  |  |
|  |  |  |  |  |
|  |  |  |  |  |
|  |  |  |  |  |
|  |  |  |  |  |
|  |  |  |  |  |
|  |  |  |  |  |
|  |  |  |  |  |

*Reqs. 1 & 2*

*Req. 2*

| | | Journal | | | | |
|---|---|---|---|---|---|---|
| DATE | | ACCOUNTS AND EXPLANATIONS | POST. REF. | DEBIT | | CREDIT |
| | | | | | | |
| | | | | | | |
| | | | | | | |
| | | | | | | |
| | | | | | | |
| | | | | | | |
| | | | | | | |
| | | | | | | |
| | | | | | | |
| | | | | | | |
| | | | | | | |
| | | | | | | |
| | | | | | | |
| | | | | | | |
| | | | | | | |
| | | | | | | |
| | | | | | | |
| | | | | | | |
| | | | | | | |
| | | | | | | |
| | | | | | | |
| | | | | | | |
| | | | | | | |
| | | | | | | |
| | | | | | | |

*Req. 3*

| ACCOUNT | DEBIT | CREDIT |
|---|---|---|
| | | |
| | | |
| | | |
| | | |
| | | |
| | | |
| | | |
| | | |
| | | |
| | | |
| | | |
| | | |
| | | |
| | | |
| | | |
| | | |
| | | |
| | | |
| | | |
| | | |
| | | |
| | | |
| | | |
| | | |

*Req. 4*

*Req. 1*

*Req. 1 (Continued)*

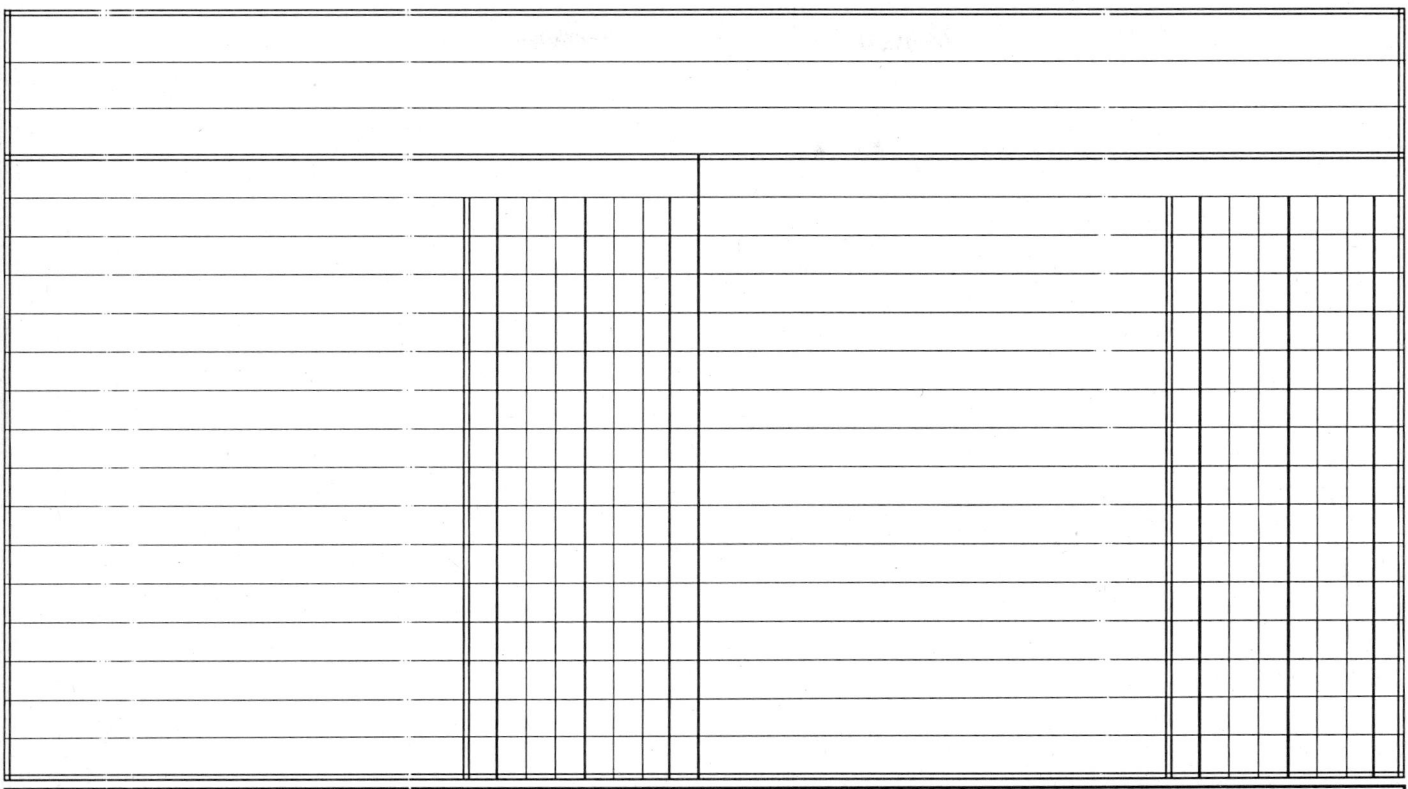

Note: If Needed, Create a Second Dollar-Column for Assets

*Req. 2*

*Rcq. 1*

| ACCOUNT TITLE | TRIAL BALANCE | | ADJUSTMENTS | | ADJUSTED TRIAL BALANCE | |
| --- | --- | --- | --- | --- | --- | --- |
| | DEBIT | CREDIT | DEBIT | CREDIT | DEBIT | CREDIT |
| Cash | | | | | | |
| Accounts receivable | | | | | | |
| Prepaid rent | | | | | | |
| Supplies | | | | | | |
| Furniture | | | | | | |
| Accumulated depreciation | | | | | | |
| Accounts payable | | | | | | |
| Salary payable | | | | | | |
| Trent Stuckey, Capital | | | | | | |
| Trent Stuckey, Withdrawals | | | | | | |
| Legal service | | | | | | |
| revenue | | | | | | |
| Salary expense | | | | | | |
| Rent expense | | | | | | |
| Utilities expense | | | | | | |
| Depreciation expense | | | | | | |
| Supplies expense | | | | | | |

*Req. 2*

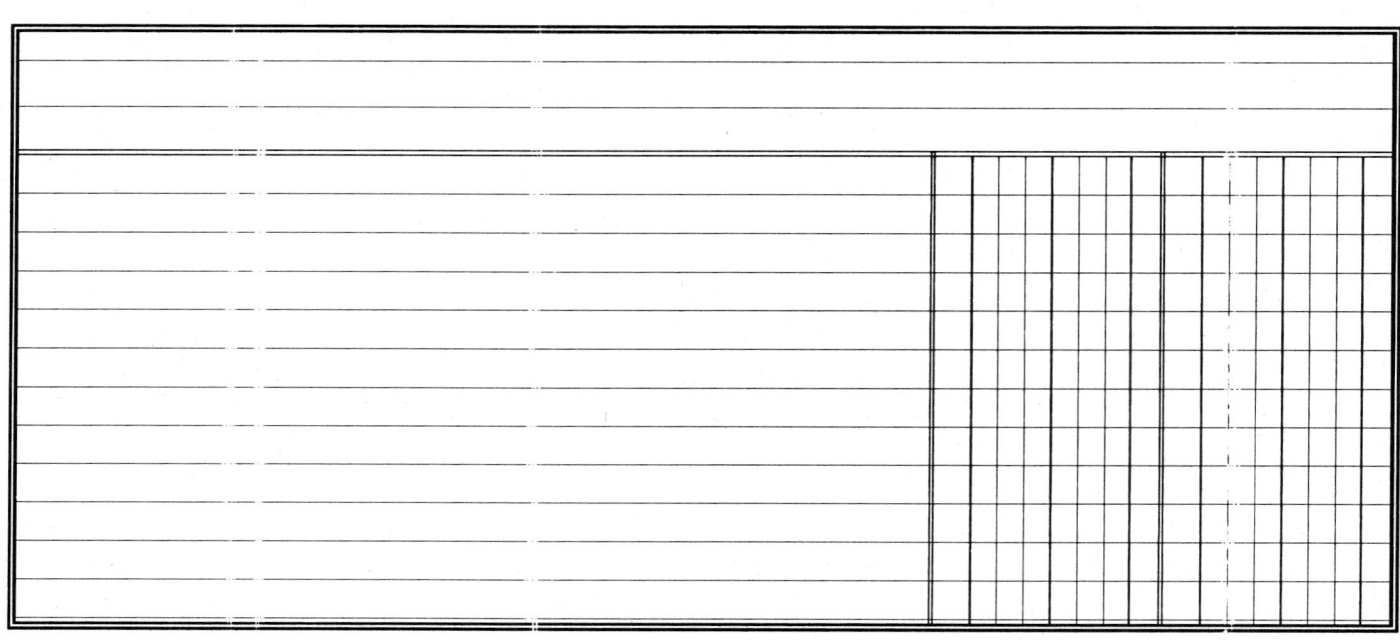

*Req. 2 (Continued)*

Note: If Needed, Create a Second Dollar-Column for Assets

NAME
SECTION
DATE

*Chapter 3*

# Decision Case 1

*Req. 1*

*Req. 2*

Req. 3

*Req. 1*

*Req. 2*

| | | | Journal | | POST.<br>REF. | DEBIT | CREDIT |
|---|---|---|---|---|---|---|---|
| DATE | | | ACCOUNTS AND EXPLANATIONS | | | | |
| | | | | | | | |
| | | | | | | | |
| | | | | | | | |
| | | | | | | | |
| | | | | | | | |
| | | | | | | | |
| | | | | | | | |
| | | | | | | | |
| | | | | | | | |
| | | | | | | | |
| | | | | | | | |
| | | | | | | | |
| | | | | | | | |
| | | | | | | | |
| | | | | | | | |
| | | | | | | | |
| | | | | | | | |
| | | | | | | | |

*Req. 3*

*Req. 1*

_____
_____
_____
_____
_____
_____
_____
_____
_____
_____

*Req. 2*

| | | Journal | | | |
|---|---|---|---|---|---|
| DATE | | ACCOUNTS AND EXPLANATIONS | POST. REF. | DEBIT | CREDIT |
| | | | | | |
| | | | | | |
| | | | | | |
| | | | | | |
| | | | | | |
| | | | | | |
| | | | | | |
| | | | | | |
| | | | | | |
| | | | | | |
| | | | | | |
| | | | | | |
| | | | | | |
| | | | | | |
| | | | | | |
| | | | | | |
| | | | | | |
| | | | | | |
| | | | | | |
| | | | | | |

*Req. 1*

*Req. 2*

*Req. 3*

*Reqs. 1 & 2*

| | | Journal | | | |
|---|---|---|---|---|---|
| DATE | | ACCOUNTS AND EXPLANATIONS | POST. REF. | DEBIT | CREDIT |
| | | | | | |
| | | | | | |
| | | | | | |
| | | | | | |
| | | | | | |
| | | | | | |
| | | | | | |
| | | | | | |
| | | | | | |
| | | | | | |
| | | | | | |
| | | | | | |
| | | | | | |
| | | | | | |
| | | | | | |
| | | | | | |

NAME
SECTION
DATE

*Reqs. 1 & 2*

| | | Journal | POST. REF. | DEBIT | CREDIT |
|---|---|---|---|---|---|
| DATE | ACCOUNTS AND EXPLANATIONS | | | | |
| | | | | | |
| | | | | | |
| | | | | | |
| | | | | | |
| | | | | | |
| | | | | | |
| | | | | | |
| | | | | | |
| | | | | | |
| | | | | | |
| | | | | | |
| | | | | | |
| | | | | | |
| | | | | | |

*Req. 3*

*Req. 4 (Continued)*

## Journal

| DATE | | ACCOUNTS AND EXPLANATIONS | POST. REF. | DEBIT | CREDIT |
|------|---|---------------------------|------------|-------|--------|
| | | | | | |
| | | | | | |
| | | | | | |
| | | | | | |
| | | | | | |
| | | | | | |
| | | | | | |
| | | | | | |
| | | | | | |
| | | | | | |
| | | | | | |
| | | | | | |
| | | | | | |
| | | | | | |
| | | | | | |
| | | | | | |
| | | | | | |
| | | | | | |

*Req. 5*

NAME
SECTION
DATE

# Chapter 3
# Internet Exercise

NAME

SECTION

DATE

Chapter 3

**Solution to
Internet Exercise**

**DE4-2**

**DE4-4**

**DE4-5**

*Req. 1*

| | | Journal | | | |
|---|---|---|---|---|---|
| DATE | | ACCOUNTS AND EXPLANATIONS | POST. REF. | DEBIT | CREDIT |
| | | | | | |
| | | | | | |
| | | | | | |
| | | | | | |
| | | | | | |
| | | | | | |
| | | | | | |
| | | | | | |
| | | | | | |
| | | | | | |
| | | | | | |

*Req. 2*

*Req. 3*

_____
_____
_____
_____
_____
_____
_____
_____
_____

**DE4-8**

### Journal

| DATE | | ACCOUNTS AND EXPLANATIONS | POST. REF. | DEBIT | CREDIT |
|------|--|---------------------------|------------|-------|--------|
| | | | | | |
| | | | | | |
| | | | | | |
| | | | | | |
| | | | | | |
| | | | | | |
| | | | | | |
| | | | | | |
| | | | | | |

**DE4-9**

**DE4-10**

### Journal

| DATE | | ACCOUNTS AND EXPLANATIONS | POST. REF. | DEBIT | CREDIT |
|------|--|---------------------------|------------|-------|--------|
| | | | | | |
| | | | | | |
| | | | | | |
| | | | | | |
| | | | | | |
| | | | | | |
| | | | | | |
| | | | | | |

## Journal

| DATE | ACCOUNTS AND EXPLANATIONS | POST. REF. | DEBIT | CREDIT |
|------|---------------------------|-----------|-------|--------|
|      |                           |           |       |        |
|      |                           |           |       |        |
|      |                           |           |       |        |
|      |                           |           |       |        |
|      |                           |           |       |        |
|      |                           |           |       |        |
|      |                           |           |       |        |

**DE4-12**

**DE4-15**

| | Millions |
|---|---|

The foldout worksheet to solve this problem can be found in the back of the book.

**E4-4**

| ACCOUNT | DEBIT | CREDIT |
|---|---|---|
| Goldsmith Testing Service | | |
| Postclosing Trial Balance | | |
| September 30, 19X6 | | |
| Cash | 3560 | |
| Acc Rec | 3650 | |
| Prepaid Rent | 600 | |
| Supplies | 1140 | |
| Equip | 32600 | |
| Accum Dep | | 2880 |
| Acct Pay | | 3600 |
| Salary Pay | | 500 |
| Goldsmith Capital | | 35170 |
| Total | 42150 | 42150 |

## Journal

| DATE | | ACCOUNTS AND EXPLANATIONS | POST. REF. | DEBIT | CREDIT |
|------|--|---------------------------|-----------|-------|--------|
| | | | | | |
| | | | | | |
| | | | | | |
| | | | | | |
| | | | | | |
| | | | | | |
| | | | | | |
| | | | | | |
| | | | | | |
| | | | | | |
| | | | | | |
| | | | | | |
| | | | | | |
| | | | | | |
| | | | | | |
| | | | | | |
| | | | | | |
| | | | | | |
| | | | | | |
| | | | | | |
| | | | | | |
| | | | | | |
| | | | | | |

## Journal

| DATE | ACCOUNTS AND EXPLANATIONS | POST. REF. | DEBIT | CREDIT |
|------|---------------------------|------------|-------|--------|
|  |  |  |  |  |
|  |  |  |  |  |
|  |  |  |  |  |
|  |  |  |  |  |
|  |  |  |  |  |
|  |  |  |  |  |
|  |  |  |  |  |
|  |  |  |  |  |
|  |  |  |  |  |
|  |  |  |  |  |
|  |  |  |  |  |
|  |  |  |  |  |
|  |  |  |  |  |
|  |  |  |  |  |
|  |  |  |  |  |
|  |  |  |  |  |
|  |  |  |  |  |
|  |  |  |  |  |
|  |  |  |  |  |
|  |  |  |  |  |
|  |  |  |  |  |
|  |  |  |  |  |
|  |  |  |  |  |
|  |  |  |  |  |

*Req. 1*

## Journal

| DATE | ACCOUNTS AND EXPLANATIONS | POST. REF. | DEBIT | CREDIT |
|------|---------------------------|------------|-------|--------|
| | | | | |
| | | | | |
| | | | | |
| | | | | |
| | | | | |
| | | | | |
| | | | | |
| | | | | |
| | | | | |
| | | | | |
| | | | | |
| | | | | |
| | | | | |
| | | | | |
| | | | | |
| | | | | |
| | | | | |
| | | | | |
| | | | | |
| | | | | |
| | | | | |
| | | | | |
| | | | | |
| | | | | |
| | | | | |
| | | | | |
| | | | | |
| | | | | |
| | | | | |
| | | | | |
| | | | | |
| | | | | |
| | | | | |
| | | | | |
| | | | | |
| | | | | |
| | | | | |
| | | | | |
| | | | | |
| | | | | |
| | | | | |
| | | | | |

*Req. 2*

_____

_____

_____

_____

_____

*Req. 1*

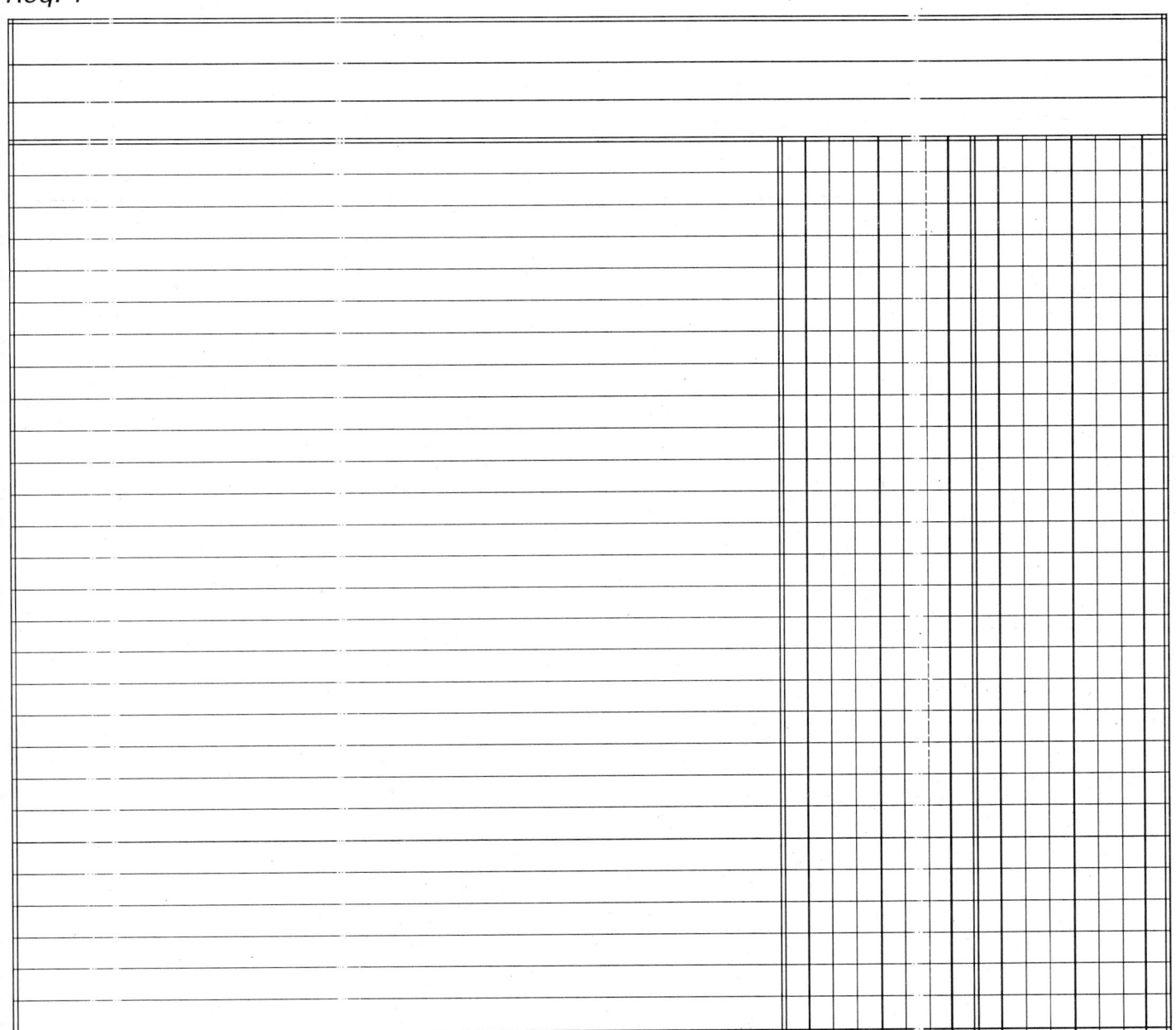

*Req. 2*

## Journal

| DATE | ACCOUNTS AND EXPLANATIONS | POST. REF. | DEBIT | CREDIT |
|---|---|---|---|---|
| example | Accounts Rec. | | 1400 | |
| | Service Rev. | | | 1400 |
| a. correcting entries | Unearned Serv. Rev. | | 1400 | |
| | Acct. Rec. | | | 1400 |
| b. | Intrest Rec | | 300 | |
| | Acct. Rec | | | 300 |
| c. | Accounts Payeble | | 2000 | |
| | Cash | | | 2000 |
| d. | Office Equipment | | 2900 | |
| | Supplies | | | 2900 |
| e. | Rent Expense | | 1800 | |
| | Prepaid Rent | | | 1800 |
| f. | Cash | | 900 | |
| | Salary Payable | | | 900 |

Req. 1

E4-11

## Journal

| DATE | ACCOUNTS AND EXPLANATIONS | POST. REF. | DEBIT | CREDIT |
|---|---|---|---|---|
| | | | | |

*Req. 1*

*Req. 2*

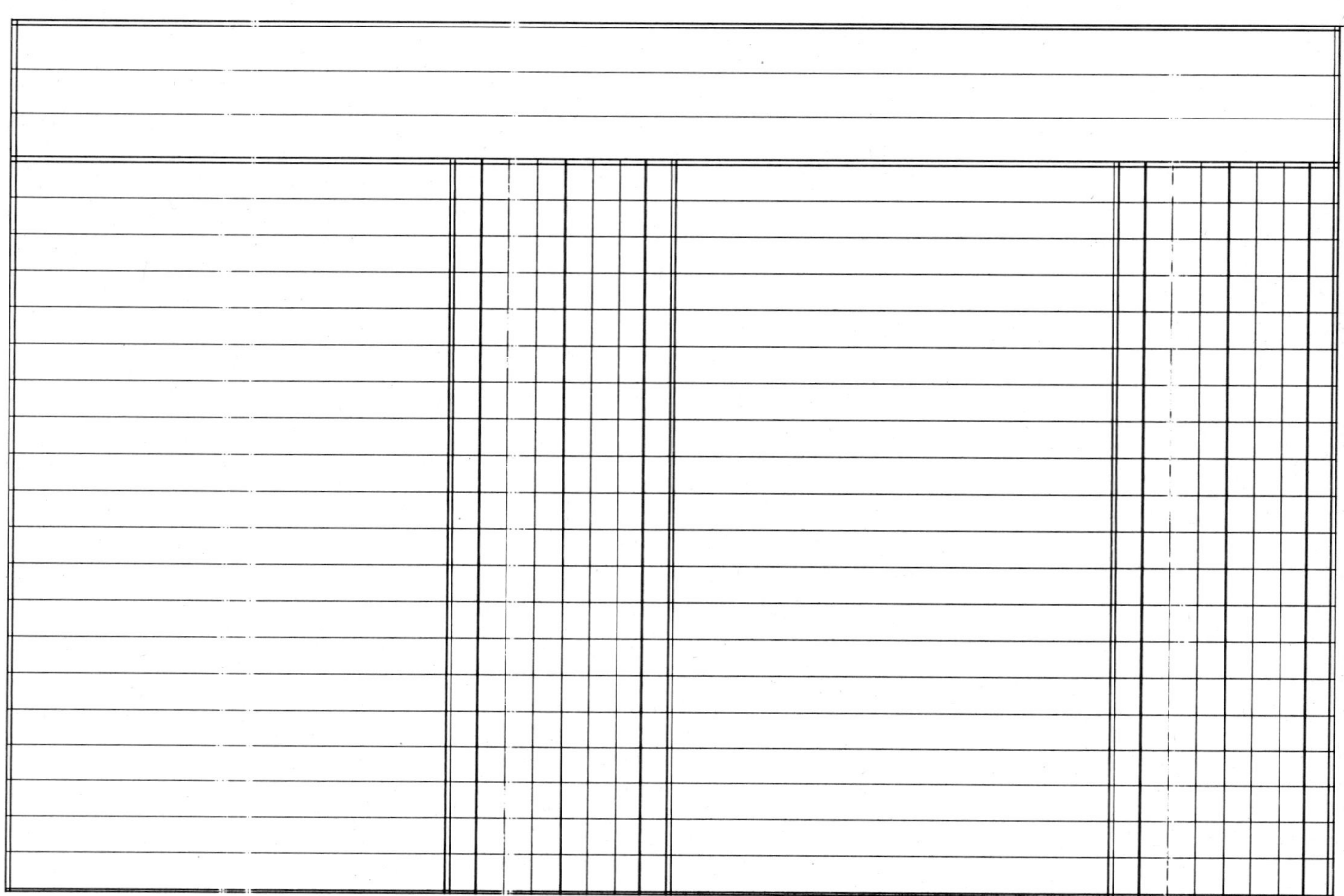

Note: If Needed, Create a Second Dollar-Column for Assets

*Req. 3*

*Req. 4*

The foldout worksheet to solve this problem can be found in the back of the book.

1.

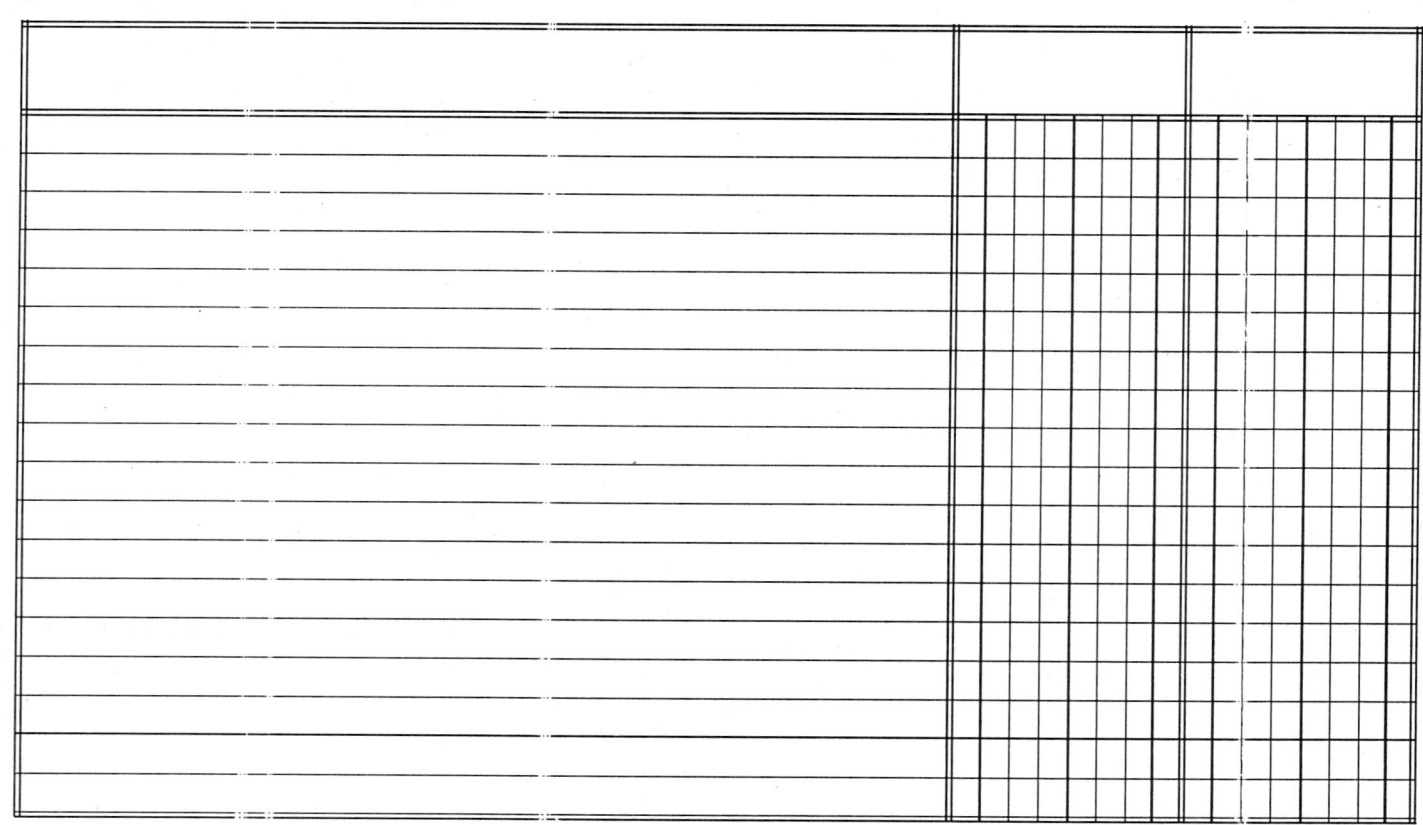

2.

3–5.

*Req. 1*

The foldout worksheet to solve this problem can be found in the back of the book.

NAME
SECTION
DATE



**P4-3A** *(Continued)*

*Req. 2*

*Req. 2 (Continued)*

Note: If Needed, Create a Second Dollar-Column for Assets

*Req. 4*

Req. 3

## Journal

| DATE | | ACCOUNTS AND EXPLANATIONS | POST. REF. | DEBIT | CREDIT |
|---|---|---|---|---|---|
| | | | | | |
| | | | | | |
| | | | | | |
| | | | | | |
| | | | | | |
| | | | | | |
| | | | | | |
| | | | | | |
| | | | | | |
| | | | | | |
| | | | | | |
| | | | | | |
| | | | | | |
| | | | | | |
| | | | | | |
| | | | | | |
| | | | | | |
| | | | | | |
| | | | | | |
| | | | | | |
| | | | | | |
| | | | | | |
| | | | | | |
| | | | | | |
| | | | | | |
| | | | | | |
| | | | | | |
| | | | | | |
| | | | | | |
| | | | | | |
| | | | | | |
| | | | | | |
| | | | | | |
| | | | | | |

*Req. 1*

Req. 2

*Reqs. 1 & 4*

| ACCOUNT | | | | | ACCOUNT NO. | | |
|---|---|---|---|---|---|---|---|
| | | JRNL. REF. | | | BALANCE | | |
| DATE | ITEM | | DEBIT | CREDIT | DEBIT | | CREDIT |
| | | | | | | | |
| | | | | | | | |
| | | | | | | | |
| | | | | | | | |
| | | | | | | | |
| | | | | | | | |

| ACCOUNT | | | | | ACCOUNT NO. | | |
|---|---|---|---|---|---|---|---|
| | | JRNL. REF. | | | BALANCE | | |
| DATE | ITEM | | DEBIT | CREDIT | DEBIT | | CREDIT |
| | | | | | | | |
| | | | | | | | |
| | | | | | | | |
| | | | | | | | |
| | | | | | | | |
| | | | | | | | |

| ACCOUNT | | | | | ACCOUNT NO. | | |
|---|---|---|---|---|---|---|---|
| | | JRNL. REF. | | | BALANCE | | |
| DATE | ITEM | | DEBIT | CREDIT | DEBIT | | CREDIT |
| | | | | | | | |
| | | | | | | | |
| | | | | | | | |
| | | | | | | | |
| | | | | | | | |
| | | | | | | | |

| ACCOUNT | | | | | ACCOUNT NO. | | |
|---|---|---|---|---|---|---|---|
| | | JRNL. REF. | | | BALANCE | | |
| DATE | ITEM | | DEBIT | CREDIT | DEBIT | | CREDIT |
| | | | | | | | |
| | | | | | | | |
| | | | | | | | |
| | | | | | | | |
| | | | | | | | |

*Reqs. 1 & 4 (Continued)*

| ACCOUNT | | | | | ACCOUNT NO. | | |
|---|---|---|---|---|---|---|---|
| | | | | | | BALANCE | |
| DATE | ITEM | JRNL. REF. | DEBIT | CREDIT | DEBIT | | CREDIT |
| | | | | | | | |
| | | | | | | | |
| | | | | | | | |
| | | | | | | | |
| | | | | | | | |

| ACCOUNT | | | | | ACCOUNT NO. | | |
|---|---|---|---|---|---|---|---|
| | | | | | | BALANCE | |
| DATE | ITEM | JRNL. REF. | DEBIT | CREDIT | DEBIT | | CREDIT |
| | | | | | | | |
| | | | | | | | |
| | | | | | | | |
| | | | | | | | |
| | | | | | | | |

| ACCOUNT | | | | | ACCOUNT NO. | | |
|---|---|---|---|---|---|---|---|
| | | | | | | BALANCE | |
| DATE | ITEM | JRNL. REF. | DEBIT | CREDIT | DEBIT | | CREDIT |
| | | | | | | | |
| | | | | | | | |
| | | | | | | | |
| | | | | | | | |
| | | | | | | | |

| ACCOUNT | | | | | ACCOUNT NO. | | |
|---|---|---|---|---|---|---|---|
| | | | | | | BALANCE | |
| DATE | ITEM | JRNL. REF. | DEBIT | CREDIT | DEBIT | | CREDIT |
| | | | | | | | |
| | | | | | | | |
| | | | | | | | |
| | | | | | | | |
| | | | | | | | |

*Reqs. 1 & 4 (Continued)*

| ACCOUNT | | | | | | ACCOUNT NO. | |
|---|---|---|---|---|---|---|---|
| | | | | | | BALANCE | |
| DATE | ITEM | JRNL. REF. | DEBIT | CREDIT | | DEBIT | CREDIT |
| | | | | | | | |
| | | | | | | | |
| | | | | | | | |
| | | | | | | | |

| ACCOUNT | | | | | | ACCOUNT NO. | |
|---|---|---|---|---|---|---|---|
| | | | | | | BALANCE | |
| DATE | ITEM | JRNL. REF. | DEBIT | CREDIT | | DEBIT | CREDIT |
| | | | | | | | |
| | | | | | | | |
| | | | | | | | |
| | | | | | | | |
| | | | | | | | |

| ACCOUNT | | | | | | ACCOUNT NO. | |
|---|---|---|---|---|---|---|---|
| | | | | | | BALANCE | |
| DATE | ITEM | JRNL. REF. | DEBIT | CREDIT | | DEBIT | CREDIT |
| | | | | | | | |
| | | | | | | | |
| | | | | | | | |
| | | | | | | | |

| ACCOUNT | | | | | | ACCOUNT NO. | |
|---|---|---|---|---|---|---|---|
| | | | | | | BALANCE | |
| DATE | ITEM | JRNL. REF. | DEBIT | CREDIT | | DEBIT | CREDIT |
| | | | | | | | |
| | | | | | | | |
| | | | | | | | |

## Reqs. 1 & 4 (Continued)

| ACCOUNT | | | | | ACCOUNT NO. | |
|---|---|---|---|---|---|---|
| | | | | | BALANCE | |
| DATE | ITEM | JRNL. REF. | DEBIT | CREDIT | DEBIT | CREDIT |
| | | | | | | |
| | | | | | | |
| | | | | | | |
| | | | | | | |
| | | | | | | |

| ACCOUNT | | | | | ACCOUNT NO. | |
|---|---|---|---|---|---|---|
| | | | | | BALANCE | |
| DATE | ITEM | JRNL. REF. | DEBIT | CREDIT | DEBIT | CREDIT |
| | | | | | | |
| | | | | | | |
| | | | | | | |
| | | | | | | |
| | | | | | | |

| ACCOUNT | | | | | ACCOUNT NO. | |
|---|---|---|---|---|---|---|
| | | | | | BALANCE | |
| DATE | ITEM | JRNL. REF. | DEBIT | CREDIT | DEBIT | CREDIT |
| | | | | | | |
| | | | | | | |
| | | | | | | |
| | | | | | | |
| | | | | | | |

| ACCOUNT | | | | | ACCOUNT NO. | |
|---|---|---|---|---|---|---|
| | | | | | BALANCE | |
| DATE | ITEM | JRNL. REF. | DEBIT | CREDIT | DEBIT | CREDIT |
| | | | | | | |
| | | | | | | |
| | | | | | | |
| | | | | | | |
| | | | | | | |

*Reqs. 1 & 4 (Continued)*

| ACCOUNT | | | | | ACCOUNT NO. | | | |
|---|---|---|---|---|---|---|---|---|
| | | | | | | BALANCE | | |
| DATE | ITEM | JRNL. REF. | DEBIT | CREDIT | DEBIT | | CREDIT | |
| | | | | | | | | |
| | | | | | | | | |
| | | | | | | | | |
| | | | | | | | | |
| | | | | | | | | |
| | | | | | | | | |

| ACCOUNT | | | | | ACCOUNT NO. | | | |
|---|---|---|---|---|---|---|---|---|
| | | | | | | BALANCE | | |
| DATE | ITEM | JRNL. REF. | DEBIT | CREDIT | DEBIT | | CREDIT | |
| | | | | | | | | |
| | | | | | | | | |
| | | | | | | | | |
| | | | | | | | | |
| | | | | | | | | |
| | | | | | | | | |
| | | | | | | | | |

| ACCOUNT | | | | | ACCOUNT NO. | | | |
|---|---|---|---|---|---|---|---|---|
| | | | | | | BALANCE | | |
| DATE | ITEM | JRNL. REF. | DEBIT | CREDIT | DEBIT | | CREDIT | |
| | | | | | | | | |
| | | | | | | | | |
| | | | | | | | | |
| | | | | | | | | |
| | | | | | | | | |
| | | | | | | | | |

| ACCOUNT | | | | | ACCOUNT NO. | | | |
|---|---|---|---|---|---|---|---|---|
| | | | | | | BALANCE | | |
| DATE | ITEM | JRNL. REF. | DEBIT | CREDIT | DEBIT | | CREDIT | |
| | | | | | | | | |
| | | | | | | | | |
| | | | | | | | | |
| | | | | | | | | |

*Reqs. 1 & 4 (Continued)*

| ACCOUNT | | | | | | ACCOUNT NO. | | | |
|---|---|---|---|---|---|---|---|---|---|
| | | | | | | | BALANCE | | |
| DATE | | ITEM | JRNL. REF. | | DEBIT | CREDIT | DEBIT | | CREDIT |
| | | | | | | | | | |
| | | | | | | | | | |
| | | | | | | | | | |
| | | | | | | | | | |
| | | | | | | | | | |
| | | | | | | | | | |

The foldout worksheet to solve this problem can be found in the back of the book.

*Req. 3*

*Req. 3 (Continued)*

*Req. 4 (Continued)*

| | | Journal | | | |
|---|---|---|---|---|---|
| DATE | | ACCOUNTS AND EXPLANATIONS | POST. REF. | DEBIT | CREDIT |
| | | | | | |
| | | | | | |
| | | | | | |
| | | | | | |
| | | | | | |
| | | | | | |
| | | | | | |
| | | | | | |
| | | | | | |
| | | | | | |
| | | | | | |
| | | | | | |
| | | | | | |
| | | | | | |
| | | | | | |
| | | | | | |
| | | | | | |
| | | | | | |
| | | | | | |
| | | | | | |
| | | | | | |
| | | | | | |
| | | | | | |
| | | | | | |
| | | | | | |
| | | | | | |
| | | | | | |
| | | | | | |
| | | | | | |
| | | | | | |
| | | | | | |
| | | | | | |
| | | | | | |
| | | | | | |
| | | | | | |
| | | | | | |
| | | | | | |
| | | | | | |
| | | | | | |
| | | | | | |

Req. 4 (Continued)

| | Journal | | | |
|---|---|---|---|---|
| DATE | ACCOUNTS AND EXPLANATIONS | POST. REF. | DEBIT | CREDIT |
| | | | | |
| | | | | |
| | | | | |
| | | | | |
| | | | | |
| | | | | |
| | | | | |
| | | | | |

Req. 5

*Req. 1*

*Reqs. 1 & 2*

*a–c*

*d*

e–f

## Journal

| DATE | ACCOUNTS AND EXPLANATIONS | POST. REF. | DEBIT | CREDIT |
|------|--------------------------|------------|-------|--------|
|  |  |  |  |  |
|  |  |  |  |  |
|  |  |  |  |  |
|  |  |  |  |  |
|  |  |  |  |  |
|  |  |  |  |  |
|  |  |  |  |  |
|  |  |  |  |  |
|  |  |  |  |  |
|  |  |  |  |  |
|  |  |  |  |  |
|  |  |  |  |  |
|  |  |  |  |  |
|  |  |  |  |  |
|  |  |  |  |  |
|  |  |  |  |  |
|  |  |  |  |  |
|  |  |  |  |  |
|  |  |  |  |  |
|  |  |  |  |  |

The foldout worksheet to solve this problem can be found in the back of the book.

*Req. 1*

## Journal

| DATE | ACCOUNTS AND EXPLANATIONS | POST. REF. | DEBIT | CREDIT |
|------|---------------------------|------------|-------|--------|
|      |                           |            |       |        |

Req. 1 (Continued)

## Journal

| DATE | ACCOUNTS AND EXPLANATIONS | POST. REF. | DEBIT | CREDIT |
|------|---------------------------|------------|-------|--------|
| | | | | |
| | | | | |
| | | | | |
| | | | | |
| | | | | |
| | | | | |
| | | | | |
| | | | | |
| | | | | |
| | | | | |
| | | | | |
| | | | | |
| | | | | |
| | | | | |
| | | | | |
| | | | | |
| | | | | |
| | | | | |
| | | | | |
| | | | | |
| | | | | |
| | | | | |
| | | | | |
| | | | | |
| | | | | |
| | | | | |
| | | | | |
| | | | | |
| | | | | |
| | | | | |
| | | | | |
| | | | | |
| | | | | |
| | | | | |

Req. 2

Req. 2 (Continued)

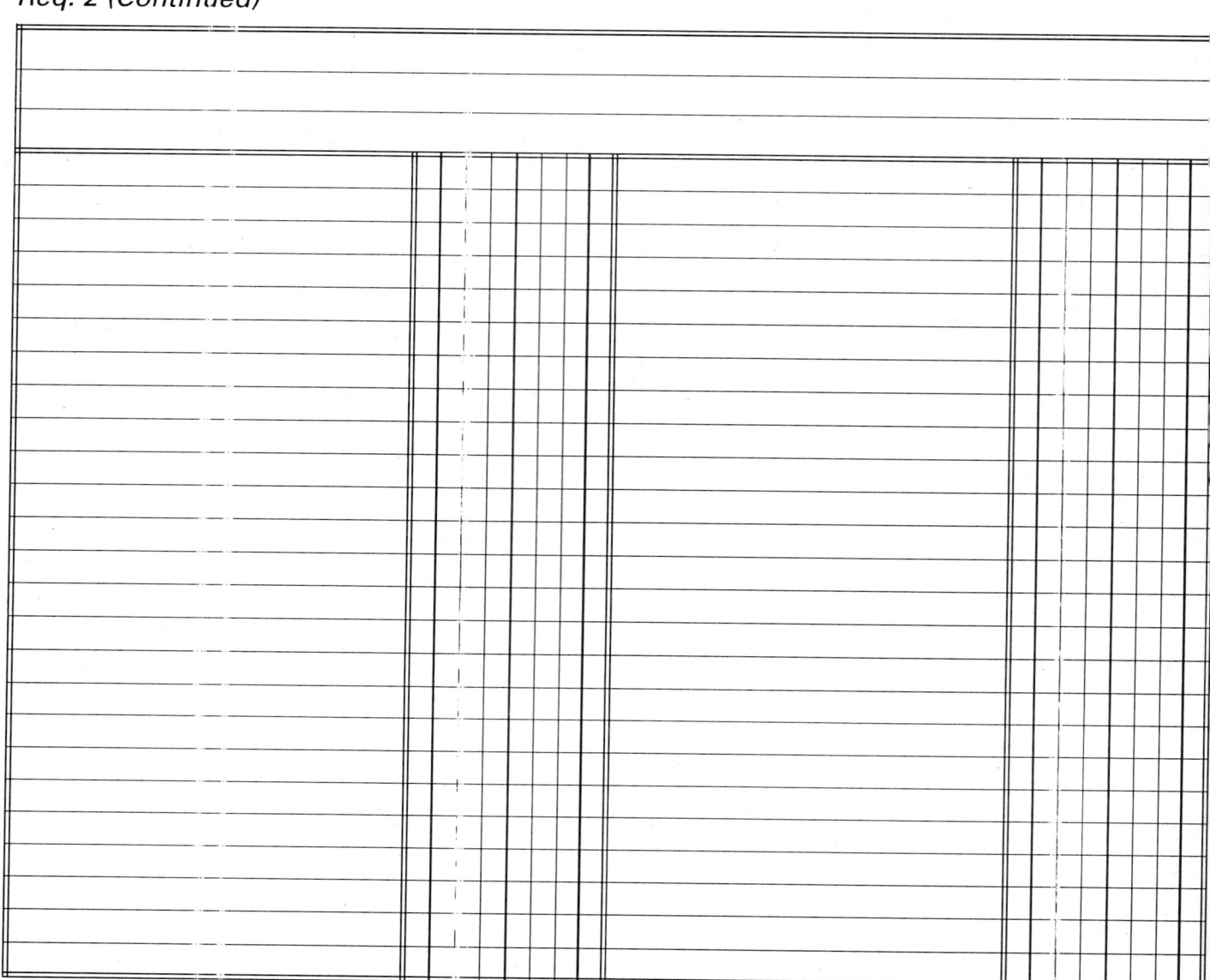

Note: If Needed, Create a Second Dollar-Column for Assets

*Req. 3*

*Req. 1*

The foldout worksheet to solve this problem can be found in the back of the book.

*Req. 2*

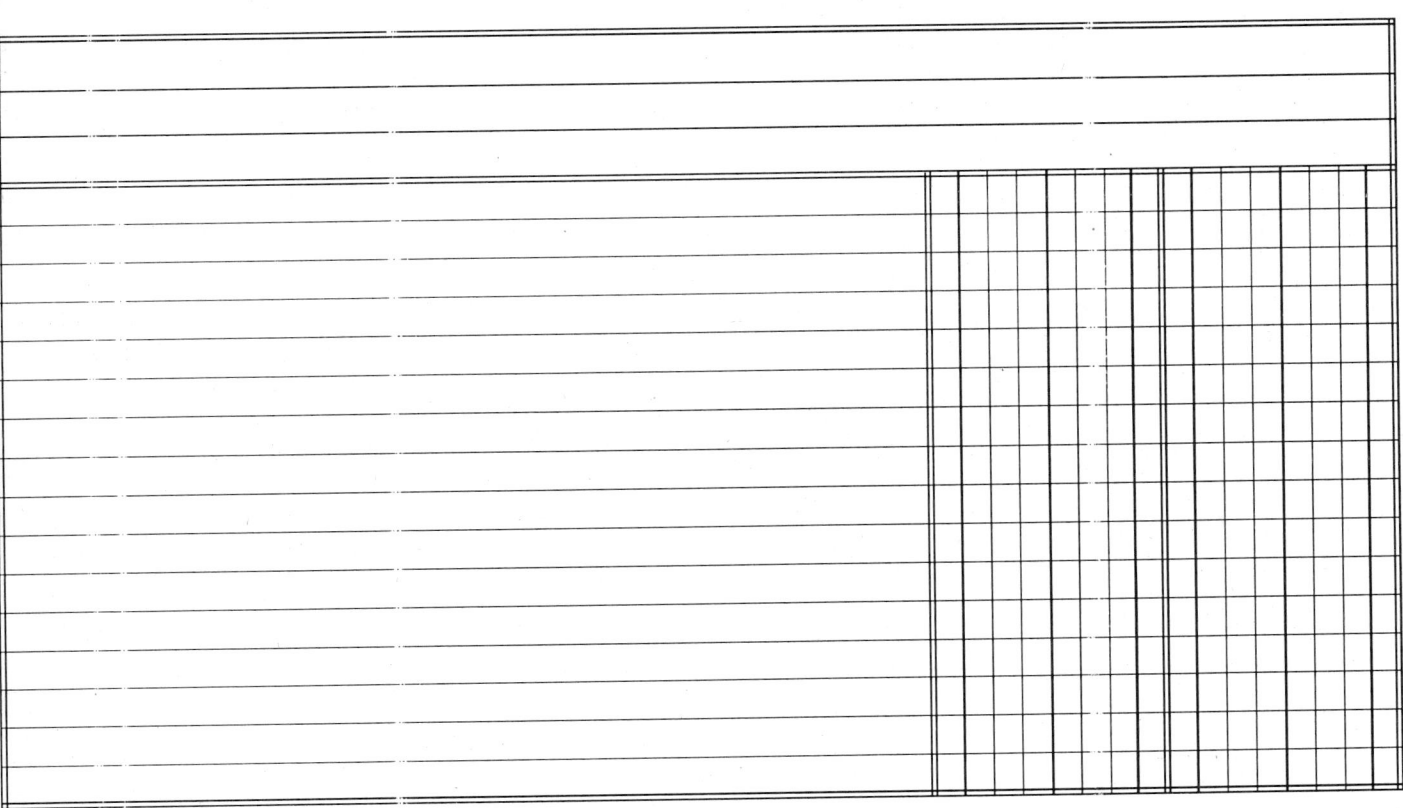

*Req. 2 (Continued)*

Note: If Needed, Create a Second Dollar-Column for Assets

*Req. 4*

Req. 3

## Journal

| DATE | ACCOUNTS AND EXPLANATIONS | POST. REF. | DEBIT | CREDIT |
|------|---------------------------|-----------|-------|--------|
| | | | | |
| | | | | |
| | | | | |
| | | | | |
| | | | | |
| | | | | |
| | | | | |
| | | | | |
| | | | | |
| | | | | |
| | | | | |
| | | | | |
| | | | | |
| | | | | |
| | | | | |
| | | | | |
| | | | | |
| | | | | |
| | | | | |
| | | | | |
| | | | | |
| | | | | |
| | | | | |
| | | | | |
| | | | | |
| | | | | |
| | | | | |
| | | | | |
| | | | | |
| | | | | |
| | | | | |
| | | | | |
| | | | | |
| | | | | |
| | | | | |
| | | | | |
| | | | | |
| | | | | |

*Req. 1*

*Req. 2*

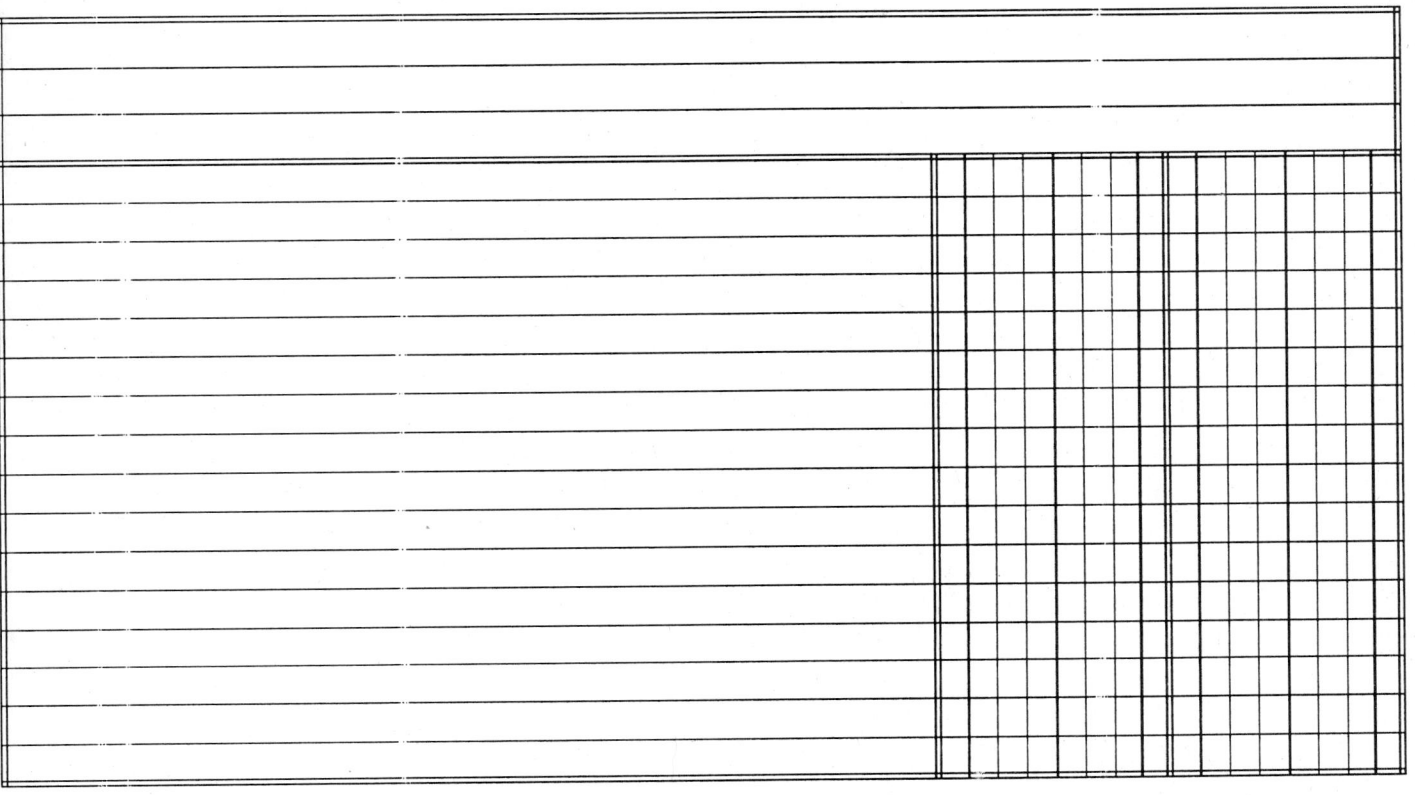

Reqs. 1 & 4

| ACCOUNT | | | | | | ACCOUNT NO. | | | |
|---|---|---|---|---|---|---|---|---|---|
| DATE | ITEM | JRNL. REF. | DEBIT | CREDIT | BALANCE | | | | |
| | | | | | DEBIT | | CREDIT | | |
| | | | | | | | | | |
| | | | | | | | | | |
| | | | | | | | | | |
| | | | | | | | | | |
| | | | | | | | | | |

| ACCOUNT | | | | | | ACCOUNT NO. | | | |
|---|---|---|---|---|---|---|---|---|---|
| DATE | ITEM | JRNL. REF. | DEBIT | CREDIT | BALANCE | | | | |
| | | | | | DEBIT | | CREDIT | | |
| | | | | | | | | | |
| | | | | | | | | | |
| | | | | | | | | | |
| | | | | | | | | | |
| | | | | | | | | | |

| ACCOUNT | | | | | | ACCOUNT NO. | | | |
|---|---|---|---|---|---|---|---|---|---|
| DATE | ITEM | JRNL. REF. | DEBIT | CREDIT | BALANCE | | | | |
| | | | | | DEBIT | | CREDIT | | |
| | | | | | | | | | |
| | | | | | | | | | |
| | | | | | | | | | |
| | | | | | | | | | |
| | | | | | | | | | |

| ACCOUNT | | | | | | ACCOUNT NO. | | | |
|---|---|---|---|---|---|---|---|---|---|
| DATE | ITEM | JRNL. REF. | DEBIT | CREDIT | BALANCE | | | | |
| | | | | | DEBIT | | CREDIT | | |
| | | | | | | | | | |
| | | | | | | | | | |
| | | | | | | | | | |
| | | | | | | | | | |
| | | | | | | | | | |

*Reqs. 1 & 4 (Continued)*

| ACCOUNT | | | | | ACCOUNT NO. | | |
|---|---|---|---|---|---|---|---|
| | | | | | | BALANCE | |
| DATE | ITEM | JRNL. REF. | DEBIT | CREDIT | DEBIT | | CREDIT |
| | | | | | | | |
| | | | | | | | |
| | | | | | | | |
| | | | | | | | |
| | | | | | | | |

| ACCOUNT | | | | | ACCOUNT NO. | | |
|---|---|---|---|---|---|---|---|
| | | | | | | BALANCE | |
| DATE | ITEM | JRNL. REF. | DEBIT | CREDIT | DEBIT | | CREDIT |
| | | | | | | | |
| | | | | | | | |
| | | | | | | | |
| | | | | | | | |
| | | | | | | | |

| ACCOUNT | | | | | ACCOUNT NO. | | |
|---|---|---|---|---|---|---|---|
| | | | | | | BALANCE | |
| DATE | ITEM | JRNL. REF. | DEBIT | CREDIT | DEBIT | | CREDIT |
| | | | | | | | |
| | | | | | | | |
| | | | | | | | |
| | | | | | | | |
| | | | | | | | |

| ACCOUNT | | | | | ACCOUNT NO. | | |
|---|---|---|---|---|---|---|---|
| | | | | | | BALANCE | |
| DATE | ITEM | JRNL. REF. | DEBIT | CREDIT | DEBIT | | CREDIT |
| | | | | | | | |
| | | | | | | | |
| | | | | | | | |
| | | | | | | | |

*Reqs. 1 & 4 (Continued)*

| ACCOUNT | | | | | ACCOUNT NO. | | |
|---|---|---|---|---|---|---|---|
| | | | | | | BALANCE | |
| DATE | ITEM | JRNL. REF. | DEBIT | CREDIT | | DEBIT | CREDIT |
| | | | | | | | |
| | | | | | | | |
| | | | | | | | |
| | | | | | | | |
| | | | | | | | |

| ACCOUNT | | | | | ACCOUNT NO. | | |
|---|---|---|---|---|---|---|---|
| | | | | | | BALANCE | |
| DATE | ITEM | JRNL. REF. | DEBIT | CREDIT | | DEBIT | CREDIT |
| | | | | | | | |
| | | | | | | | |
| | | | | | | | |
| | | | | | | | |
| | | | | | | | |
| | | | | | | | |

| ACCOUNT | | | | | ACCOUNT NO. | | |
|---|---|---|---|---|---|---|---|
| | | | | | | BALANCE | |
| DATE | ITEM | JRNL. REF. | DEBIT | CREDIT | | DEBIT | CREDIT |
| | | | | | | | |
| | | | | | | | |
| | | | | | | | |
| | | | | | | | |
| | | | | | | | |
| | | | | | | | |

| ACCOUNT | | | | | ACCOUNT NO. | | |
|---|---|---|---|---|---|---|---|
| | | | | | | BALANCE | |
| DATE | ITEM | JRNL. REF. | DEBIT | CREDIT | | DEBIT | CREDIT |
| | | | | | | | |
| | | | | | | | |
| | | | | | | | |
| | | | | | | | |
| | | | | | | | |

*Reqs. 1 & 4 (Continued)*

| ACCOUNT | | | | | | ACCOUNT NO. | | |
|---|---|---|---|---|---|---|---|---|
| | | | | | | BALANCE | | |
| DATE | ITEM | JRNL. REF. | DEBIT | CREDIT | | DEBIT | | CREDIT |
| | | | | | | | | |
| | | | | | | | | |
| | | | | | | | | |
| | | | | | | | | |
| | | | | | | | | |

| ACCOUNT | | | | | | ACCOUNT NO. | | |
|---|---|---|---|---|---|---|---|---|
| | | | | | | BALANCE | | |
| DATE | ITEM | JRNL. REF. | DEBIT | CREDIT | | DEBIT | | CREDIT |
| | | | | | | | | |
| | | | | | | | | |
| | | | | | | | | |
| | | | | | | | | |
| | | | | | | | | |

| ACCOUNT | | | | | | ACCOUNT NO. | | |
|---|---|---|---|---|---|---|---|---|
| | | | | | | BALANCE | | |
| DATE | ITEM | JRNL. REF. | DEBIT | CREDIT | | DEBIT | | CREDIT |
| | | | | | | | | |
| | | | | | | | | |
| | | | | | | | | |
| | | | | | | | | |
| | | | | | | | | |

| ACCOUNT | | | | | | ACCOUNT NO. | | |
|---|---|---|---|---|---|---|---|---|
| | | | | | | BALANCE | | |
| DATE | ITEM | JRNL. REF. | DEBIT | CREDIT | | DEBIT | | CREDIT |
| | | | | | | | | |
| | | | | | | | | |
| | | | | | | | | |

*Reqs. 1 & 4 (Continued)*

| ACCOUNT | | | | | ACCOUNT NO. | | |
|---|---|---|---|---|---|---|---|
| DATE | ITEM | JRNL. REF. | DEBIT | CREDIT | BALANCE | | |
| | | | | | DEBIT | CREDIT | |
| | | | | | | | |
| | | | | | | | |
| | | | | | | | |
| | | | | | | | |
| | | | | | | | |
| | | | | | | | |

| ACCOUNT | | | | | ACCOUNT NO. | | |
|---|---|---|---|---|---|---|---|
| DATE | ITEM | JRNL. REF. | DEBIT | CREDIT | BALANCE | | |
| | | | | | DEBIT | CREDIT | |
| | | | | | | | |
| | | | | | | | |
| | | | | | | | |
| | | | | | | | |
| | | | | | | | |
| | | | | | | | |

| ACCOUNT | | | | | ACCOUNT NO. | | |
|---|---|---|---|---|---|---|---|
| DATE | ITEM | JRNL. REF. | DEBIT | CREDIT | BALANCE | | |
| | | | | | DEBIT | CREDIT | |
| | | | | | | | |
| | | | | | | | |
| | | | | | | | |
| | | | | | | | |
| | | | | | | | |

| ACCOUNT | | | | | ACCOUNT NO. | | |
|---|---|---|---|---|---|---|---|
| DATE | ITEM | JRNL. REF. | DEBIT | CREDIT | BALANCE | | |
| | | | | | DEBIT | CREDIT | |
| | | | | | | | |
| | | | | | | | |
| | | | | | | | |
| | | | | | | | |
| | | | | | | | |

*Reqs. 1 & 4 (Continued)*

| ACCOUNT | | | | | ACCOUNT NO. | | |
|---|---|---|---|---|---|---|---|
| | | | | | BALANCE | | |
| DATE | ITEM | JRNL. REF. | DEBIT | CREDIT | DEBIT | | CREDIT |
| | | | | | | | |
| | | | | | | | |
| | | | | | | | |
| | | | | | | | |
| | | | | | | | |
| | | | | | | | |

*Req. 2*

The foldout worksheet to solve this problem can be found in the back of the book.

*Req. 3*

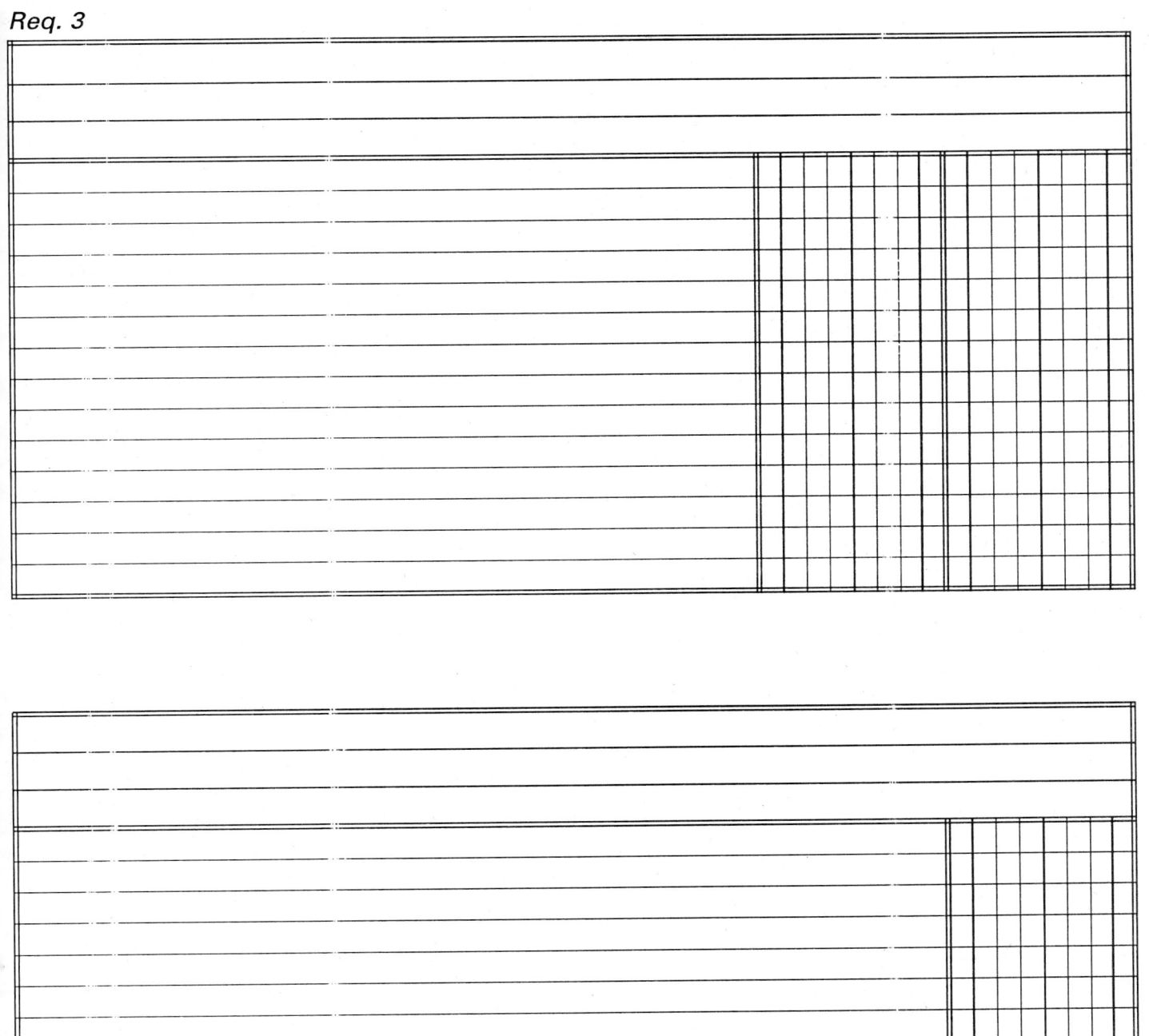

*Req. 3 (Continued)*

*Req. 4 (Continued)*

## Journal

| DATE | ACCOUNTS AND EXPLANATIONS | POST. REF. | DEBIT | CREDIT |
|------|---------------------------|-----------|-------|--------|
|      |                           |           |       |        |

*Req. 4 (Continued)*

## Journal

| DATE | | ACCOUNTS AND EXPLANATIONS | POST. REF. | DEBIT | CREDIT |
|------|--|---------------------------|------------|-------|--------|
| | | | | | |
| | | | | | |
| | | | | | |
| | | | | | |
| | | | | | |
| | | | | | |
| | | | | | |
| | | | | | |
| | | | | | |

Req. 5

*Req. 1*

*Reqs. 1 & 2*

*a–c*

*d*

NAME

SECTION

DATE

*e − f*

Chapter 4

**P4-7B**

# Journal

| DATE | ACCOUNTS AND EXPLANATIONS | POST. REF. | DEBIT | CREDIT |
|------|---------------------------|------------|-------|--------|
|      |                           |            |       |        |
|      |                           |            |       |        |
|      |                           |            |       |        |
|      |                           |            |       |        |
|      |                           |            |       |        |
|      |                           |            |       |        |
|      |                           |            |       |        |
|      |                           |            |       |        |
|      |                           |            |       |        |
|      |                           |            |       |        |
|      |                           |            |       |        |
|      |                           |            |       |        |
|      |                           |            |       |        |
|      |                           |            |       |        |
|      |                           |            |       |        |
|      |                           |            |       |        |
|      |                           |            |       |        |
|      |                           |            |       |        |
|      |                           |            |       |        |
|      |                           |            |       |        |
|      |                           |            |       |        |
|      |                           |            |       |        |
|      |                           |            |       |        |
|      |                           |            |       |        |
|      |                           |            |       |        |
|      |                           |            |       |        |
|      |                           |            |       |        |
|      |                           |            |       |        |
|      |                           |            |       |        |
|      |                           |            |       |        |

NAME
SECTION
DATE

Chapter 4

**Decision Case 1**

*(Continued,*

Note: If Needed, Create a Second Dollar-Column for Assets

NAME
SECTION
DATE

*Chapter 4*

# Decision Case 1
*(Continued)*

The foldout worksheet to solve this problem can be found in the back of the book.

*Reqs. 1–5*

*Reqs. 1, 2, & 3*

*Reqs. 2 & 3*

| | | POST. REF. | DEBIT | CREDIT |
|---|---|---|---|---|
| **Journal** | | | | |
| DATE | ACCOUNTS AND EXPLANATIONS | | | |
| | | | | |
| | | | | |
| | | | | |
| | | | | |
| | | | | |
| | | | | |
| | | | | |
| | | | | |
| | | | | |
| | | | | |
| | | | | |
| | | | | |
| | | | | |
| | | | | |
| | | | | |
| | | | | |
| | | | | |
| | | | | |
| | | | | |
| | | | | |
| | | | | |
| | | | | |
| | | | | |
| | | | | |
| | | | | |
| | | | | |
| | | | | |
| | | | | |
| | | | | |

*Req. 4*

| DATE | ACCOUNTS AND EXPLANATIONS | POST. REF. | DEBIT | CREDIT |
|------|---------------------------|-----------|-------|--------|
| | | | | |

Chapter 4

# Internet Exercise

# Solutions to
# Internet Exercises

# Solutions to Internet Exercises

## Journal

| DATE | ACCOUNTS AND EXPLANATIONS | POST. REF. | DEBIT | CREDIT |
|------|---------------------------|------------|-------|--------|
|      |                           |            |       |        |
|      |                           |            |       |        |
|      |                           |            |       |        |
|      |                           |            |       |        |
|      |                           |            |       |        |
|      |                           |            |       |        |
|      |                           |            |       |        |
|      |                           |            |       |        |
|      |                           |            |       |        |
|      |                           |            |       |        |
|      |                           |            |       |        |
|      |                           |            |       |        |
|      |                           |            |       |        |

**DE5-5**

## Journal

| DATE | ACCOUNTS AND EXPLANATIONS | POST. REF. | DEBIT | CREDIT |
|------|---------------------------|------------|-------|--------|
|      |                           |            |       |        |
|      |                           |            |       |        |
|      |                           |            |       |        |
|      |                           |            |       |        |
|      |                           |            |       |        |
|      |                           |            |       |        |
|      |                           |            |       |        |
|      |                           |            |       |        |
|      |                           |            |       |        |
|      |                           |            |       |        |
|      |                           |            |       |        |
|      |                           |            |       |        |
|      |                           |            |       |        |
|      |                           |            |       |        |

## Journal

| DATE | ACCOUNTS AND EXPLANATIONS | POST. REF. | DEBIT | CREDIT |
|------|---------------------------|------------|-------|--------|
|      |                           |            |       |        |
|      |                           |            |       |        |
|      |                           |            |       |        |
|      |                           |            |       |        |
|      |                           |            |       |        |
|      |                           |            |       |        |
|      |                           |            |       |        |
|      |                           |            |       |        |
|      |                           |            |       |        |
|      |                           |            |       |        |

## Journal

| DATE | ACCOUNTS AND EXPLANATIONS | POST. REF. | DEBIT | CREDIT |
|------|---------------------------|------------|-------|--------|
|      |                           |            |       |        |
|      |                           |            |       |        |
|      |                           |            |       |        |
|      |                           |            |       |        |
|      |                           |            |       |        |
|      |                           |            |       |        |
|      |                           |            |       |        |
|      |                           |            |       |        |
|      |                           |            |       |        |
|      |                           |            |       |        |
|      |                           |            |       |        |
|      |                           |            |       |        |
|      |                           |            |       |        |
|      |                           |            |       |        |
|      |                           |            |       |        |
|      |                           |            |       |        |
|      |                           |            |       |        |
|      |                           |            |       |        |

**DE5-9**

| | | Journal | | | |
|---|---|---|---|---|---|
| DATE | | ACCOUNTS AND EXPLANATIONS | POST. REF. | DEBIT | CREDIT |
| | | | | | |
| | | | | | |
| | | | | | |
| | | | | | |
| | | | | | |
| | | | | | |
| | | | | | |
| | | | | | |
| | | | | | |

**DE5-11**

## Journal

| DATE | ACCOUNTS AND EXPLANATIONS | POST. REF. | DEBIT | CREDIT |
|------|---------------------------|------------|-------|--------|
|      |                           |            |       |        |
|      |                           |            |       |        |
|      |                           |            |       |        |
|      |                           |            |       |        |
|      |                           |            |       |        |
|      |                           |            |       |        |
|      |                           |            |       |        |
|      |                           |            |       |        |
|      |                           |            |       |        |
|      |                           |            |       |        |
|      |                           |            |       |        |
|      |                           |            |       |        |
|      |                           |            |       |        |
|      |                           |            |       |        |
|      |                           |            |       |        |
|      |                           |            |       |        |
|      |                           |            |       |        |
|      |                           |            |       |        |
|      |                           |            |       |        |

*Reqs.1 & 2*

DE5-15

| | | MILLIONS |
|---|---|---|
| | | |

**DE5-17**

**DE5-18**

**DE5-19**

*Req. 1*

*Req. 2*

*Req. 3*

## Journal

| DATE | | ACCOUNTS AND EXPLANATIONS | POST. REF. | DEBIT | CREDIT |
|------|---|---------------------------|------------|-------|--------|
| June | 3 | Inventory | | 300 | |
| | | Accounts Payable | | | 300 |
| | 7 | Accounts Payable | | 300 | |
| | | Inventory | | | 300 |
| | 9 | Inventory (Freight-In) | | 30 | |
| | | Cash | | | 30 |
| | 10 | Accounts Receivable | | 2200 | |
| | | Sales Rev. | | | 2200 |
| | 10 | Cost of G.S. | | 1300 | |
| | | Inventory | | | 1300 |
| | 12 | Accounts Payable | | 400 | |
| | | Cash | | | 392 |
| | | Inventory (Disc.) | | | 8 |
| | 16 | Sales Returns & Allowances | | 800 | |
| | | Accounts Receivable | | | 800 |
| | 23 | Cash | | 1372 | |
| | | Sales Discount | | 28 | |
| | | Acct. Rec. | | | 1400 |

400
x 2%
8

400
- 8
392

## Journal

| DATE | | ACCOUNTS AND EXPLANATIONS | POST. REF. | DEBIT | CREDIT |
|---|---|---|---|---|---|
| May | 15 | Inventory | | 10536 | |
| | | Accounts Payable | | | 10536 |
| | 19 | Accounts Payable | | 5002 | |
| | | Inventory | | | 5002 |
| | 22 | Accounts Payable | | 5534 | |
| | | Inventory (Discount 2%) | | | 110 |
| | | Cash | | | 5423 |

## Journal

Purchaser

| DATE | | ACCOUNTS AND EXPLANATIONS | POST. REF. | DEBIT | CREDIT |
|---|---|---|---|---|---|
| May | 2 | Inventory | | 5000 | |
| | | Accounts Payable | | | 5000 |
| | 4 | Accounts Payable | | 800 | |
| | | Inventory | | | 800 |
| | 14 | Cash | | 4074 | |
| | | Note Payable (short term) | | | 4074 |
| | 14 | Accounts Pay | | 4200 | |
| | | Cash | | | 4074 |
| | | Inventory | | | 126 |
| June | 14 | Note Pay | | 4074 | |
| | | Intrest Exp | | 41 | |
| | | Cash | | | 4115 |

## Journal   Seller

| DATE | | ACCOUNTS AND EXPLANATIONS | POST. REF. | DEBIT | CREDIT |
|---|---|---|---|---|---|
| April | 30 | Accts Receivable | | 5000 | |
| | | Sales Revenue | | | 5000 |
| | 30 | Cost of Goods Sold | | 3000 | |
| | | Inventory | | | 3000 |
| | | | | | |
| May | 5 | Sales Returns & Allowance | | 800 | |
| | | Acct. Rec. | | | 800 |
| | 5 | Inventory | | 480 | |
| | | Cost of G.S. | | | 480 |
| | | | | | |
| | 15 | Cash | | 4074 | |
| | | Sales Discount | | 126 | |
| | | Acct. Rec. | | | 4200 |

5 **E5-6**

## Journal

| DATE | | ACCOUNTS AND EXPLANATIONS | POST. REF. | DEBIT | CREDIT |
|---|---|---|---|---|---|
| Jan. | 31 | Closing Entries | | | |
| | | Sales Revenue | | 15470 | |
| | | Intrest Revenue | | 20 | |
| | | Income Summary | | | 15490 |
| | | | | | |
| | | Income Summary | | 3513 | |
| | | Other Expense | | | 516 |
| | | Selling Expense | | | 2784 |
| | | Intrest Expense | | | 4 |
| | | Gen. & Admin. Exp | | | 269 |

|  Income Summary  |  |
|---|---|
|  | 15490 |

|  Owner Capital  |  |
|---|---|
|  |  |

## Journal

| DATE | ACCOUNTS AND EXPLANATIONS | POST. REF. | DEBIT | CREDIT |
|------|---------------------------|-----------|-------|--------|
|      |                           |           |       |        |
|      |                           |           |       |        |
|      |                           |           |       |        |
|      |                           |           |       |        |
|      |                           |           |       |        |
|      |                           |           |       |        |
|      |                           |           |       |        |
|      |                           |           |       |        |
|      |                           |           |       |        |
|      |                           |           |       |        |
|      |                           |           |       |        |
|      |                           |           |       |        |
|      |                           |           |       |        |
|      |                           |           |       |        |
|      |                           |           |       |        |
|      |                           |           |       |        |
|      |                           |           |       |        |
|      |                           |           |       |        |
|      |                           |           |       |        |
|      |                           |           |       |        |

E5-9

Reqs. 1 & 2

Req. 2

## Journal

| DATE | ACCOUNTS AND EXPLANATIONS | POST. REF. | DEBIT | CREDIT |
|------|---------------------------|------------|-------|--------|
|  |  |  |  |  |
|  |  |  |  |  |
|  |  |  |  |  |
|  |  |  |  |  |
|  |  |  |  |  |
|  |  |  |  |  |
|  |  |  |  |  |
|  |  |  |  |  |
|  |  |  |  |  |
|  |  |  |  |  |
|  |  |  |  |  |
|  |  |  |  |  |
|  |  |  |  |  |
|  |  |  |  |  |
|  |  |  |  |  |
|  |  |  |  |  |
|  |  |  |  |  |
|  |  |  |  |  |
|  |  |  |  |  |
|  |  |  |  |  |
|  |  |  |  |  |
|  |  |  |  |  |
|  |  |  |  |  |
|  |  |  |  |  |
|  |  |  |  |  |
|  |  |  |  |  |
|  |  |  |  |  |
|  |  |  |  |  |
|  |  |  |  |  |
|  |  |  |  |  |
|  |  |  |  |  |
|  |  |  |  |  |
|  |  |  |  |  |

Req. 2

## Journal

| DATE | ACCOUNTS AND EXPLANATIONS | POST. REF. | DEBIT | CREDIT |
|------|---------------------------|------------|-------|--------|
|  |  |  |  |  |
|  |  |  |  |  |
|  |  |  |  |  |
|  |  |  |  |  |
|  |  |  |  |  |
|  |  |  |  |  |
|  |  |  |  |  |
|  |  |  |  |  |
|  |  |  |  |  |
|  |  |  |  |  |
|  |  |  |  |  |
|  |  |  |  |  |
|  |  |  |  |  |
|  |  |  |  |  |
|  |  |  |  |  |
|  |  |  |  |  |
|  |  |  |  |  |
|  |  |  |  |  |
|  |  |  |  |  |
|  |  |  |  |  |
|  |  |  |  |  |
|  |  |  |  |  |
|  |  |  |  |  |
|  |  |  |  |  |
|  |  |  |  |  |

NAME

SECTION

DATE

Req. 1

## Journal

| DATE | ACCOUNTS AND EXPLANATIONS | POST. REF. | DEBIT | CREDIT |
|------|---------------------------|------------|-------|--------|
|  |  |  |  |  |
|  |  |  |  |  |
|  |  |  |  |  |
|  |  |  |  |  |
|  |  |  |  |  |
|  |  |  |  |  |
|  |  |  |  |  |
|  |  |  |  |  |
|  |  |  |  |  |
|  |  |  |  |  |
|  |  |  |  |  |
|  |  |  |  |  |
|  |  |  |  |  |
|  |  |  |  |  |
|  |  |  |  |  |
|  |  |  |  |  |
|  |  |  |  |  |
|  |  |  |  |  |
|  |  |  |  |  |
|  |  |  |  |  |
|  |  |  |  |  |
|  |  |  |  |  |
|  |  |  |  |  |
|  |  |  |  |  |
|  |  |  |  |  |
|  |  |  |  |  |
|  |  |  |  |  |
|  |  |  |  |  |
|  |  |  |  |  |
|  |  |  |  |  |
|  |  |  |  |  |
|  |  |  |  |  |
|  |  |  |  |  |
|  |  |  |  |  |
|  |  |  |  |  |
|  |  |  |  |  |
|  |  |  |  |  |
|  |  |  |  |  |

## Journal

| DATE | ACCOUNTS AND EXPLANATIONS | POST. REF. | DEBIT | CREDIT |
|---|---|---|---|---|
| | | | | |
| | | | | |
| | | | | |
| | | | | |
| | | | | |
| | | | | |
| | | | | |
| | | | | |
| | | | | |
| | | | | |
| | | | | |
| | | | | |
| | | | | |
| | | | | |
| | | | | |
| | | | | |
| | | | | |
| | | | | |
| | | | | |
| | | | | |
| | | | | |
| | | | | |
| | | | | |
| | | | | |
| | | | | |
| | | | | |
| | | | | |

*Req. 2*

AME
ECTION
ATE

*Req. 1*

*Req. 2*

Req. 1

|  |  |  |  |  |  |  |  |  |  |  |  |  |  |  |  |  |  |  |  |  |  |  |  |  |  |  |  |  |  |  |
|--|--|--|--|--|--|--|--|--|--|--|--|--|--|--|--|--|--|--|--|--|--|--|--|--|--|--|--|--|--|--|
|  |  |  |  |  |  |  |  |  |  |  |  |  |  |  |  |  |  |  |  |  |  |  |  |  |  |  |  |  |  |  |

*Req. 2*

*Req. 1*

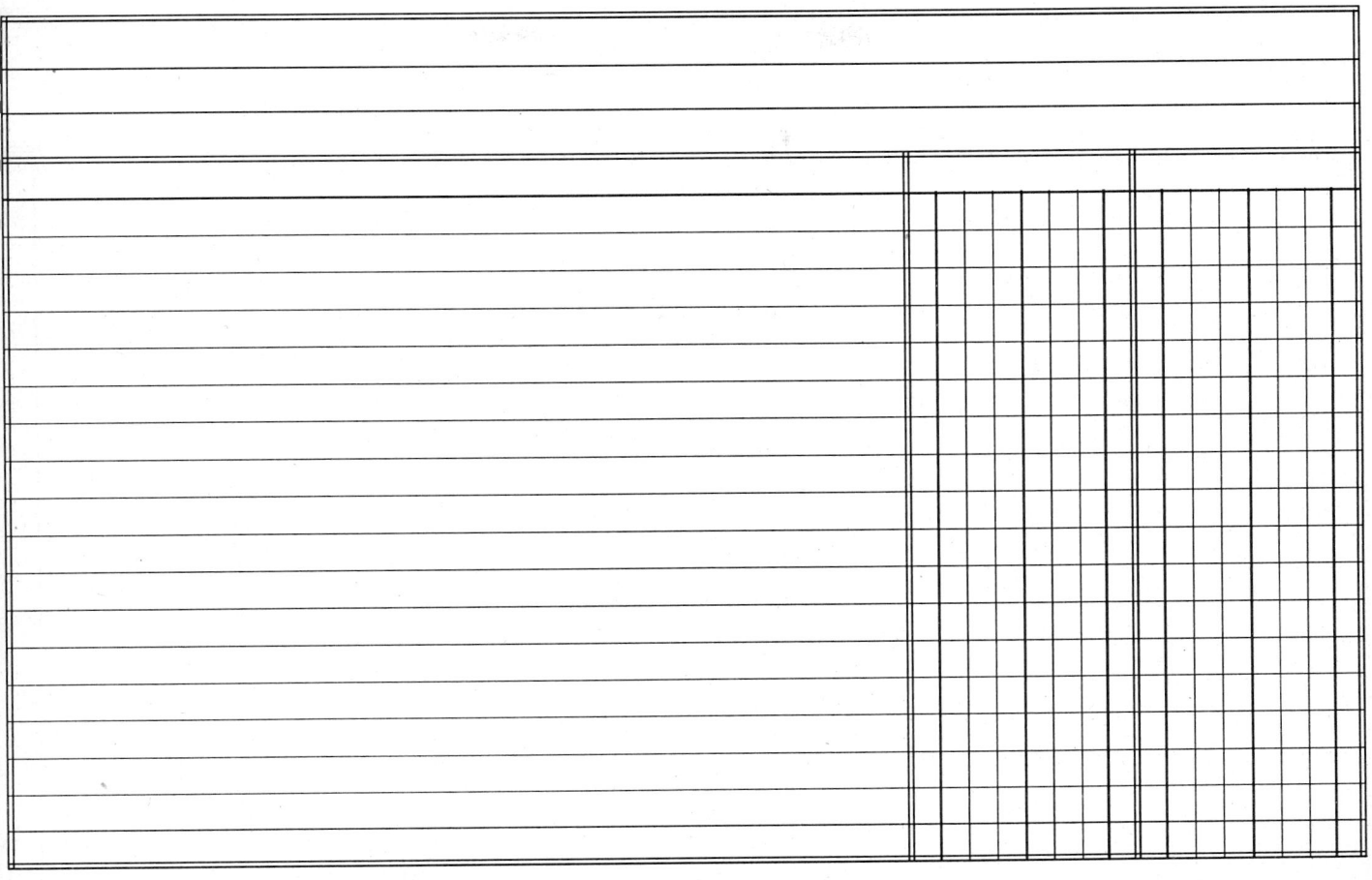

*Req. 2*

Req. 1

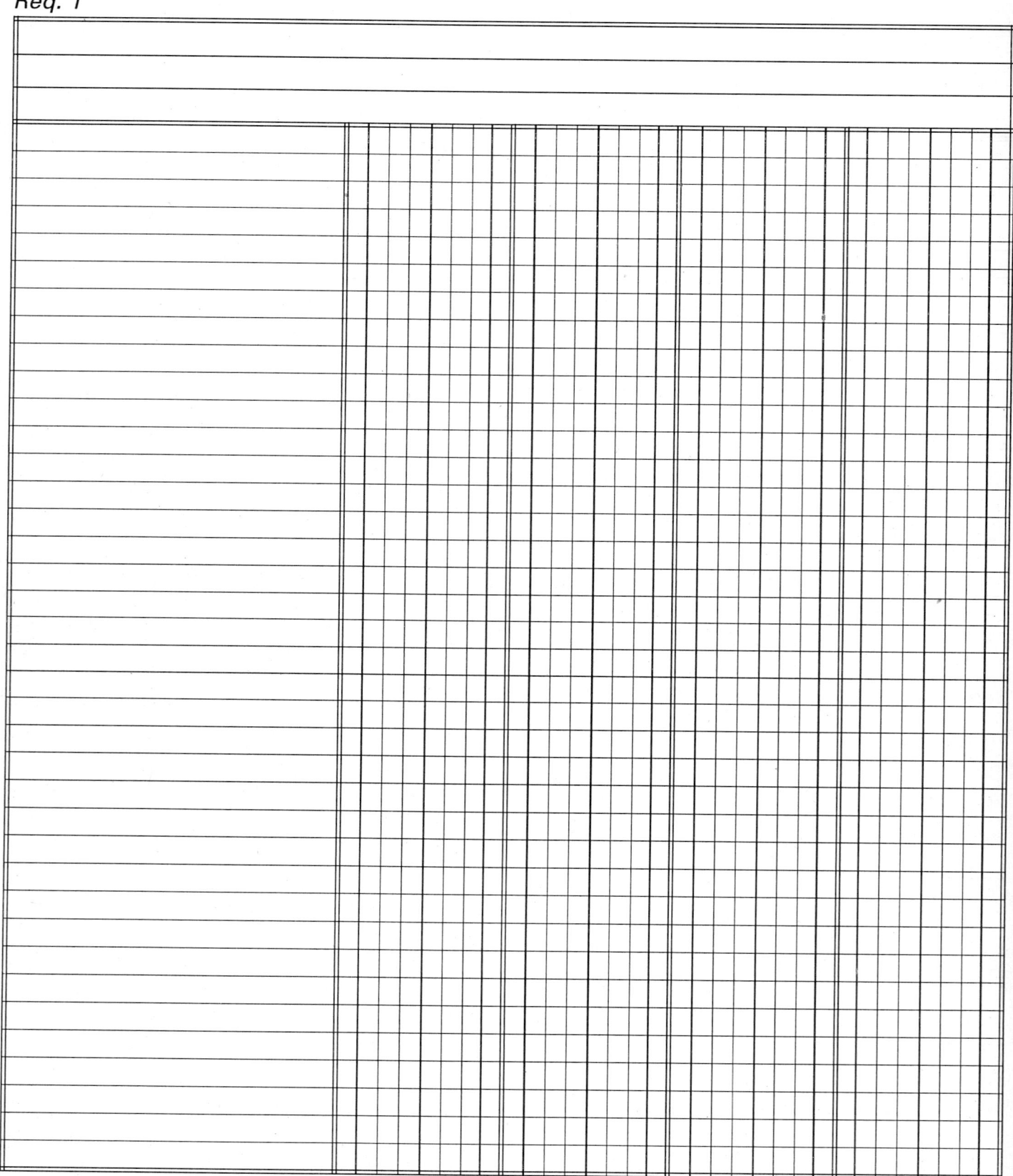

*Reqs. 2 & 3*

## Journal

| DATE | ACCOUNTS AND EXPLANATIONS | POST. REF. | DEBIT | CREDIT |
|------|--------------------------|-----------|-------|--------|
|  |  |  |  |  |
|  |  |  |  |  |
|  |  |  |  |  |
|  |  |  |  |  |
|  |  |  |  |  |
|  |  |  |  |  |
|  |  |  |  |  |
|  |  |  |  |  |
|  |  |  |  |  |
|  |  |  |  |  |
|  |  |  |  |  |
|  |  |  |  |  |
|  |  |  |  |  |
|  |  |  |  |  |
|  |  |  |  |  |
|  |  |  |  |  |
|  |  |  |  |  |
|  |  |  |  |  |
|  |  |  |  |  |
|  |  |  |  |  |
|  |  |  |  |  |
|  |  |  |  |  |
|  |  |  |  |  |
|  |  |  |  |  |

## Journal

| DATE | ACCOUNTS AND EXPLANATIONS | POST. REF. | DEBIT | CREDIT |
|------|---------------------------|-----------|-------|--------|
|  |  |  |  |  |
|  |  |  |  |  |
|  |  |  |  |  |
|  |  |  |  |  |
|  |  |  |  |  |
|  |  |  |  |  |
|  |  |  |  |  |
|  |  |  |  |  |
|  |  |  |  |  |
|  |  |  |  |  |
|  |  |  |  |  |
|  |  |  |  |  |
|  |  |  |  |  |
|  |  |  |  |  |
|  |  |  |  |  |
|  |  |  |  |  |
|  |  |  |  |  |
|  |  |  |  |  |
|  |  |  |  |  |

NAME
SECTION
DATE

E5-3B

Req. 1

## Journal

| DATE | ACCOUNTS AND EXPLANATIONS | POST. REF. | DEBIT | CREDIT |
|------|--------------------------|------------|-------|--------|
|      |                          |            |       |        |
|      |                          |            |       |        |
|      |                          |            |       |        |
|      |                          |            |       |        |
|      |                          |            |       |        |
|      |                          |            |       |        |
|      |                          |            |       |        |
|      |                          |            |       |        |
|      |                          |            |       |        |
|      |                          |            |       |        |
|      |                          |            |       |        |
|      |                          |            |       |        |
|      |                          |            |       |        |
|      |                          |            |       |        |
|      |                          |            |       |        |
|      |                          |            |       |        |
|      |                          |            |       |        |
|      |                          |            |       |        |
|      |                          |            |       |        |
|      |                          |            |       |        |
|      |                          |            |       |        |
|      |                          |            |       |        |
|      |                          |            |       |        |
|      |                          |            |       |        |
|      |                          |            |       |        |
|      |                          |            |       |        |
|      |                          |            |       |        |
|      |                          |            |       |        |
|      |                          |            |       |        |
|      |                          |            |       |        |

## Journal

| DATE | ACCOUNTS AND EXPLANATIONS | POST. REF. | DEBIT | CREDIT |
|------|---------------------------|------------|-------|--------|
|      |                           |            |       |        |
|      |                           |            |       |        |
|      |                           |            |       |        |
|      |                           |            |       |        |
|      |                           |            |       |        |
|      |                           |            |       |        |
|      |                           |            |       |        |
|      |                           |            |       |        |
|      |                           |            |       |        |
|      |                           |            |       |        |
|      |                           |            |       |        |
|      |                           |            |       |        |
|      |                           |            |       |        |
|      |                           |            |       |        |
|      |                           |            |       |        |
|      |                           |            |       |        |
|      |                           |            |       |        |
|      |                           |            |       |        |

The foldout worksheet to solve this problem can be found in the back of the book.

*Req. 1*

## Journal

| DATE | | ACCOUNTS AND EXPLANATIONS | POST. REF. | DEBIT | CREDIT |
|---|---|---|---|---|---|
| | | | | | |
| | | | | | |
| | | | | | |
| | | | | | |
| | | | | | |
| | | | | | |
| | | | | | |
| | | | | | |
| | | | | | |
| | | | | | |
| | | | | | |
| | | | | | |
| | | | | | |
| | | | | | |
| | | | | | |
| | | | | | |
| | | | | | |
| | | | | | |
| | | | | | |
| | | | | | |
| | | | | | |
| | | | | | |
| | | | | | |
| | | | | | |
| | | | | | |
| | | | | | |
| | | | | | |
| | | | | | |
| | | | | | |
| | | | | | |
| | | | | | |
| | | | | | |
| | | | | | |
| | | | | | |
| | | | | | |
| | | | | | |
| | | | | | |
| | | | | | |
| | | | | | |
| | | | | | |
| | | | | | |
| | | | | | |

## Journal

| DATE | ACCOUNTS AND EXPLANATIONS | POST. REF. | DEBIT | CREDIT |
|------|---------------------------|-----------|-------|--------|
|  |  |  |  |  |
|  |  |  |  |  |
|  |  |  |  |  |
|  |  |  |  |  |
|  |  |  |  |  |
|  |  |  |  |  |
|  |  |  |  |  |
|  |  |  |  |  |
|  |  |  |  |  |
|  |  |  |  |  |
|  |  |  |  |  |
|  |  |  |  |  |
|  |  |  |  |  |
|  |  |  |  |  |
|  |  |  |  |  |
|  |  |  |  |  |
|  |  |  |  |  |
|  |  |  |  |  |
|  |  |  |  |  |
|  |  |  |  |  |
|  |  |  |  |  |
|  |  |  |  |  |
|  |  |  |  |  |
|  |  |  |  |  |
|  |  |  |  |  |
|  |  |  |  |  |

*Req. 2*

*Req. 1*

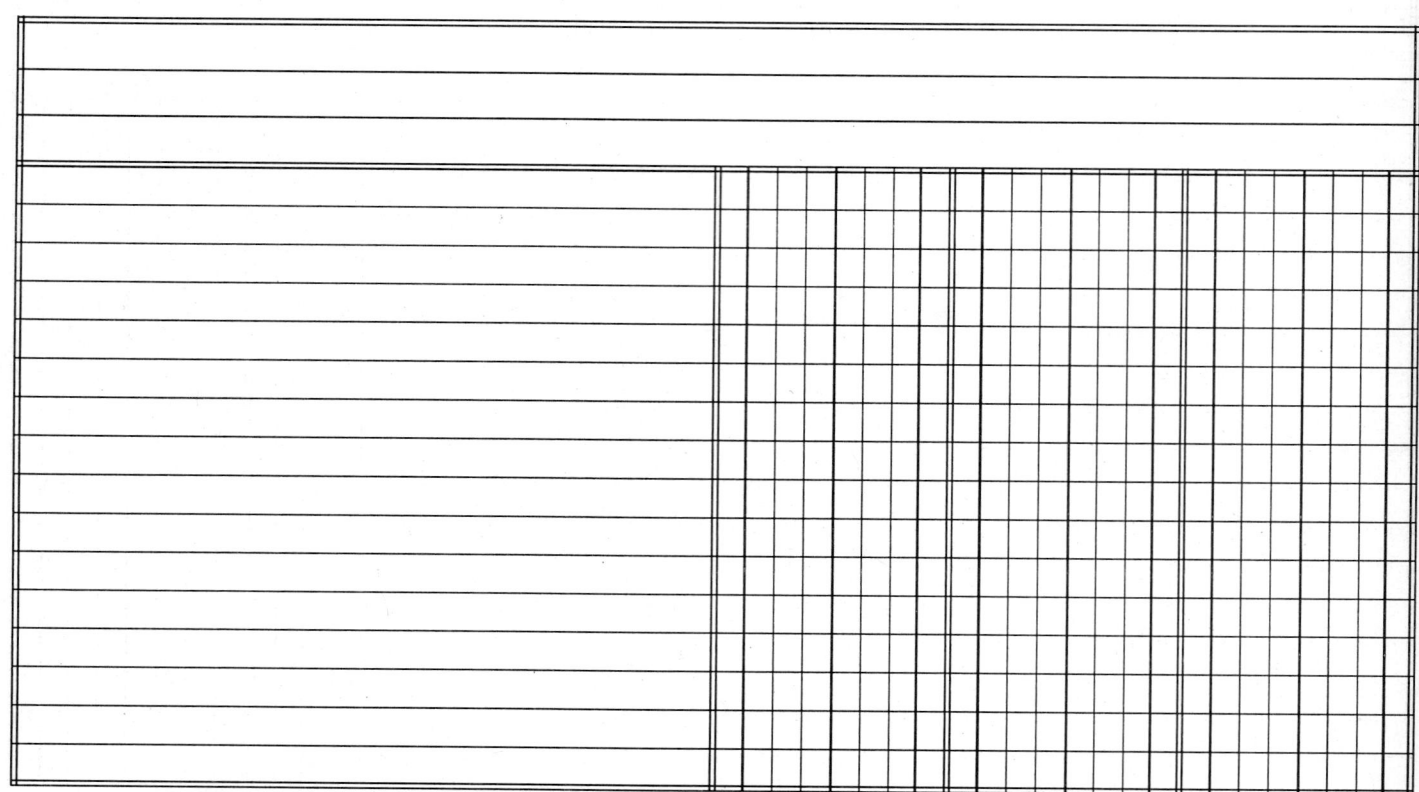

*Req. 1*

*Req. 2*

*Req. 1*

*Req. 2*

*Req. 1*

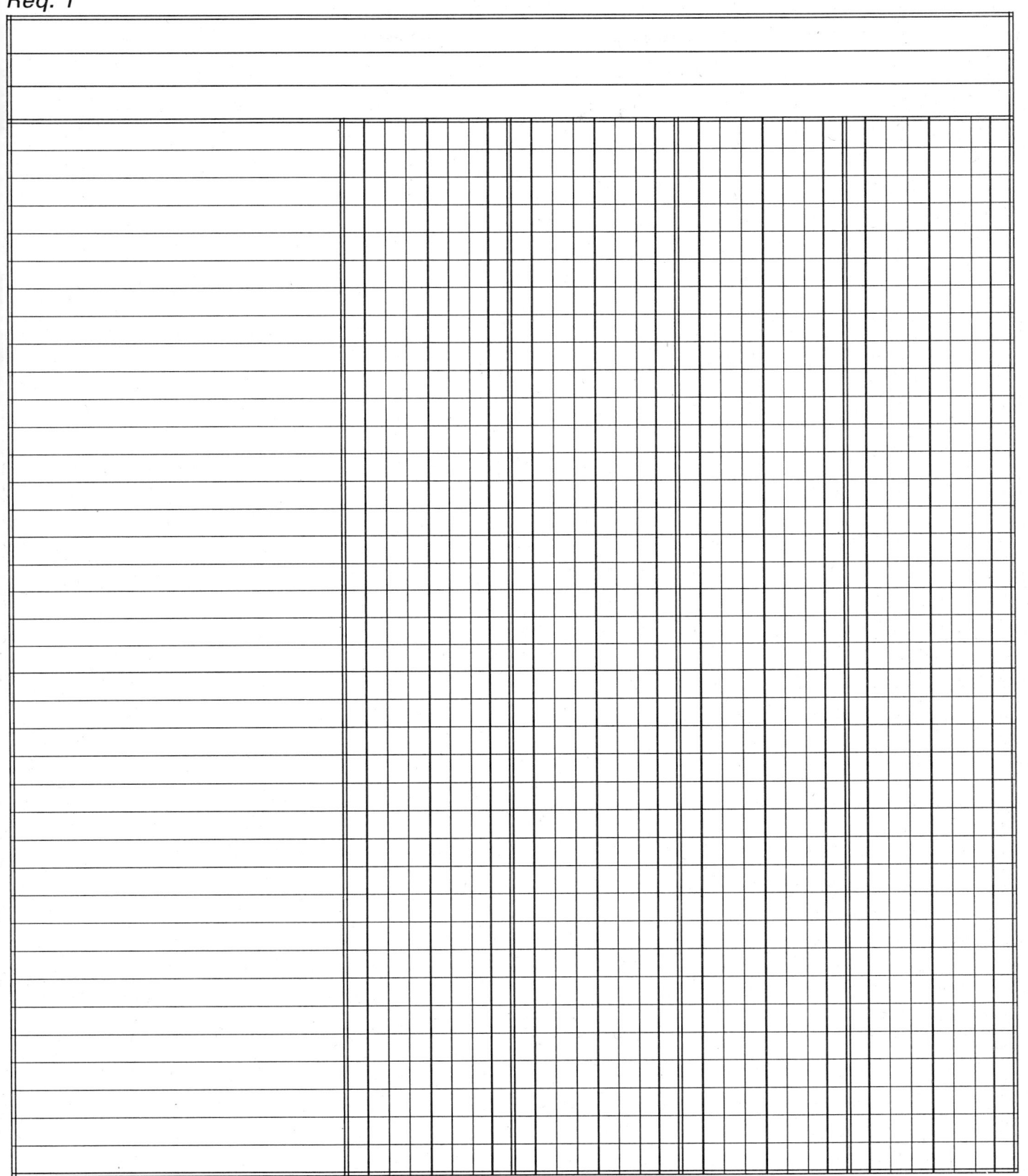

*Reqs. 2 & 3*

# Decision Case 1

*Req. 1*

*Req. 2*

*Req. 2*

*Reqs. 3 & 4*

*Req. 1*

| | | **Journal** | | | |
|---|---|---|---|---|---|
| DATE | | ACCOUNTS AND EXPLANATIONS | POST. REF. | DEBIT | CREDIT |
| | | | | | |
| | | | | | |
| | | | | | |
| | | | | | |
| | | | | | |
| | | | | | |
| | | | | | |
| | | | | | |
| | | | | | |
| | | | | | |
| | | | | | |
| | | | | | |
| | | | | | |
| | | | | | |
| | | | | | |
| | | | | | |
| | | | | | |
| | | | | | |

*Req. 2*

## Journal

| DATE | ACCOUNTS AND EXPLANATIONS | POST. REF. | DEBIT | CREDIT |
|------|---------------------------|------------|-------|--------|
|      |                           |            |       |        |
|      |                           |            |       |        |
|      |                           |            |       |        |
|      |                           |            |       |        |
|      |                           |            |       |        |
|      |                           |            |       |        |
|      |                           |            |       |        |
|      |                           |            |       |        |
|      |                           |            |       |        |
|      |                           |            |       |        |
|      |                           |            |       |        |
|      |                           |            |       |        |
|      |                           |            |       |        |
|      |                           |            |       |        |
|      |                           |            |       |        |
|      |                           |            |       |        |
|      |                           |            |       |        |
|      |                           |            |       |        |
|      |                           |            |       |        |
|      |                           |            |       |        |
|      |                           |            |       |        |
|      |                           |            |       |        |
|      |                           |            |       |        |
|      |                           |            |       |        |
|      |                           |            |       |        |
|      |                           |            |       |        |
|      |                           |            |       |        |

## Journal

| DATE | ACCOUNTS AND EXPLANATIONS | POST. REF. | DEBIT | CREDIT |
|------|---------------------------|------------|-------|--------|
|      |                           |            |       |        |
|      |                           |            |       |        |
|      |                           |            |       |        |
|      |                           |            |       |        |
|      |                           |            |       |        |
|      |                           |            |       |        |
|      |                           |            |       |        |
|      |                           |            |       |        |
|      |                           |            |       |        |
|      |                           |            |       |        |
|      |                           |            |       |        |
|      |                           |            |       |        |
|      |                           |            |       |        |

## Journal

| DATE | ACCOUNTS AND EXPLANATIONS | POST. REF. | DEBIT | CREDIT |
|------|---------------------------|------------|-------|--------|
|      |                           |            |       |        |
|      |                           |            |       |        |
|      |                           |            |       |        |
|      |                           |            |       |        |
|      |                           |            |       |        |
|      |                           |            |       |        |
|      |                           |            |       |        |
|      |                           |            |       |        |
|      |                           |            |       |        |
|      |                           |            |       |        |
|      |                           |            |       |        |
|      |                           |            |       |        |
|      |                           |            |       |        |
|      |                           |            |       |        |
|      |                           |            |       |        |
|      |                           |            |       |        |
|      |                           |            |       |        |
|      |                           |            |       |        |
|      |                           |            |       |        |
|      |                           |            |       |        |
|      |                           |            |       |        |
|      |                           |            |       |        |

## Journal

| DATE | ACCOUNTS AND EXPLANATIONS | POST. REF. | DEBIT | CREDIT |
|------|---------------------------|------------|-------|--------|
|  |  |  |  |  |
|  |  |  |  |  |
|  |  |  |  |  |
|  |  |  |  |  |
|  |  |  |  |  |
|  |  |  |  |  |
|  |  |  |  |  |
|  |  |  |  |  |
|  |  |  |  |  |
|  |  |  |  |  |
|  |  |  |  |  |
|  |  |  |  |  |
|  |  |  |  |  |
|  |  |  |  |  |

# Journal

| DATE | ACCOUNTS AND EXPLANATIONS | POST. REF. | DEBIT | CREDIT |
|------|---------------------------|-----------|-------|--------|
| | | | | |
| | | | | |
| | | | | |
| | | | | |
| | | | | |
| | | | | |
| | | | | |
| | | | | |
| | | | | |
| | | | | |
| | | | | |
| | | | | |
| | | | | |
| | | | | |
| | | | | |
| | | | | |
| | | | | |
| | | | | |
| | | | | |
| | | | | |
| | | | | |
| | | | | |
| | | | | |
| | | | | |
| | | | | |
| | | | | |
| | | | | |
| | | | | |
| | | | | |
| | | | | |
| | | | | |
| | | | | |
| | | | | |
| | | | | |
| | | | | |
| | | | | |
| | | | | |
| | | | | |
| | | | | |

Req. 1

## Journal

| DATE | ACCOUNTS AND EXPLANATIONS | POST. REF. | DEBIT | CREDIT |
|---|---|---|---|---|
|  |  |  |  |  |
|  |  |  |  |  |
|  |  |  |  |  |
|  |  |  |  |  |
|  |  |  |  |  |
|  |  |  |  |  |
|  |  |  |  |  |
|  |  |  |  |  |
|  |  |  |  |  |
|  |  |  |  |  |
|  |  |  |  |  |
|  |  |  |  |  |
|  |  |  |  |  |
|  |  |  |  |  |
|  |  |  |  |  |
|  |  |  |  |  |
|  |  |  |  |  |
|  |  |  |  |  |
|  |  |  |  |  |
|  |  |  |  |  |
|  |  |  |  |  |
|  |  |  |  |  |
|  |  |  |  |  |
|  |  |  |  |  |
|  |  |  |  |  |
|  |  |  |  |  |
|  |  |  |  |  |
|  |  |  |  |  |
|  |  |  |  |  |
|  |  |  |  |  |

Req. 2

*Req. 1*

## Journal

| DATE | ACCOUNTS AND EXPLANATIONS | POST. REF. | DEBIT | CREDIT |
|------|---------------------------|------------|-------|--------|
|  |  |  |  |  |
|  |  |  |  |  |
|  |  |  |  |  |
|  |  |  |  |  |
|  |  |  |  |  |
|  |  |  |  |  |
|  |  |  |  |  |
|  |  |  |  |  |
|  |  |  |  |  |
|  |  |  |  |  |
|  |  |  |  |  |
|  |  |  |  |  |
|  |  |  |  |  |
|  |  |  |  |  |
|  |  |  |  |  |
|  |  |  |  |  |
|  |  |  |  |  |
|  |  |  |  |  |
|  |  |  |  |  |
|  |  |  |  |  |
|  |  |  |  |  |
|  |  |  |  |  |
|  |  |  |  |  |
|  |  |  |  |  |
|  |  |  |  |  |
|  |  |  |  |  |
|  |  |  |  |  |
|  |  |  |  |  |
|  |  |  |  |  |
|  |  |  |  |  |
|  |  |  |  |  |
|  |  |  |  |  |

*Req. 2*

The foldout worksheet to solve this problem can be found in the back of the book.

**P5S-4**

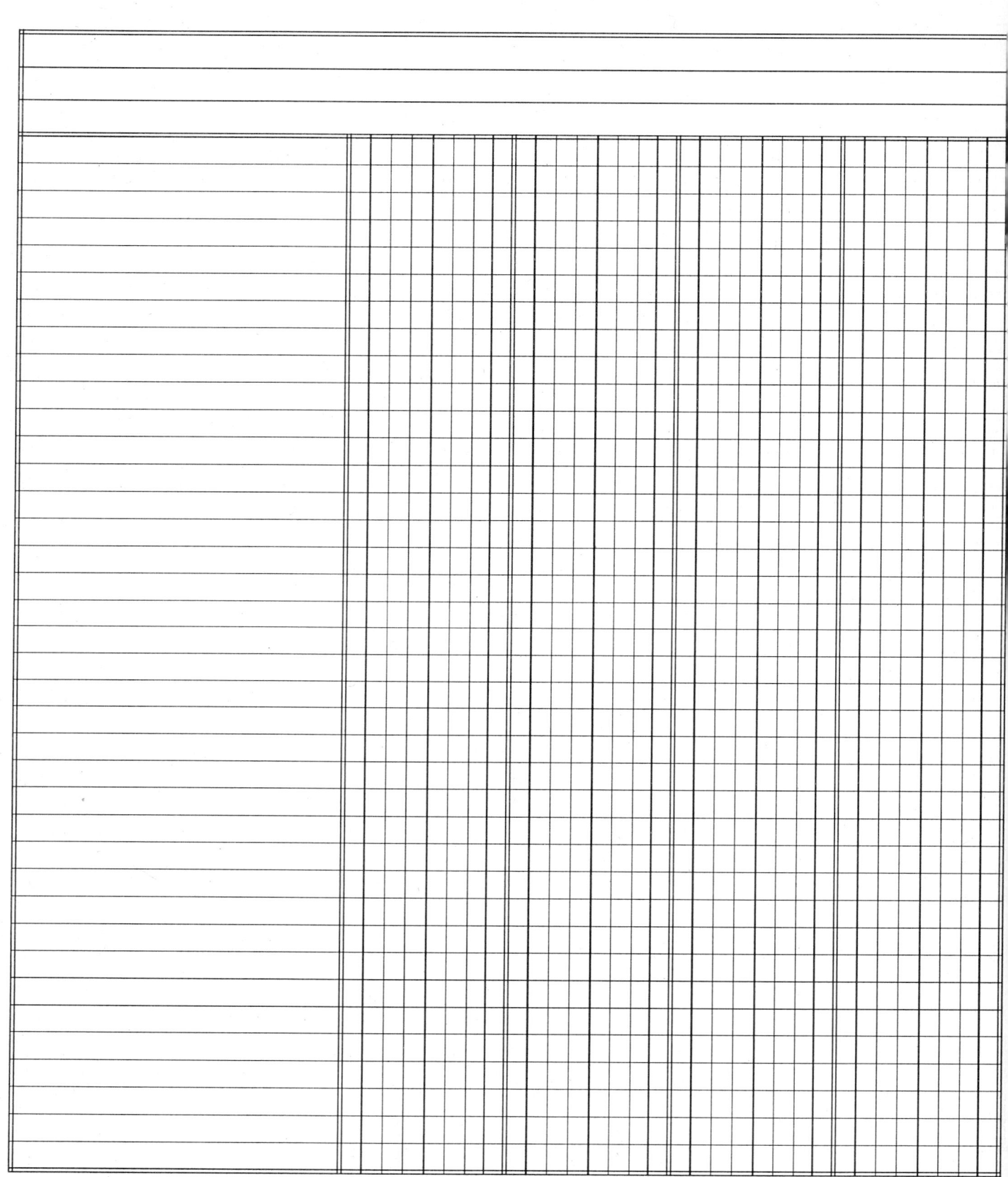

## Journal

| DATE | ACCOUNTS AND EXPLANATIONS | POST. REF. | DEBIT | CREDIT |
|------|---------------------------|------------|-------|--------|
|  |  |  |  |  |
|  |  |  |  |  |
|  |  |  |  |  |
|  |  |  |  |  |
|  |  |  |  |  |
|  |  |  |  |  |
|  |  |  |  |  |
|  |  |  |  |  |
|  |  |  |  |  |
|  |  |  |  |  |
|  |  |  |  |  |
|  |  |  |  |  |
|  |  |  |  |  |
|  |  |  |  |  |
|  |  |  |  |  |
|  |  |  |  |  |
|  |  |  |  |  |
|  |  |  |  |  |
|  |  |  |  |  |
|  |  |  |  |  |
|  |  |  |  |  |
|  |  |  |  |  |
|  |  |  |  |  |
|  |  |  |  |  |
|  |  |  |  |  |
|  |  |  |  |  |
|  |  |  |  |  |
|  |  |  |  |  |
|  |  |  |  |  |
|  |  |  |  |  |
|  |  |  |  |  |
|  |  |  |  |  |
|  |  |  |  |  |
|  |  |  |  |  |
|  |  |  |  |  |
|  |  |  |  |  |

**Computations:**

## Journal

| DATE | ACCOUNTS AND EXPLANATIONS | POST. REF. | DEBIT | CREDIT |
|------|---------------------------|------------|-------|--------|
| | | | | |
| | | | | |
| | | | | |
| | | | | |
| | | | | |
| | | | | |
| | | | | |
| | | | | |
| | | | | |
| | | | | |
| | | | | |
| | | | | |
| | | | | |
| | | | | |
| | | | | |
| | | | | |
| | | | | |
| | | | | |
| | | | | |
| | | | | |
| | | | | |
| | | | | |
| | | | | |
| | | | | |
| | | | | |
| | | | | |
| | | | | |
| | | | | |
| | | | | |
| | | | | |

NAME
SECTION
DATE

Chapter 5

**Solutions to
Internet Exercises**

The foldout worksheet to solve this problem can be found in the back of the book.

The foldout worksheet to solve this problem can be found in the back of the book.

The foldout worksheet to solve this problem can be found in the back of the book.

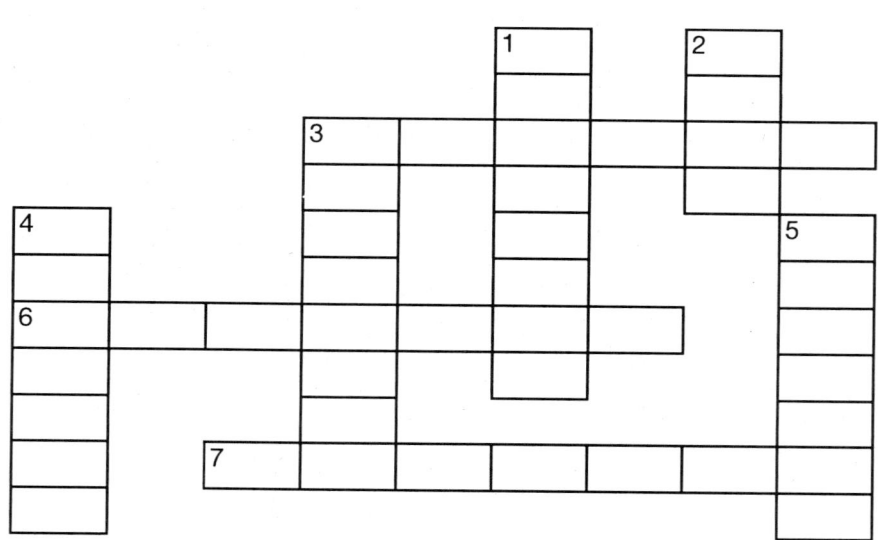

**DE6-5**

**DE6-6**

DE6-8

**DE6-10**

**DE6-12**

**E6-2**

**E6-3**

**E6-4**

# E6-5

NAME
SECTION
DATE

## Cash Receipts Journal

PAGE

| DATE | DEBITS | | | CREDITS | | | | |
| | CASH | SALES DISCOUNTS | ACCOUNTS RECEIVABLE | SALES REVENUE | OTHER ACCOUNTS | | | COST OF GOODS SOLD DR. INVENTORY CR. |
| | | | | | ACCOUNT TITLE | POST REF. | AMOUNT | |
| | | | | | | | | |
| | | | | | | | | |
| | | | | | | | | |
| | | | | | | | | |
| | | | | | | | | |
| | | | | | | | | |
| | | | | | | | | |

# E6-6

| OSTING EFERENCE | CLASSIFICATION | POSTING REFERENCE | CLASSIFICATION |
|---|---|---|---|
| a | | g | |
| b | | h | |
| c | | i | |
| d | | j | |
| e | | k | |
| f | | l | |

# E6-7

# E6-8

| Journal | | | | |
|---|---|---|---|---|
| DATE | ACCOUNTS AND EXPLANATIONS | POST. REF. | DEBIT | CREDIT |
| | | | | |
| | | | | |
| | | | | |
| | | | | |
| | | | | |
| | | | | |
| | | | | |
| | | | | |
| | | | | |
| | | | | |
| | | | | |
| | | | | |
| | | | | |
| | | | | |
| | | | | |
| | | | | |
| | | | | |
| | | | | |

Chapter 6

## Purchases Journal

| DATE | ACCOUNT CREDITED | TERMS | POST. REF. | CREDITS | DEBITS | | | | |
|------|------------------|-------|-----------|---------|--------|--|--|--|--|
| | | | | ACCOUNTS PAYABLE | INVENTORY | SUPPLIES | OTHER ACCOUNTS | | |
| | | | | | | | ACCOUNT TITLE | POST. REF. | AMOUNT |
| | | | | | | | | | |
| | | | | | | | | | |
| | | | | | | | | | |
| | | | | | | | | | |
| | | | | | | | | | |
| | | | | | | | | | |

| ACCOUNT | | | | | ACCOUNT NO. | | |
|---|---|---|---|---|---|---|---|
| | | | | | BALANCE | | |
| DATE | ITEM | JRNL. REF. | DEBIT | CREDIT | DEBIT | | CREDIT |
| | | | | | | | |
| | | | | | | | |
| | | | | | | | |

| ACCOUNT | | | | | ACCOUNT NO. | | |
|---|---|---|---|---|---|---|---|
| | | | | | BALANCE | | |
| DATE | ITEM | JRNL. REF. | DEBIT | CREDIT | DEBIT | | CREDIT |
| | | | | | | | |
| | | | | | | | |
| | | | | | | | |

| ACCOUNT | | | | | ACCOUNT NO. | | |
|---|---|---|---|---|---|---|---|
| | | | | | BALANCE | | |
| DATE | ITEM | JRNL. REF. | DEBIT | CREDIT | DEBIT | | CREDIT |
| | | | | | | | |
| | | | | | | | |
| | | | | | | | |

| ACCOUNT | | | | | ACCOUNT NO. | | |
|---|---|---|---|---|---|---|---|
| | | | | | BALANCE | | |
| DATE | ITEM | JRNL. REF. | DEBIT | CREDIT | DEBIT | | CREDIT |
| | | | | | | | |
| | | | | | | | |
| | | | | | | | |

*Req. 2*

| ACCOUNT | | | | | ACCOUNT NO. | |
|---|---|---|---|---|---|---|
| | | JRNL. REF. | | | BALANCE | |
| DATE | ITEM | | DEBIT | CREDIT | DEBIT | CREDIT |
| | | | | | | |
| | | | | | | |
| | | | | | | |

| ACCOUNT | | | | | ACCOUNT NO. | |
|---|---|---|---|---|---|---|
| | | JRNL. REF. | | | BALANCE | |
| DATE | ITEM | | DEBIT | CREDIT | DEBIT | CREDIT |
| | | | | | | |
| | | | | | | |
| | | | | | | |

| ACCOUNT | | | | | ACCOUNT NO. | |
|---|---|---|---|---|---|---|
| | | JRNL. REF. | | | BALANCE | |
| DATE | ITEM | | DEBIT | CREDIT | DEBIT | CREDIT |
| | | | | | | |
| | | | | | | |
| | | | | | | |

*Req. 3*

Chapter 6

Reqs. 1–3

# Cash Disbursements Journal

PAGE

| DATE | ACCOUNT DEBITED | DEBITS | | CREDITS | |
|---|---|---|---|---|---|
| | | OTHER ACCOUNTS | ACCOUNTS PAYABLE | INVENTORY | CASH |
| | | | | | |
| | | | | | |
| | | | | | |
| | | | | | |
| | | | | | |
| | | | | | |
| | | | | | |
| | | | | | |
| | | | | | |
| | | | | | |
| | | | | | |
| | | | | | |
| | | | | | |

BIWHEEL JOURNAL ENTRIES

SCHWINN JOURNAL ENTRIES

## General Journal

| DATE | ACCOUNT TITLE | DEBIT | CREDIT |
|------|---------------|-------|--------|
|      |               |       |        |
|      |               |       |        |
|      |               |       |        |
|      |               |       |        |
|      |               |       |        |
|      |               |       |        |
|      |               |       |        |
|      |               |       |        |
|      |               |       |        |

| DATE | ACCOUNT TITLE | DEBIT | CREDIT |
|------|---------------|-------|--------|
|      |               |       |        |
|      |               |       |        |
|      |               |       |        |
|      |               |       |        |
|      |               |       |        |
|      |               |       |        |
|      |               |       |        |
|      |               |       |        |
|      |               |       |        |

Reqs. 1–3

*Reqs. 1 and 3*

## Sales Journal

| DATE | ACCOUNT DEBITED | POST. REF. | ACCOUNTS RECEIVABLE DR. SALES REVENUE CR. | COST OF GOODS SOLD DR. INVENTORY CR. |
|------|-----------------|------------|-------------------------------------------|--------------------------------------|
|      |                 |            |                                           |                                      |
|      |                 |            |                                           |                                      |
|      |                 |            |                                           |                                      |
|      |                 |            |                                           |                                      |
|      |                 |            |                                           |                                      |
|      |                 |            |                                           |                                      |
|      |                 |            |                                           |                                      |
|      |                 |            |                                           |                                      |

Reqs. 1–3 *(Continued)*

## Cash Receipts Journal

PAGE

| DATE | DEBITS | | | CREDITS | | | |
| | CASH | SALES DISCOUNTS | ACCOUNTS RECEIVABLE | SALES REVENUE | OTHER ACCOUNTS | | COST OF GOODS SOLD DR. INVENTORY CR. |
| | | | | | ACCOUNT TITLE | POST REF. | AMOUNT | |

*Reqs. 1 and 3 (Continued)*

## Journal

| DATE | ACCOUNTS AND EXPLANATIONS | POST. REF. | DEBIT | CREDIT |
|------|---------------------------|------------|-------|--------|
|  |  |  |  |  |
|  |  |  |  |  |
|  |  |  |  |  |
|  |  |  |  |  |
|  |  |  |  |  |
|  |  |  |  |  |
|  |  |  |  |  |
|  |  |  |  |  |
|  |  |  |  |  |
|  |  |  |  |  |
|  |  |  |  |  |
|  |  |  |  |  |
|  |  |  |  |  |
|  |  |  |  |  |
|  |  |  |  |  |
|  |  |  |  |  |

*Req. 1*

*Req. 2*

NAME
SECTION
DATE

**P6-3A** *(Continued)*

*Req. 3*

## Cash Receipts Journal

PAGE

| DATE | DEBITS | | | CREDITS | | | | | |
|------|--------|--|--|---------|--|--|--|--|--|
| | CASH | SALES DISCOUNTS | ACCOUNTS RECEIVABLE | SALES REVENUE | OTHER ACCOUNTS | | | COST OF GOODS SOLD DR. INVENTORY CR. |
| | | | | | ACCOUNT TITLE | POST REF. | AMOUNT | |

P6-4A

*Reqs. 1–3*

# Purchases Journal

| DATE | ACCOUNT CREDITED | TERMS | POST. REF. | CREDITS | DEBITS | | OTHER ACCOUNTS | | |
|------|------------------|-------|-----------|---------|--------|--|----------------|--|--|
| | | | | ACCOUNTS PAYABLE | INVENTORY | SUPPLIES | ACCOUNT TITLE | POST. REF. | AMOUNT |
| | | | | | | | | | |
| | | | | | | | | | |
| | | | | | | | | | |
| | | | | | | | | | |
| | | | | | | | | | |
| | | | | | | | | | |
| | | | | | | | | | |
| | | | | | | | | | |
| | | | | | | | | | |
| | | | | | | | | | |

Chapter 6

P6-4A *(Continued)*

*Reqs. 1–3 (Continued)*

# Cash Disbursements Journal

PAGE

| DATE | ACCOUNT DEBITED | POST REF. | DEBITS | | CREDITS | |
|------|-----------------|-----------|--------|--------|--------|--------|
| | | | OTHER ACCOUNTS | ACCOUNTS PAYABLE | INVENTORY | CASH |
| | | | | | | |
| | | | | | | |
| | | | | | | |
| | | | | | | |
| | | | | | | |
| | | | | | | |
| | | | | | | |
| | | | | | | |
| | | | | | | |
| | | | | | | |
| | | | | | | |
| | | | | | | |
| | | | | | | |
| | | | | | | |
| | | | | | | |
| | | | | | | |
| | | | | | | |
| | | | | | | |
| | | | | | | |

*Reqs. 1–3 (Continued)*

| | | **Journal** | | | |
|---|---|---|---|---|---|
| DATE | | ACCOUNTS AND EXPLANATIONS | POST. REF. | DEBIT | CREDIT |
| | | | | | |
| | | | | | |
| | | | | | |
| | | | | | |
| | | | | | |
| | | | | | |
| | | | | | |
| | | | | | |
| | | | | | |

| ACCOUNT | | | | | ACCOUNT NO. | | | |
|---|---|---|---|---|---|---|---|---|
| | | | | | | BALANCE | | |
| DATE | ITEM | JRNL. REF. | DEBIT | CREDIT | DEBIT | | CREDIT | |
| | | | | | | | | |
| | | | | | | | | |
| | | | | | | | | |
| | | | | | | | | |
| | | | | | | | | |

| ACCOUNT | | | | | ACCOUNT NO. | | | |
|---|---|---|---|---|---|---|---|---|
| | | | | | | BALANCE | | |
| DATE | ITEM | JRNL. REF. | DEBIT | CREDIT | DEBIT | | CREDIT | |
| | | | | | | | | |
| | | | | | | | | |
| | | | | | | | | |
| | | | | | | | | |
| | | | | | | | | |
| | | | | | | | | |

| ACCOUNT | | | | | ACCOUNT NO. | | | |
|---|---|---|---|---|---|---|---|---|
| | | | | | | BALANCE | | |
| DATE | ITEM | JRNL. REF. | DEBIT | CREDIT | DEBIT | | CREDIT | |
| | | | | | | | | |
| | | | | | | | | |
| | | | | | | | | |
| | | | | | | | | |
| | | | | | | | | |
| | | | | | | | | |

| ACCOUNT | | | | | ACCOUNT NO. | | | |
|---|---|---|---|---|---|---|---|---|
| | | | | | | BALANCE | | |
| DATE | ITEM | JRNL. REF. | DEBIT | CREDIT | DEBIT | | CREDIT | |
| | | | | | | | | |
| | | | | | | | | |
| | | | | | | | | |
| | | | | | | | | |
| | | | | | | | | |
| | | | | | | | | |

| ACCOUNT  INVENTORY | | | | | ACCOUNT NO. | |
|---|---|---|---|---|---|---|
| | | JRNL. REF. | | | BALANCE | |
| DATE | ITEM | | DEBIT | CREDIT | DEBIT | CREDIT |
| | | | | | | |
| | | | | | | |
| | | | | | | |
| | | | | | | |
| | | | | | | |
| | | | | | | |
| | | | | | | |
| | | | | | | |

| ACCOUNT | | | | | ACCOUNT NO. | |
|---|---|---|---|---|---|---|
| | | JRNL. REF. | | | BALANCE | |
| DATE | ITEM | | DEBIT | CREDIT | DEBIT | CREDIT |
| | | | | | | |
| | | | | | | |
| | | | | | | |
| | | | | | | |
| | | | | | | |
| | | | | | | |

| ACCOUNT | | | | | ACCOUNT NO. | |
|---|---|---|---|---|---|---|
| | | JRNL. REF. | | | BALANCE | |
| DATE | ITEM | | DEBIT | CREDIT | DEBIT | CREDIT |
| | | | | | | |
| | | | | | | |
| | | | | | | |
| | | | | | | |
| | | | | | | |
| | | | | | | |

| ACCOUNT | | | | | ACCOUNT NO. | |
|---|---|---|---|---|---|---|
| | | JRNL. REF. | | | BALANCE | |
| DATE | ITEM | | DEBIT | CREDIT | DEBIT | CREDIT |
| | | | | | | |
| | | | | | | |
| | | | | | | |
| | | | | | | |
| | | | | | | |

| ACCOUNT | | | | | ACCOUNT NO. | | | | |
|---|---|---|---|---|---|---|---|---|---|
| | | | | | | BALANCE | | | |
| DATE | ITEM | JRNL. REF. | DEBIT | CREDIT | DEBIT | | CREDIT | | |
| | | | | | | | | | |
| | | | | | | | | | |
| | | | | | | | | | |
| | | | | | | | | | |
| | | | | | | | | | |

| ACCOUNT | | | | | ACCOUNT NO. | | | | |
|---|---|---|---|---|---|---|---|---|---|
| | | | | | | BALANCE | | | |
| DATE | ITEM | JRNL. REF. | DEBIT | CREDIT | DEBIT | | CREDIT | | |
| | | | | | | | | | |
| | | | | | | | | | |
| | | | | | | | | | |
| | | | | | | | | | |
| | | | | | | | | | |

| ACCOUNT | | | | | ACCOUNT NO. | | | | |
|---|---|---|---|---|---|---|---|---|---|
| | | | | | | BALANCE | | | |
| DATE | ITEM | JRNL. REF. | DEBIT | CREDIT | DEBIT | | CREDIT | | |
| | | | | | | | | | |
| | | | | | | | | | |
| | | | | | | | | | |
| | | | | | | | | | |
| | | | | | | | | | |

| ACCOUNT | | | | | ACCOUNT NO. | | | | |
|---|---|---|---|---|---|---|---|---|---|
| | | | | | | BALANCE | | | |
| DATE | ITEM | JRNL. REF. | DEBIT | CREDIT | DEBIT | | CREDIT | | |
| | | | | | | | | | |
| | | | | | | | | | |
| | | | | | | | | | |
| | | | | | | | | | |
| | | | | | | | | | |

| ACCOUNT | | | | | ACCOUNT NO. | | |
|---|---|---|---|---|---|---|---|
| | | | | | | BALANCE | |
| DATE | ITEM | JRNL. REF. | DEBIT | CREDIT | | DEBIT | CREDIT |
| | | | | | | | |
| | | | | | | | |
| | | | | | | | |
| | | | | | | | |
| | | | | | | | |
| | | | | | | | |

| ACCOUNT | | | | | ACCOUNT NO. | | |
|---|---|---|---|---|---|---|---|
| | | | | | | BALANCE | |
| DATE | ITEM | JRNL. REF. | DEBIT | CREDIT | | DEBIT | CREDIT |
| | | | | | | | |
| | | | | | | | |
| | | | | | | | |
| | | | | | | | |
| | | | | | | | |
| | | | | | | | |

| ACCOUNT | | | | | ACCOUNT NO. | | |
|---|---|---|---|---|---|---|---|
| | | | | | | BALANCE | |
| DATE | ITEM | JRNL. REF. | DEBIT | CREDIT | | DEBIT | CREDIT |
| | | | | | | | |
| | | | | | | | |
| | | | | | | | |
| | | | | | | | |
| | | | | | | | |
| | | | | | | | |

| ACCOUNT | | | | | ACCOUNT NO. | | |
|---|---|---|---|---|---|---|---|
| | | | | | | BALANCE | |
| DATE | ITEM | JRNL. REF. | DEBIT | CREDIT | | DEBIT | CREDIT |
| | | | | | | | |
| | | | | | | | |
| | | | | | | | |
| | | | | | | | |
| | | | | | | | |

| ACCOUNT | | | | | ACCOUNT NO. | | | |
|---|---|---|---|---|---|---|---|---|
| | | | | | | BALANCE | | |
| DATE | ITEM | JRNL. REF. | DEBIT | CREDIT | DEBIT | | CREDIT | |
| | | | | | | | | |
| | | | | | | | | |
| | | | | | | | | |
| | | | | | | | | |
| | | | | | | | | |

| ACCOUNT | | | | | ACCOUNT NO. | | | |
|---|---|---|---|---|---|---|---|---|
| | | | | | | BALANCE | | |
| DATE | ITEM | JRNL. REF. | DEBIT | CREDIT | DEBIT | | CREDIT | |
| | | | | | | | | |
| | | | | | | | | |
| | | | | | | | | |
| | | | | | | | | |
| | | | | | | | | |

| ACCOUNT | | | | | ACCOUNT NO. | | | |
|---|---|---|---|---|---|---|---|---|
| | | | | | | BALANCE | | |
| DATE | ITEM | JRNL. REF. | DEBIT | CREDIT | DEBIT | | CREDIT | |
| | | | | | | | | |
| | | | | | | | | |
| | | | | | | | | |
| | | | | | | | | |
| | | | | | | | | |

| ACCOUNT | | | | | ACCOUNT NO. | | | |
|---|---|---|---|---|---|---|---|---|
| | | | | | | BALANCE | | |
| DATE | ITEM | JRNL. REF. | DEBIT | CREDIT | DEBIT | | CREDIT | |
| | | | | | | | | |
| | | | | | | | | |
| | | | | | | | | |
| | | | | | | | | |

*Reqs. 3–5*

| | | Sales Journal | | | | |
|---|---|---|---|---|---|---|
| DATE | INVOICE NO. | ACCOUNT DEBITED | POST. REF. | ACCOUNTS RECEIVABLE DR. SALES REVENUE CR. | COST OF GOODS SOLD DR. INVENTORY CR. | |
| | | | | | | |
| | | | | | | |
| | | | | | | |
| | | | | | | |
| | | | | | | |
| | | | | | | |
| | | | | | | |
| | | | | | | |
| | | | | | | |

*Req. 6*

# Cash Receipts Journal

PAGE

| DATE | DEBITS | | | CREDITS | | | | COST OF GOODS SOLD DR. INVENTORY CR. |
|------|--------|--|--|---------|--|--|--|--|
| | CASH | SALES DISCOUNTS | ACCOUNTS RECEIVABLE | SALES REVENUE | OTHER ACCOUNTS | | | |
| | | | | | ACCOUNT TITLE | POST REF. | AMOUNT | |

**P6-5A**(Continued)

## Purchases Journal

PAGE

| DATE | ACCOUNT CREDITED | TERMS | POST. REF. | CREDITS | DEBITS | | OTHER ACCOUNTS | | |
|------|------------------|-------|-----------|---------|--------|--------|----------------|--------|--------|
| | | | | ACCOUNTS PAYABLE | INVENTORY | SUPPLIES | ACCOUNT TITLE | POST. REF. | AMOUNT |
| | | | | | | | | | |
| | | | | | | | | | |
| | | | | | | | | | |
| | | | | | | | | | |
| | | | | | | | | | |
| | | | | | | | | | |
| | | | | | | | | | |

NAME
SECTION
DATE

P6-5A *(Continued)*

# Cash Disbursements Journal

PAGE

| DATE | CK. NO. | ACCOUNT DEBITED | POST. REF. | DEBITS | | CREDITS | |
|------|---------|-----------------|------------|--------|--------|-----------|------|
| | | | | OTHER ACCOUNTS | ACCOUNTS PAYABLE | INVENTORY | CASH |
| | | | | | | | |
| | | | | | | | |
| | | | | | | | |
| | | | | | | | |
| | | | | | | | |
| | | | | | | | |
| | | | | | | | |
| | | | | | | | |
| | | | | | | | |
| | | | | | | | |
| | | | | | | | |
| | | | | | | | |

## General Journal

| DATE | | ACCOUNTS AND EXPLANATIONS | POST. REF. | DEBIT | CREDIT |
|---|---|---|---|---|---|
| | | | | | |
| | | | | | |
| | | | | | |
| | | | | | |
| | | | | | |
| | | | | | |
| | | | | | |
| | | | | | |
| | | | | | |
| | | | | | |
| | | | | | |
| | | | | | |
| | | | | | |

Reqs. 1–3

*Reqs. 1 and 3*

| | | Sales Journal | | | | |
|---|---|---|---|---|---|---|
| DATE | | ACCOUNT DEBITED | POST. REF. | ACCOUNTS RECEIVABLE DR. SALES REVENUE CR. | COST OF GOODS SOLD DR. INVENTORY CR. | |
| | | | | | | |
| | | | | | | |
| | | | | | | |
| | | | | | | |
| | | | | | | |
| | | | | | | |
| | | | | | | |
| | | | | | | |
| | | | | | | |

Chapter 6

P6-2B *(Continued)*

Reqs. 1–3 *(Continued)*

## Cash Receipts Journal

PAGE

| | DEBITS | | | CREDITS | | | | | |
|---|---|---|---|---|---|---|---|---|---|
| | | | | | | OTHER ACCOUNTS | | | COST OF GOODS SOLD DR. INVENTORY CR. |
| DATE | CASH | SALES DISCOUNTS | ACCOUNTS RECEIVABLE | SALES REVENUE | | ACCOUNT TITLE | POST REF. | AMOUNT | |

*Reqs. 1 and 3 (Continued)*

| | | General Journal | | | |
|---|---|---|---|---|---|
| DATE | | ACCOUNTS AND EXPLANATIONS | | DEBIT | CREDIT |
| | | | | | |
| | | | | | |
| | | | | | |
| | | | | | |
| | | | | | |
| | | | | | |
| | | | | | |
| | | | | | |
| | | | | | |
| | | | | | |
| | | | | | |
| | | | | | |
| | | | | | |
| | | | | | |
| | | | | | |
| | | | | | |
| | | | | | |

*Req. 1*

*Req. 2*

**P6-3B** *(Continued)*

Req. 3

## Cash Receipts Journal

PAGE

| DATE | DEBITS | | | CREDITS | | | | |
|------|--------|--------|--------|---------|--------|--------|--------|--------|
| | CASH | SALES DISCOUNTS | ACCOUNTS RECEIVABLE | SALES REVENUE | OTHER ACCOUNTS | | | COST OF GOODS SOLD DR. INVENTORY CR. |
| | | | | | ACCOUNT TITLE | POST REF. | AMOUNT | |

NAME
SECTION
DATE

**P6-4B**

Reqs. 1–3

# Purchases Journal

| DATE | ACCOUNT CREDITED | TERMS | POST. REF. | CREDITS | DEBITS | | OTHER ACCOUNTS | | |
|------|------------------|-------|-----------|---------|--------|--|----------------|--|--|
| | | | | ACCOUNTS PAYABLE | INVENTORY | SUPPLIES | ACCOUNT TITLE | POST. REF. | AMOUNT |
| | | | | | | | | | |
| | | | | | | | | | |
| | | | | | | | | | |
| | | | | | | | | | |
| | | | | | | | | | |
| | | | | | | | | | |
| | | | | | | | | | |
| | | | | | | | | | |
| | | | | | | | | | |

Reqs. 1–3 *(Continued)*

# Cash Disbursements Journal

PAGE

| DATE | ACCOUNT DEBITED | POST REF. | DEBITS | | CREDITS | |
| | | | OTHER ACCOUNTS | ACCOUNTS PAYABLE | INVENTORY | CASH |
| --- | --- | --- | --- | --- | --- | --- |
| | | | | | | |
| | | | | | | |
| | | | | | | |
| | | | | | | |
| | | | | | | |
| | | | | | | |
| | | | | | | |
| | | | | | | |
| | | | | | | |
| | | | | | | |

*Reqs. 1–3 (Continued)*

## Journal

| DATE | ACCOUNTS AND EXPLANATIONS | POST. REF. | DEBIT | CREDIT |
|------|---------------------------|------------|-------|--------|
|      |                           |            |       |        |
|      |                           |            |       |        |
|      |                           |            |       |        |
|      |                           |            |       |        |
|      |                           |            |       |        |
|      |                           |            |       |        |
|      |                           |            |       |        |
|      |                           |            |       |        |

| ACCOUNT | | | | | | ACCOUNT NO. | |
|---|---|---|---|---|---|---|---|
| | | | | | | BALANCE | |
| DATE | ITEM | JRNL. REF. | DEBIT | CREDIT | | DEBIT | CREDIT |
| | | | | | | | |
| | | | | | | | |
| | | | | | | | |
| | | | | | | | |
| | | | | | | | |

| ACCOUNT | | | | | | ACCOUNT NO. | |
|---|---|---|---|---|---|---|---|
| | | | | | | BALANCE | |
| DATE | ITEM | JRNL. REF. | DEBIT | CREDIT | | DEBIT | CREDIT |
| | | | | | | | |
| | | | | | | | |
| | | | | | | | |
| | | | | | | | |
| | | | | | | | |

| ACCOUNT | | | | | | ACCOUNT NO. | |
|---|---|---|---|---|---|---|---|
| | | | | | | BALANCE | |
| DATE | ITEM | JRNL. REF. | DEBIT | CREDIT | | DEBIT | CREDIT |
| | | | | | | | |
| | | | | | | | |
| | | | | | | | |
| | | | | | | | |
| | | | | | | | |

| ACCOUNT | | | | | | ACCOUNT NO. | |
|---|---|---|---|---|---|---|---|
| | | | | | | BALANCE | |
| DATE | ITEM | JRNL. REF. | DEBIT | CREDIT | | DEBIT | CREDIT |
| | | | | | | | |
| | | | | | | | |
| | | | | | | | |
| | | | | | | | |
| | | | | | | | |

| ACCOUNT  INVENTORY | | | | | ACCOUNT NO. | |
|---|---|---|---|---|---|---|
| | | | | | BALANCE | |
| DATE | ITEM | JRNL. REF. | DEBIT | CREDIT | DEBIT | CREDIT |
| | | | | | | |
| | | | | | | |
| | | | | | | |
| | | | | | | |
| | | | | | | |
| | | | | | | |
| | | | | | | |

| ACCOUNT | | | | | ACCOUNT NO. | |
|---|---|---|---|---|---|---|
| | | | | | BALANCE | |
| DATE | ITEM | JRNL. REF. | DEBIT | CREDIT | DEBIT | CREDIT |
| | | | | | | |
| | | | | | | |
| | | | | | | |
| | | | | | | |

| ACCOUNT | | | | | ACCOUNT NO. | |
|---|---|---|---|---|---|---|
| | | | | | BALANCE | |
| DATE | ITEM | JRNL. REF. | DEBIT | CREDIT | DEBIT | CREDIT |
| | | | | | | |
| | | | | | | |
| | | | | | | |
| | | | | | | |

| ACCOUNT | | | | | ACCOUNT NO. | |
|---|---|---|---|---|---|---|
| | | | | | BALANCE | |
| DATE | ITEM | JRNL. REF. | DEBIT | CREDIT | DEBIT | CREDIT |
| | | | | | | |
| | | | | | | |
| | | | | | | |

| ACCOUNT | | | | | ACCOUNT NO. | | |
|---|---|---|---|---|---|---|---|
| | | | | | | BALANCE | |
| DATE | ITEM | JRNL. REF. | DEBIT | CREDIT | DEBIT | CREDIT | |
| | | | | | | | |
| | | | | | | | |
| | | | | | | | |
| | | | | | | | |
| | | | | | | | |

| ACCOUNT | | | | | ACCOUNT NO. | | |
|---|---|---|---|---|---|---|---|
| | | | | | | BALANCE | |
| DATE | ITEM | JRNL. REF. | DEBIT | CREDIT | DEBIT | CREDIT | |
| | | | | | | | |
| | | | | | | | |
| | | | | | | | |
| | | | | | | | |
| | | | | | | | |

| ACCOUNT | | | | | ACCOUNT NO. | | |
|---|---|---|---|---|---|---|---|
| | | | | | | BALANCE | |
| DATE | ITEM | JRNL. REF. | DEBIT | CREDIT | DEBIT | CREDIT | |
| | | | | | | | |
| | | | | | | | |
| | | | | | | | |
| | | | | | | | |
| | | | | | | | |

| ACCOUNT | | | | | ACCOUNT NO. | | |
|---|---|---|---|---|---|---|---|
| | | | | | | BALANCE | |
| DATE | ITEM | JRNL. REF. | DEBIT | CREDIT | DEBIT | CREDIT | |
| | | | | | | | |
| | | | | | | | |
| | | | | | | | |
| | | | | | | | |
| | | | | | | | |

| ACCOUNT | | | | | ACCOUNT NO. | | |
|---|---|---|---|---|---|---|---|
| | | | | | BALANCE | | |
| DATE | ITEM | JRNL. REF. | DEBIT | CREDIT | DEBIT | CREDIT | |
| | | | | | | | |
| | | | | | | | |
| | | | | | | | |
| | | | | | | | |
| | | | | | | | |

| ACCOUNT | | | | | ACCOUNT NO. | | |
|---|---|---|---|---|---|---|---|
| | | | | | BALANCE | | |
| DATE | ITEM | JRNL. REF. | DEBIT | CREDIT | DEBIT | CREDIT | |
| | | | | | | | |
| | | | | | | | |
| | | | | | | | |
| | | | | | | | |
| | | | | | | | |

| ACCOUNT | | | | | ACCOUNT NO. | | |
|---|---|---|---|---|---|---|---|
| | | | | | BALANCE | | |
| DATE | ITEM | JRNL. REF. | DEBIT | CREDIT | DEBIT | CREDIT | |
| | | | | | | | |
| | | | | | | | |
| | | | | | | | |
| | | | | | | | |
| | | | | | | | |

| ACCOUNT | | | | | ACCOUNT NO. | | |
|---|---|---|---|---|---|---|---|
| | | | | | BALANCE | | |
| DATE | ITEM | JRNL. REF. | DEBIT | CREDIT | DEBIT | CREDIT | |
| | | | | | | | |
| | | | | | | | |
| | | | | | | | |
| | | | | | | | |

| ACCOUNT | | | | | | ACCOUNT NO. | | | |
|---|---|---|---|---|---|---|---|---|---|
| | | | | | | | BALANCE | | |
| DATE | ITEM | JRNL. REF. | DEBIT | CREDIT | | DEBIT | | CREDIT | |
| | | | | | | | | | |
| | | | | | | | | | |
| | | | | | | | | | |
| | | | | | | | | | |
| | | | | | | | | | |
| | | | | | | | | | |

| ACCOUNT | | | | | | ACCOUNT NO. | | | |
|---|---|---|---|---|---|---|---|---|---|
| | | | | | | | BALANCE | | |
| DATE | ITEM | JRNL. REF. | DEBIT | CREDIT | | DEBIT | | CREDIT | |
| | | | | | | | | | |
| | | | | | | | | | |
| | | | | | | | | | |
| | | | | | | | | | |
| | | | | | | | | | |
| | | | | | | | | | |

| ACCOUNT | | | | | | ACCOUNT NO. | | | |
|---|---|---|---|---|---|---|---|---|---|
| | | | | | | | BALANCE | | |
| DATE | ITEM | JRNL. REF. | DEBIT | CREDIT | | DEBIT | | CREDIT | |
| | | | | | | | | | |
| | | | | | | | | | |
| | | | | | | | | | |
| | | | | | | | | | |
| | | | | | | | | | |
| | | | | | | | | | |

| ACCOUNT | | | | | | ACCOUNT NO. | | | |
|---|---|---|---|---|---|---|---|---|---|
| | | | | | | | BALANCE | | |
| DATE | ITEM | JRNL. REF. | DEBIT | CREDIT | | DEBIT | | CREDIT | |
| | | | | | | | | | |
| | | | | | | | | | |
| | | | | | | | | | |
| | | | | | | | | | |
| | | | | | | | | | |

Reqs. 3–5

| | | Sales Journal | | | | |
|---|---|---|---|---|---|---|
| DATE | INVOICE NO | ACCOUNT DEBITED | POST. REF. | ACCOUNTS RECEIVABLE DR. SALES REVENUE CR. | | COST OF GOODS SOLD DR. INVENTORY CR. |
| | | | | | | |
| | | | | | | |
| | | | | | | |
| | | | | | | |
| | | | | | | |
| | | | | | | |
| | | | | | | |
| | | | | | | |

Req. 6

Chapter 6

P6-5B (Continued)

## Cash Receipts Journal

PAGE

| DATE | DEBITS | | | CREDITS | | | | |
|---|---|---|---|---|---|---|---|---|
| | CASH | SALES DISCOUNTS | ACCOUNTS RECEIVABLE | SALES REVENUE | OTHER ACCOUNTS | | | COST OF GOODS SOLD DR. INVENTORY CR. |
| | | | | | ACCOUNT TITLE | POST REF. | AMOUNT | |

**6-5B** *(Continued)*

# Purchases Journal

PAGE ____

| DATE | ACCOUNT CREDITED | TERMS | POST. REF. | CREDITS | DEBITS | | OTHER ACCOUNTS | | |
|------|------------------|-------|-----------|---------|--------|--|----------------|--|--|
| | | | | ACCOUNTS PAYABLE | INVENTORY | SUPPLIES | ACCOUNT TITLE | POST. REF. | AMOUNT |
| | | | | | | | | | |
| | | | | | | | | | |
| | | | | | | | | | |
| | | | | | | | | | |
| | | | | | | | | | |
| | | | | | | | | | |
| | | | | | | | | | |

# P6-5B *(Continued)*

## Cash Disbursements Journal

PAGE

| DATE | CK. NO. | ACCOUNT DEBITED | POST. REF. | DEBITS | | CREDITS | |
| | | | | OTHER ACCOUNTS | ACCOUNTS PAYABLE | INVENTORY | CASH |
|---|---|---|---|---|---|---|---|
| | | | | | | | |
| | | | | | | | |
| | | | | | | | |
| | | | | | | | |
| | | | | | | | |
| | | | | | | | |
| | | | | | | | |
| | | | | | | | |
| | | | | | | | |
| | | | | | | | |
| | | | | | | | |
| | | | | | | | |
| | | | | | | | |
| | | | | | | | |

## General Journal

| DATE | ACCOUNTS AND EXPLANATIONS | POST. REF. | DEBIT | CREDIT |
|------|---------------------------|------------|-------|--------|
| | | | | |
| | | | | |
| | | | | |
| | | | | |
| | | | | |
| | | | | |
| | | | | |
| | | | | |
| | | | | |
| | | | | |
| | | | | |
| | | | | |
| | | | | |
| | | | | |

## Sales Journal

| DATE | INVOICE NO. | ACCOUNT DEBITED | POST. REF. | ACCOUNTS RECEIVABLE DR. SALES REVENUE CR. |
|------|-------------|-----------------|------------|-------------------------------------------|
|      |             |                 |            |                                           |
|      |             |                 |            |                                           |
|      |             |                 |            |                                           |
|      |             |                 |            |                                           |
|      |             |                 |            |                                           |
|      |             |                 |            |                                           |
|      |             |                 |            |                                           |
|      |             |                 |            |                                           |
|      |             |                 |            |                                           |
|      |             |                 |            |                                           |

# Decision Case 1 *(Continued)*

## Cash Receipts Journal

PAGE

| DATE | DEBITS | | | CREDITS | | | |
|---|---|---|---|---|---|---|---|
| | CASH | SALES DISCOUNTS | ACCOUNTS RECEIVABLE | SALES REVENUE | OTHER ACCOUNTS | | |
| | | | | | ACCOUNT TITLE | POST REF. | AMOUNT |
| | | | | | | | |

NAME

SECTION

DATE

Chapter 6

**Decision Case 1**

*(Continued*

# Comprehensive Problem 1 for Part 1

*Reqs. 1–5*

| ACCOUNT | | | | | ACCOUNT NO. | |
|---|---|---|---|---|---|---|
| | | | | | BALANCE | |
| DATE | ITEM | JRNL. REF. | DEBIT | CREDIT | DEBIT | CREDIT |
| | | | | | | |
| | | | | | | |
| | | | | | | |
| | | | | | | |

| ACCOUNT | | | | | ACCOUNT NO. | |
|---|---|---|---|---|---|---|
| | | | | | BALANCE | |
| DATE | ITEM | JRNL. REF. | DEBIT | CREDIT | DEBIT | CREDIT |
| | | | | | | |
| | | | | | | |
| | | | | | | |
| | | | | | | |

| ACCOUNT | | | | | ACCOUNT NO. | |
|---|---|---|---|---|---|---|
| | | | | | BALANCE | |
| DATE | ITEM | JRNL. REF. | DEBIT | CREDIT | DEBIT | CREDIT |
| | | | | | | |
| | | | | | | |
| | | | | | | |
| | | | | | | |

| ACCOUNT | | | | | ACCOUNT NO. | |
|---|---|---|---|---|---|---|
| | | | | | BALANCE | |
| DATE | ITEM | JRNL. REF. | DEBIT | CREDIT | DEBIT | CREDIT |
| | | | | | | |
| | | | | | | |
| | | | | | | |
| | | | | | | |

*Reqs. 1–5*

| ACCOUNT | | | | | ACCOUNT NO. | | |
|---|---|---|---|---|---|---|---|
| | | JRNL. REF. | | | BALANCE | | |
| DATE | ITEM | | DEBIT | CREDIT | DEBIT | | CREDIT |
| | | | | | | | |
| | | | | | | | |
| | | | | | | | |
| | | | | | | | |
| | | | | | | | |
| | | | | | | | |

| ACCOUNT | | | | | ACCOUNT NO. | | |
|---|---|---|---|---|---|---|---|
| | | JRNL. REF. | | | BALANCE | | |
| DATE | ITEM | | DEBIT | CREDIT | DEBIT | | CREDIT |
| | | | | | | | |
| | | | | | | | |
| | | | | | | | |
| | | | | | | | |
| | | | | | | | |
| | | | | | | | |

| ACCOUNT | | | | | ACCOUNT NO. | | |
|---|---|---|---|---|---|---|---|
| | | JRNL. REF. | | | BALANCE | | |
| DATE | ITEM | | DEBIT | CREDIT | DEBIT | | CREDIT |
| | | | | | | | |
| | | | | | | | |
| | | | | | | | |
| | | | | | | | |
| | | | | | | | |
| | | | | | | | |

| ACCOUNT | | | | | ACCOUNT NO. | | |
|---|---|---|---|---|---|---|---|
| | | JRNL. REF. | | | BALANCE | | |
| DATE | ITEM | | DEBIT | CREDIT | DEBIT | | CREDIT |
| | | | | | | | |
| | | | | | | | |
| | | | | | | | |
| | | | | | | | |
| | | | | | | | |

NAME
SECTION
DATE

*Chapter 6*

# Comprehensive Problem 1 for Part 1

*(Continued)*

*Reqs. 1–5 (Continued)*

ACCOUNT          ACCOUNT NO.

| DATE | ITEM | JRNL. REF. | DEBIT | CREDIT | BALANCE DEBIT | CREDIT |
|------|------|-----------|-------|--------|-------|--------|
|      |      |           |       |        |       |        |
|      |      |           |       |        |       |        |
|      |      |           |       |        |       |        |
|      |      |           |       |        |       |        |

ACCOUNT          ACCOUNT NO.

| DATE | ITEM | JRNL. REF. | DEBIT | CREDIT | BALANCE DEBIT | CREDIT |
|------|------|-----------|-------|--------|-------|--------|
|      |      |           |       |        |       |        |
|      |      |           |       |        |       |        |
|      |      |           |       |        |       |        |
|      |      |           |       |        |       |        |

ACCOUNT          ACCOUNT NO.

| DATE | ITEM | JRNL. REF. | DEBIT | CREDIT | BALANCE DEBIT | CREDIT |
|------|------|-----------|-------|--------|-------|--------|
|      |      |           |       |        |       |        |
|      |      |           |       |        |       |        |
|      |      |           |       |        |       |        |
|      |      |           |       |        |       |        |

ACCOUNT          ACCOUNT NO.

| DATE | ITEM | JRNL. REF. | DEBIT | CREDIT | BALANCE DEBIT | CREDIT |
|------|------|-----------|-------|--------|-------|--------|
|      |      |           |       |        |       |        |
|      |      |           |       |        |       |        |
|      |      |           |       |        |       |        |
|      |      |           |       |        |       |        |

NAME
SECTION
DATE

*Chapter 6*

# Comprehensive Problem 1 for Part 1

Reqs. 1–5 (Continued)

(Continued

| ACCOUNT | | | | | | ACCOUNT NO. | |
|---|---|---|---|---|---|---|---|
| | | | | | | BALANCE | |
| DATE | ITEM | JRNL. REF. | DEBIT | CREDIT | | DEBIT | CREDIT |
| | | | | | | | |
| | | | | | | | |
| | | | | | | | |
| | | | | | | | |
| | | | | | | | |
| | | | | | | | |

| ACCOUNT | | | | | | ACCOUNT NO. | |
|---|---|---|---|---|---|---|---|
| | | | | | | BALANCE | |
| DATE | ITEM | JRNL. REF. | DEBIT | CREDIT | | DEBIT | CREDIT |
| | | | | | | | |
| | | | | | | | |
| | | | | | | | |
| | | | | | | | |
| | | | | | | | |
| | | | | | | | |
| | | | | | | | |

| ACCOUNT | | | | | | ACCOUNT NO. | |
|---|---|---|---|---|---|---|---|
| | | | | | | BALANCE | |
| DATE | ITEM | JRNL. REF. | DEBIT | CREDIT | | DEBIT | CREDIT |
| | | | | | | | |
| | | | | | | | |
| | | | | | | | |
| | | | | | | | |
| | | | | | | | |
| | | | | | | | |
| | | | | | | | |

| ACCOUNT | | | | | | ACCOUNT NO. | |
|---|---|---|---|---|---|---|---|
| | | | | | | BALANCE | |
| DATE | ITEM | JRNL. REF. | DEBIT | CREDIT | | DEBIT | CREDIT |
| | | | | | | | |
| | | | | | | | |
| | | | | | | | |
| | | | | | | | |
| | | | | | | | |
| | | | | | | | |

AME
ECTION
ATE

*Chapter 6*

# Comprehensive Problem 1 for Part 1

*(Continued)*

*eqs. 1–5 (Continued)*

| ACCOUNT | | | | | ACCOUNT NO. | | |
|---|---|---|---|---|---|---|---|
| | | | | | | BALANCE | |
| DATE | ITEM | JRNL. REF. | DEBIT | CREDIT | DEBIT | | CREDIT |
| | | | | | | | |
| | | | | | | | |
| | | | | | | | |
| | | | | | | | |
| | | | | | | | |

| ACCOUNT | | | | | ACCOUNT NO. | | |
|---|---|---|---|---|---|---|---|
| | | | | | | BALANCE | |
| DATE | ITEM | JRNL. REF. | DEBIT | CREDIT | DEBIT | | CREDIT |
| | | | | | | | |
| | | | | | | | |
| | | | | | | | |
| | | | | | | | |
| | | | | | | | |

| ACCOUNT | | | | | ACCOUNT NO. | | |
|---|---|---|---|---|---|---|---|
| | | | | | | BALANCE | |
| DATE | ITEM | JRNL. REF. | DEBIT | CREDIT | DEBIT | | CREDIT |
| | | | | | | | |
| | | | | | | | |
| | | | | | | | |
| | | | | | | | |
| | | | | | | | |
| | | | | | | | |
| | | | | | | | |
| | | | | | | | |
| | | | | | | | |
| | | | | | | | |

# Comprehensive Problem 1 for Part

*Reqs. 1–5 (Continued)*

*(Continued*

| ACCOUNT | | | | | | ACCOUNT NO. | |
|---|---|---|---|---|---|---|---|
| | | JRNL. REF. | | | | BALANCE | |
| DATE | ITEM | | DEBIT | CREDIT | | DEBIT | CREDIT |
| | | | | | | | |
| | | | | | | | |
| | | | | | | | |
| | | | | | | | |
| | | | | | | | |
| | | | | | | | |
| | | | | | | | |
| | | | | | | | |

| ACCOUNT | | | | | | ACCOUNT NO. | |
|---|---|---|---|---|---|---|---|
| | | JRNL. REF. | | | | BALANCE | |
| DATE | ITEM | | DEBIT | CREDIT | | DEBIT | CREDIT |
| | | | | | | | |
| | | | | | | | |
| | | | | | | | |
| | | | | | | | |
| | | | | | | | |
| | | | | | | | |
| | | | | | | | |

| ACCOUNT | | | | | | ACCOUNT NO. | |
|---|---|---|---|---|---|---|---|
| | | JRNL. REF. | | | | BALANCE | |
| DATE | ITEM | | DEBIT | CREDIT | | DEBIT | CREDIT |
| | | | | | | | |
| | | | | | | | |
| | | | | | | | |
| | | | | | | | |

*Req. 2*

The worksheet to solve this problem can be found on page 495.

AME
ECTION
ATE

*Chapter 6*

# Comprehensive
# Problem 1 *(Continued)*

*Req. 3*

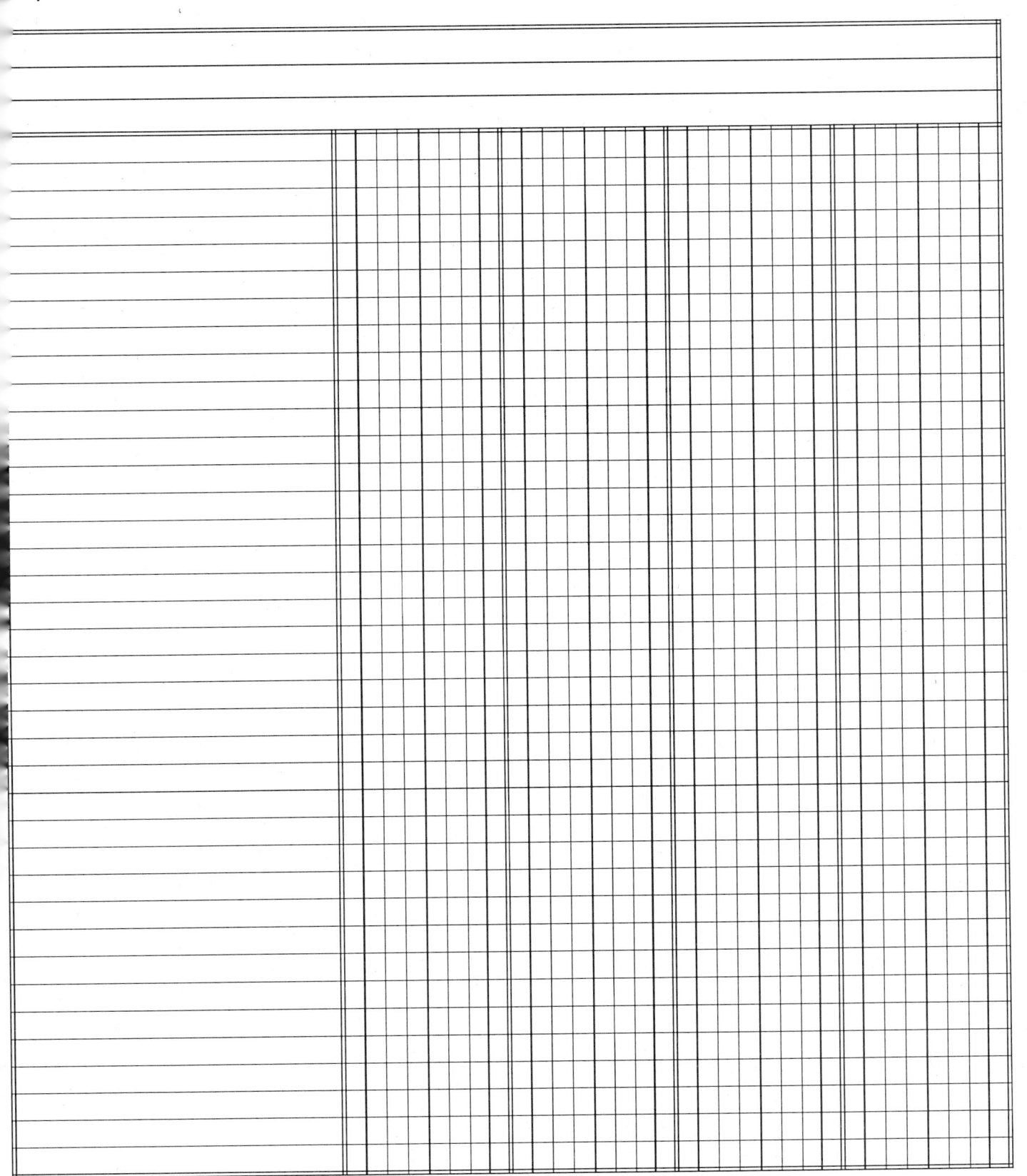

NAME
SECTION
DATE

Chapter 6

**Comprehensive
Problem 1** *(Continued*

*Req. 3 (Continued)*

*Req. 3 (Continued)*

NAME
SECTION
DATE

Chapter 6

**Comprehensive
Problem 1** (Continued)

Req. 4

| | Journal | | | | |
|---|---|---|---|---|---|
| DATE | ACCOUNTS AND EXPLANATIONS | POST. REF. | DEBIT | CREDIT | |
| | | | | | |
| | | | | | |
| | | | | | |
| | | | | | |
| | | | | | |
| | | | | | |
| | | | | | |
| | | | | | |
| | | | | | |
| | | | | | |
| | | | | | |
| | | | | | |
| | | | | | |
| | | | | | |
| | | | | | |
| | | | | | |
| | | | | | |
| | | | | | |
| | | | | | |
| | | | | | |
| | | | | | |
| | | | | | |
| | | | | | |
| | | | | | |
| | | | | | |
| | | | | | |
| | | | | | |
| | | | | | |
| | | | | | |
| | | | | | |
| | | | | | |
| | | | | | |
| | | | | | |
| | | | | | |
| | | | | | |

AME
ECTION
ATE

Chapter 6

**Comprehensive
Problem 1** (Continued)

Req. 4 (Continued)

## Journal

| DATE | ACCOUNTS AND EXPLANATIONS | POST. REF. | DEBIT | CREDIT |
|------|---------------------------|-----------|-------|--------|
|  |  |  |  |  |
|  |  |  |  |  |
|  |  |  |  |  |
|  |  |  |  |  |
|  |  |  |  |  |
|  |  |  |  |  |
|  |  |  |  |  |
|  |  |  |  |  |
|  |  |  |  |  |
|  |  |  |  |  |
|  |  |  |  |  |
|  |  |  |  |  |
|  |  |  |  |  |
|  |  |  |  |  |
|  |  |  |  |  |
|  |  |  |  |  |
|  |  |  |  |  |
|  |  |  |  |  |
|  |  |  |  |  |
|  |  |  |  |  |
|  |  |  |  |  |
|  |  |  |  |  |
|  |  |  |  |  |
|  |  |  |  |  |
|  |  |  |  |  |
|  |  |  |  |  |
|  |  |  |  |  |
|  |  |  |  |  |
|  |  |  |  |  |
|  |  |  |  |  |
|  |  |  |  |  |
|  |  |  |  |  |
|  |  |  |  |  |
|  |  |  |  |  |

NAME

SECTION

DATE

Chapter 6

**Comprehensive**
**Problem 1** *(Continued*

*Req. 6*

**Current Ratio**

**Debt Ratio**

**Gross Margin Percentage**

**Inventory Turnover**

*Reqs. 1, 3, & 6*

| ACCOUNT | | | | | ACCOUNT NO. | | |
|---|---|---|---|---|---|---|---|
| | | JRNL. REF. | | | BALANCE | | |
| DATE | ITEM | | DEBIT | CREDIT | DEBIT | CREDIT | |
| | | | | | | | |
| | | | | | | | |
| | | | | | | | |

| ACCOUNT | | | | | ACCOUNT NO. | | |
|---|---|---|---|---|---|---|---|
| | | JRNL. REF. | | | BALANCE | | |
| DATE | ITEM | | DEBIT | CREDIT | DEBIT | CREDIT | |
| | | | | | | | |
| | | | | | | | |
| | | | | | | | |

| ACCOUNT | | | | | ACCOUNT NO. | | |
|---|---|---|---|---|---|---|---|
| | | JRNL. REF. | | | BALANCE | | |
| DATE | ITEM | | DEBIT | CREDIT | DEBIT | CREDIT | |
| | | | | | | | |
| | | | | | | | |
| | | | | | | | |

NAME
SECTION
DATE

Chapter 6

**Comprehensive
Problem 2**(Continued

## Reqs. 1, 3, & 6 (Continued)

| ACCOUNT | | | | | ACCOUNT NO. | | |
|---|---|---|---|---|---|---|---|
| | | | | | BALANCE | | |
| DATE | ITEM | JRNL. REF. | DEBIT | CREDIT | DEBIT | CREDIT | |
| | | | | | | | |

| ACCOUNT | | | | | ACCOUNT NO. | | |
|---|---|---|---|---|---|---|---|
| | | | | | BALANCE | | |
| DATE | ITEM | JRNL. REF. | DEBIT | CREDIT | DEBIT | CREDIT | |
| | | | | | | | |

| ACCOUNT | | | | | ACCOUNT NO. | | |
|---|---|---|---|---|---|---|---|
| | | | | | BALANCE | | |
| DATE | ITEM | JRNL. REF. | DEBIT | CREDIT | DEBIT | CREDIT | |
| | | | | | | | |

| ACCOUNT | | | | | ACCOUNT NO. | | |
|---|---|---|---|---|---|---|---|
| | | | | | BALANCE | | |
| DATE | ITEM | JRNL. REF. | DEBIT | CREDIT | DEBIT | CREDIT | |
| | | | | | | | |

NAME
SECTION
DATE

*Reqs. 1, 3, & 6 (Continued)*

| ACCOUNT | | | | | ACCOUNT NO. | |
|---|---|---|---|---|---|---|
| | | | | | BALANCE | |
| DATE | ITEM | JRNL. REF. | DEBIT | CREDIT | DEBIT | CREDIT |
| | | | | | | |
| | | | | | | |
| | | | | | | |

| ACCOUNT | | | | | ACCOUNT NO. | |
|---|---|---|---|---|---|---|
| | | | | | BALANCE | |
| DATE | ITEM | JRNL. REF. | DEBIT | CREDIT | DEBIT | CREDIT |
| | | | | | | |
| | | | | | | |
| | | | | | | |
| | | | | | | |

| ACCOUNT | | | | | ACCOUNT NO. | |
|---|---|---|---|---|---|---|
| | | | | | BALANCE | |
| DATE | ITEM | JRNL. REF. | DEBIT | CREDIT | DEBIT | CREDIT |
| | | | | | | |
| | | | | | | |
| | | | | | | |
| | | | | | | |

| ACCOUNT | | | | | ACCOUNT NO. | |
|---|---|---|---|---|---|---|
| | | | | | BALANCE | |
| DATE | ITEM | JRNL. REF. | DEBIT | CREDIT | DEBIT | CREDIT |
| | | | | | | |
| | | | | | | |
| | | | | | | |
| | | | | | | |

NAME
SECTION
DATE

Chapter 6

Comprehensive
Problem 2 (Continued)

Reqs. 1, 3, & 6 (Continued)

| ACCOUNT | | | | | ACCOUNT NO. | |
|---|---|---|---|---|---|---|
| | | JRNL. | | | BALANCE | |
| DATE | ITEM | REF. | DEBIT | CREDIT | DEBIT | CREDIT |
| | | | | | | |
| | | | | | | |
| | | | | | | |
| | | | | | | |

| ACCOUNT | | | | | ACCOUNT NO. | |
|---|---|---|---|---|---|---|
| | | JRNL. | | | BALANCE | |
| DATE | ITEM | REF. | DEBIT | CREDIT | DEBIT | CREDIT |
| | | | | | | |
| | | | | | | |
| | | | | | | |
| | | | | | | |

| ACCOUNT | | | | | ACCOUNT NO. | |
|---|---|---|---|---|---|---|
| | | JRNL. | | | BALANCE | |
| DATE | ITEM | REF. | DEBIT | CREDIT | DEBIT | CREDIT |
| | | | | | | |
| | | | | | | |
| | | | | | | |
| | | | | | | |

| ACCOUNT | | | | | ACCOUNT NO. | |
|---|---|---|---|---|---|---|
| | | JRNL. | | | BALANCE | |
| DATE | ITEM | REF. | DEBIT | CREDIT | DEBIT | CREDIT |
| | | | | | | |
| | | | | | | |
| | | | | | | |

AME
ECTION
ATE

Chapter 6

# Comprehensive
# Problem 2 *(Continued)*

*eqs. 1, 3, & 6 (Continued)*

| ACCOUNT | | | | | ACCOUNT NO. | |
|---|---|---|---|---|---|---|
| | | | | | BALANCE | |
| DATE | ITEM | JRNL. REF. | DEBIT | CREDIT | DEBIT | CREDIT |
| | | | | | | |
| | | | | | | |
| | | | | | | |
| | | | | | | |

| ACCOUNT | | | | | ACCOUNT NO. | |
|---|---|---|---|---|---|---|
| | | | | | BALANCE | |
| DATE | ITEM | JRNL. REF. | DEBIT | CREDIT | DEBIT | CREDIT |
| | | | | | | |
| | | | | | | |
| | | | | | | |
| | | | | | | |

| ACCOUNT | | | | | ACCOUNT NO. | |
|---|---|---|---|---|---|---|
| | | | | | BALANCE | |
| DATE | ITEM | JRNL. REF. | DEBIT | CREDIT | DEBIT | CREDIT |
| | | | | | | |
| | | | | | | |
| | | | | | | |
| | | | | | | |

| ACCOUNT | | | | | ACCOUNT NO. | |
|---|---|---|---|---|---|---|
| | | | | | BALANCE | |
| DATE | ITEM | JRNL. REF. | DEBIT | CREDIT | DEBIT | CREDIT |
| | | | | | | |
| | | | | | | |
| | | | | | | |
| | | | | | | |

NAME
SECTION
DATE

Chapter 6

# Comprehensiv
# Problem 2 (Continue

## Reqs. 1, 3, & 6 (Continued)

| ACCOUNT | | | | | ACCOUNT NO. | | |
|---|---|---|---|---|---|---|---|
| DATE | ITEM | JRNL. REF. | DEBIT | CREDIT | BALANCE | | |
| | | | | | DEBIT | CREDIT | |
| | | | | | | | |
| | | | | | | | |
| | | | | | | | |
| | | | | | | | |

| ACCOUNT | | | | | ACCOUNT NO. | | |
|---|---|---|---|---|---|---|---|
| DATE | ITEM | JRNL. REF. | DEBIT | CREDIT | BALANCE | | |
| | | | | | DEBIT | CREDIT | |
| | | | | | | | |
| | | | | | | | |
| | | | | | | | |
| | | | | | | | |

| ACCOUNT | | | | | ACCOUNT NO. | | |
|---|---|---|---|---|---|---|---|
| DATE | ITEM | JRNL. REF. | DEBIT | CREDIT | BALANCE | | |
| | | | | | DEBIT | CREDIT | |
| | | | | | | | |
| | | | | | | | |
| | | | | | | | |
| | | | | | | | |

| ACCOUNT | | | | | ACCOUNT NO. | | |
|---|---|---|---|---|---|---|---|
| DATE | ITEM | JRNL. REF. | DEBIT | CREDIT | BALANCE | | |
| | | | | | DEBIT | CREDIT | |
| | | | | | | | |
| | | | | | | | |
| | | | | | | | |

AME
ECTION
ATE

Chapter 6

# Comprehensive
# Problem 2 (Continued)

*Reqs. 1, 3, & 6 (Continued)*

| ACCOUNT | | | | | ACCOUNT NO. | |
|---------|------|------------|-------|--------|-------------|--------|
| | | | | | BALANCE | |
| DATE | ITEM | JRNL. REF. | DEBIT | CREDIT | DEBIT | CREDIT |
| | | | | | | |
| | | | | | | |
| | | | | | | |
| | | | | | | |

| ACCOUNT | | | | | ACCOUNT NO. | |
|---------|------|------------|-------|--------|-------------|--------|
| | | | | | BALANCE | |
| DATE | ITEM | JRNL. REF. | DEBIT | CREDIT | DEBIT | CREDIT |
| | | | | | | |
| | | | | | | |
| | | | | | | |
| | | | | | | |
| | | | | | | |

| ACCOUNT | | | | | ACCOUNT NO. | |
|---------|------|------------|-------|--------|-------------|--------|
| | | | | | BALANCE | |
| DATE | ITEM | JRNL. REF. | DEBIT | CREDIT | DEBIT | CREDIT |
| | | | | | | |
| | | | | | | |
| | | | | | | |
| | | | | | | |
| | | | | | | |

| ACCOUNT | | | | | ACCOUNT NO. | |
|---------|------|------------|-------|--------|-------------|--------|
| | | | | | BALANCE | |
| DATE | ITEM | JRNL. REF. | DEBIT | CREDIT | DEBIT | CREDIT |
| | | | | | | |
| | | | | | | |
| | | | | | | |
| | | | | | | |

NAME
SECTION
DATE

Chapter 6

# Comprehensiv
# Problem 2(Continue

*Reqs. 1, 3, & 6 (Continued)*

| ACCOUNT | | | | | ACCOUNT NO. | |
|---|---|---|---|---|---|---|
| | | JRNL. REF. | | | BALANCE | |
| DATE | ITEM | | DEBIT | CREDIT | DEBIT | CREDIT |
| | | | | | | |
| | | | | | | |
| | | | | | | |
| | | | | | | |
| | | | | | | |

| ACCOUNT | | | | | ACCOUNT NO. | |
|---|---|---|---|---|---|---|
| | | JRNL. REF. | | | BALANCE | |
| DATE | ITEM | | DEBIT | CREDIT | DEBIT | CREDIT |
| | | | | | | |
| | | | | | | |
| | | | | | | |
| | | | | | | |
| | | | | | | |

AME
ECTION
ATE

Chapter 6

# Comprehensive
# Problem 2 (Continued)

*eqs. 1, 3, & 7 (Continued)*

CCOUNTS RECEIVABLE SUBSIDARY LEDGER

ACCOUNT _____ ACCOUNT NO. _____

| DATE | ITEM | JRNL. REF. | DEBIT | CREDIT | BALANCE DEBIT | BALANCE CREDIT |
|------|------|------------|-------|--------|---------------|----------------|
|      |      |            |       |        |               |                |
|      |      |            |       |        |               |                |
|      |      |            |       |        |               |                |

ACCOUNT _____ ACCOUNT NO. _____

| DATE | ITEM | JRNL. REF. | DEBIT | CREDIT | BALANCE DEBIT | BALANCE CREDIT |
|------|------|------------|-------|--------|---------------|----------------|
|      |      |            |       |        |               |                |
|      |      |            |       |        |               |                |
|      |      |            |       |        |               |                |
|      |      |            |       |        |               |                |

ACCOUNT _____ ACCOUNT NO. _____

| DATE | ITEM | JRNL. REF. | DEBIT | CREDIT | BALANCE DEBIT | BALANCE CREDIT |
|------|------|------------|-------|--------|---------------|----------------|
|      |      |            |       |        |               |                |
|      |      |            |       |        |               |                |
|      |      |            |       |        |               |                |

ACCOUNT _____ ACCOUNT NO. _____

| DATE | ITEM | JRNL. REF. | DEBIT | CREDIT | BALANCE DEBIT | BALANCE CREDIT |
|------|------|------------|-------|--------|---------------|----------------|
|      |      |            |       |        |               |                |
|      |      |            |       |        |               |                |
|      |      |            |       |        |               |                |

NAME
SECTION
DATE

Chapter 6

# Comprehensiv
# Problem 2 (Continue

*Reqs. 1, 3, & 7 (Continued)*

ACCOUNTS PAYABLE SUBSIDARY LEDGER

| ACCOUNT | | | | | ACCOUNT NO. | | |
|---|---|---|---|---|---|---|---|
| | | | | | | BALANCE | |
| DATE | ITEM | JRNL. REF. | DEBIT | CREDIT | DEBIT | DEBIT | CREDIT |
| | | | | | | | |
| | | | | | | | |
| | | | | | | | |
| | | | | | | | |
| | | | | | | | |

| ACCOUNT | | | | | ACCOUNT NO. | | |
|---|---|---|---|---|---|---|---|
| | | | | | | BALANCE | |
| DATE | ITEM | JRNL. REF. | DEBIT | CREDIT | DEBIT | DEBIT | CREDIT |
| | | | | | | | |
| | | | | | | | |
| | | | | | | | |
| | | | | | | | |
| | | | | | | | |

| ACCOUNT | | | | | ACCOUNT NO. | | |
|---|---|---|---|---|---|---|---|
| | | | | | | BALANCE | |
| DATE | ITEM | JRNL. REF. | DEBIT | CREDIT | DEBIT | DEBIT | CREDIT |
| | | | | | | | |
| | | | | | | | |
| | | | | | | | |
| | | | | | | | |
| | | | | | | | |

| ACCOUNT | | | | | ACCOUNT NO. | | |
|---|---|---|---|---|---|---|---|
| | | | | | | BALANCE | |
| DATE | ITEM | JRNL. REF. | DEBIT | CREDIT | DEBIT | DEBIT | CREDIT |
| | | | | | | | |
| | | | | | | | |
| | | | | | | | |
| | | | | | | | |
| | | | | | | | |

AME
CTION
ATE
*eq. 2*

Chapter 6

# Comprehensive
# Problem 2 *(Continued)*

(Alternate Working Papers for Special Journals can be found after General Journal Pages)

## General Journal

| DATE | ACCOUNTS AND EXPLANATIONS | POST. REF. | DEBIT | CREDIT |
|------|----------------------------|------------|-------|--------|
|      |                            |            |       |        |
|      |                            |            |       |        |
|      |                            |            |       |        |
|      |                            |            |       |        |
|      |                            |            |       |        |
|      |                            |            |       |        |
|      |                            |            |       |        |
|      |                            |            |       |        |
|      |                            |            |       |        |
|      |                            |            |       |        |
|      |                            |            |       |        |
|      |                            |            |       |        |
|      |                            |            |       |        |
|      |                            |            |       |        |
|      |                            |            |       |        |
|      |                            |            |       |        |
|      |                            |            |       |        |
|      |                            |            |       |        |
|      |                            |            |       |        |
|      |                            |            |       |        |
|      |                            |            |       |        |
|      |                            |            |       |        |
|      |                            |            |       |        |

NAME

SECTION

DATE

Req. 2

Chapter 6

# Comprehensiv
# Problem 2(Continue

## General Journal

| DATE | ACCOUNTS AND EXPLANATIONS | POST. REF. | DEBIT | CREDIT |
|------|---------------------------|------------|-------|--------|
|  |  |  |  |  |
|  |  |  |  |  |
|  |  |  |  |  |
|  |  |  |  |  |
|  |  |  |  |  |
|  |  |  |  |  |
|  |  |  |  |  |
|  |  |  |  |  |
|  |  |  |  |  |
|  |  |  |  |  |
|  |  |  |  |  |
|  |  |  |  |  |
|  |  |  |  |  |
|  |  |  |  |  |
|  |  |  |  |  |
|  |  |  |  |  |
|  |  |  |  |  |
|  |  |  |  |  |
|  |  |  |  |  |
|  |  |  |  |  |
|  |  |  |  |  |
|  |  |  |  |  |
|  |  |  |  |  |
|  |  |  |  |  |
|  |  |  |  |  |
|  |  |  |  |  |
|  |  |  |  |  |
|  |  |  |  |  |
|  |  |  |  |  |
|  |  |  |  |  |
|  |  |  |  |  |
|  |  |  |  |  |
|  |  |  |  |  |
|  |  |  |  |  |
|  |  |  |  |  |
|  |  |  |  |  |
|  |  |  |  |  |
|  |  |  |  |  |
|  |  |  |  |  |
|  |  |  |  |  |

*Req. 2 (Continued)*

## General Journal

| DATE | ACCOUNTS AND EXPLANATIONS | POST. REF. | DEBIT | CREDIT |
|------|---------------------------|-----------|-------|--------|
|      |                           |           |       |        |
|      |                           |           |       |        |
|      |                           |           |       |        |
|      |                           |           |       |        |
|      |                           |           |       |        |
|      |                           |           |       |        |
|      |                           |           |       |        |
|      |                           |           |       |        |
|      |                           |           |       |        |
|      |                           |           |       |        |
|      |                           |           |       |        |
|      |                           |           |       |        |
|      |                           |           |       |        |
|      |                           |           |       |        |
|      |                           |           |       |        |
|      |                           |           |       |        |
|      |                           |           |       |        |
|      |                           |           |       |        |
|      |                           |           |       |        |
|      |                           |           |       |        |
|      |                           |           |       |        |

NAME
SECTION
DATE

Chapter 6

Comprehensive
Problem 2 (Continued

*Req. 2 (Continued)*

## General Journal

| DATE | | ACCOUNTS AND EXPLANATIONS | POST. REF. | DEBIT | CREDIT |
|------|---|---------------------------|------------|-------|--------|
| | | | | | |
| | | | | | |
| | | | | | |
| | | | | | |
| | | | | | |
| | | | | | |
| | | | | | |
| | | | | | |
| | | | | | |
| | | | | | |
| | | | | | |
| | | | | | |
| | | | | | |
| | | | | | |
| | | | | | |
| | | | | | |
| | | | | | |
| | | | | | |
| | | | | | |
| | | | | | |
| | | | | | |
| | | | | | |
| | | | | | |
| | | | | | |
| | | | | | |
| | | | | | |
| | | | | | |
| | | | | | |
| | | | | | |
| | | | | | |
| | | | | | |
| | | | | | |
| | | | | | |
| | | | | | |
| | | | | | |
| | | | | | |

*Reqs. 2 & 3 (Continued)*

(Alternate Working Papers)

## Sales Journal

| DATE | ACCOUNT DEBITED | POST. REF. | ACCOUNTS RECEIVABLE DR. SALES REVENUE CR. | COST OF GOODS SOLD DR. INVENTORY CR. |
|------|-----------------|------------|-------------------------------------------|--------------------------------------|
|      |                 |            |                                           |                                      |
|      |                 |            |                                           |                                      |
|      |                 |            |                                           |                                      |
|      |                 |            |                                           |                                      |
|      |                 |            |                                           |                                      |
|      |                 |            |                                           |                                      |
|      |                 |            |                                           |                                      |
|      |                 |            |                                           |                                      |
|      |                 |            |                                           |                                      |
|      |                 |            |                                           |                                      |

Chapter 6

# Comprehensive Problem 2 *(Continued)*

Reqs. 2 & 3 *(Continued)*

## Cash Receipts Journal

PAGE

| DATE | DEBITS | | | CREDITS | | | | |
| | CASH | SALES DISCOUNTS | ACCOUNTS RECEIVABLE | SALES REVENUE | OTHER ACCOUNTS | | | COST OF GOODS SOLD DR. INVENTORY CR. |
| | | | | | ACCOUNT TITLE | POST REF. | AMOUNT | |
| | | | | | | | | |
| | | | | | | | | |
| | | | | | | | | |
| | | | | | | | | |
| | | | | | | | | |
| | | | | | | | | |
| | | | | | | | | |
| | | | | | | | | |
| | | | | | | | | |
| | | | | | | | | |
| | | | | | | | | |
| | | | | | | | | |
| | | | | | | | | |
| | | | | | | | | |
| | | | | | | | | |

# Comprehensive
# Problem 2 *(Continued)*

*Reqs. 2 & 3 (Continued)*

(Alternate Working Papers)

## Purchases Journal

PAGE

| DATE | ACCOUNT CREDITED | TERMS | POST. REF. | CREDITS | DEBITS | | | |
|---|---|---|---|---|---|---|---|---|
| | | | | ACCOUNTS PAYABLE | INVENTORY | SUPPLIES | OTHER ACCOUNTS | |
| | | | | | | | ACCOUNT TITLE | POST. REF. | AMOUNT |

# Comprehensive
# Problem 2 *(Continued)*

*Reqs. 2 & 3 (Continued)*

(Alternate Working Papers)

## Cash Disbursements Journal

PAGE _____

| DATE | CK. NO. | ACCOUNT DEBITED | POST. REF. | DEBITS | | CREDITS | |
| | | | | OTHER ACCOUNTS | ACCOUNTS PAYABLE | INVENTORY | CASH |
|---|---|---|---|---|---|---|---|
| | | | | | | | |
| | | | | | | | |
| | | | | | | | |
| | | | | | | | |
| | | | | | | | |
| | | | | | | | |
| | | | | | | | |
| | | | | | | | |
| | | | | | | | |
| | | | | | | | |
| | | | | | | | |
| | | | | | | | |

*Reqs. 2, 3, & 7 (Continued)*

## General Journal

| DATE | ACCOUNTS AND EXPLANATIONS | POST. REF. | DEBIT | CREDIT |
|------|---------------------------|------------|-------|--------|
|      |                           |            |       |        |
|      |                           |            |       |        |
|      |                           |            |       |        |
|      |                           |            |       |        |
|      |                           |            |       |        |
|      |                           |            |       |        |
|      |                           |            |       |        |
|      |                           |            |       |        |
|      |                           |            |       |        |
|      |                           |            |       |        |
|      |                           |            |       |        |
|      |                           |            |       |        |
|      |                           |            |       |        |
|      |                           |            |       |        |
|      |                           |            |       |        |
|      |                           |            |       |        |
|      |                           |            |       |        |
|      |                           |            |       |        |
|      |                           |            |       |        |
|      |                           |            |       |        |
|      |                           |            |       |        |
|      |                           |            |       |        |
|      |                           |            |       |        |
|      |                           |            |       |        |

NAME
SECTION
DATE

Chapter 6

Comprehensive
Problem 2 (Continued)

Reqs. 2, 3, & 7 (Continued)

## General Journal

| DATE | ACCOUNTS AND EXPLANATIONS | POST. REF. | DEBIT | CREDIT |
|------|---------------------------|------------|-------|--------|
|      |                           |            |       |        |

NAME
SECTION
DATE

Chapter 6

# Comprehensive
# Problem 2 (Continued)

*Reqs. 2, 3, & 7 (Continued)*

## General Journal

| DATE | ACCOUNTS AND EXPLANATIONS | POST. REF. | DEBIT | CREDIT |
|------|---------------------------|-----------|-------|--------|
|  |  |  |  |  |
|  |  |  |  |  |
|  |  |  |  |  |
|  |  |  |  |  |
|  |  |  |  |  |
|  |  |  |  |  |
|  |  |  |  |  |
|  |  |  |  |  |
|  |  |  |  |  |
|  |  |  |  |  |
|  |  |  |  |  |
|  |  |  |  |  |
|  |  |  |  |  |
|  |  |  |  |  |
|  |  |  |  |  |
|  |  |  |  |  |
|  |  |  |  |  |
|  |  |  |  |  |
|  |  |  |  |  |
|  |  |  |  |  |
|  |  |  |  |  |
|  |  |  |  |  |
|  |  |  |  |  |
|  |  |  |  |  |
|  |  |  |  |  |

*Req. 4*

The worksheet to solve this problem can be found on page 496.

Req. 5

NAME
SECTION
DATE

Chapter 6

# Comprehensive
# Problem 2 (Continued

*Req. 5 (Continued)*

NAME
SECTION
DATE

Chapter 6

# Comprehensive
# Problem 2 (Continued)

Req. 7

| ACCOUNT | DEBIT | CREDIT |
|---------|-------|--------|
|  |  |  |
|  |  |  |
|  |  |  |
|  |  |  |
|  |  |  |
|  |  |  |
|  |  |  |
|  |  |  |
|  |  |  |
|  |  |  |
|  |  |  |
|  |  |  |
|  |  |  |
|  |  |  |
|  |  |  |
|  |  |  |
|  |  |  |
|  |  |  |
|  |  |  |
|  |  |  |
|  |  |  |
|  |  |  |
|  |  |  |
|  |  |  |

NAME
SECTION
DATE

Req. 2

St. James Technology

Work Sheet

For the Month Ended January 31, 19XX

| ACCOUNT TITLE | TRIAL BALANCE DEBIT | TRIAL BALANCE CREDIT | ADJUSTMENTS DEBIT | ADJUSTMENTS CREDIT | INCOME STATEMENT DEBIT | INCOME STATEMENT CREDIT | BALANCE SHEET DEBIT | BALANCE SHEET CREDIT |
|---|---|---|---|---|---|---|---|---|
| Cash | 16430 | | | | | | | |
| Accounts receivable | 19090 | | | | | | | |
| Inventory | 65400 | | | | | | | |
| Supplies | 2700 | | | | | | | |
| Buildings | 188170 | | | | | | | |
| Accumulated depreciation-building | | 36000 | | | | | | |
| Fixtures | 45600 | | | | | | | |
| Accumulated depreciation-fixtures | | 5800 | | | | | | |
| Accounts payable | | 28300 | | | | | | |
| Salary payable | | | | | | | | |
| Interest payable | | | | | | | | |
| Unearned sales revenue | | 6560 | | | | | | |
| Note payable, long term | | 87000 | | | | | | |
| Meg Louder, Capital | | 144980 | | | | | | |
| Meg Louder, Withdrawals | 9200 | | | | | | | |
| Sales revenue | | 187970 | | | | | | |
| Sales discounts | 7300 | | | | | | | |
| Sales returns and allowances | 8140 | | | | | | | |
| Cost of goods sold | 103000 | | | | | | | |
| Selling expense | 21520 | | | | | | | |
| General expense | 10060 | | | | | | | |
| Interest expense | | | | | | | | |
| | 496610 | 496610 | | | | | | |
| Net income | | | | | | | | |

NAME
SECTION
DATE
Req. 4

Chapter 6

# Comprehensiv
# Problem 2 (Cont.

**Anacomp Meter Company**

**Work Sheet**

**For the Month Ended August 31, 19XX**

| ACCOUNT TITLE | TRIAL BALANCE | | ADJUSTMENTS | | INCOME STATEMENT | | BALANCE SHEET | |
|---|---|---|---|---|---|---|---|---|
| | DEBIT | CREDIT | DEBIT | CREDIT | DEBIT | CREDIT | DEBIT | CREDIT |
| Cash | | | | | | | | |
| Accounts receivable | | | | | | | | |
| Interest receivable | | | | | | | | |
| Inventory | | | | | | | | |
| Supplies | | | | | | | | |
| Prepaid Insurance | | | | | | | | |
| Note receivable, long-term | | | | | | | | |
| Furniture | | | | | | | | |
| Accumulated depreciation | | | | | | | | |
| Accounts payable | | | | | | | | |
| Salary payable | | | | | | | | |
| Interest payable | | | | | | | | |
| Unearned sales revenue | | | | | | | | |
| Note payable, long-term | | | | | | | | |
| Peter Firestone, Capital | | | | | | | | |
| Peter Firestone, Withdrawals | | | | | | | | |
| Sales revenue | | | | | | | | |
| Sales discounts | | | | | | | | |
| Sales returns and allowances | | | | | | | | |
| Interest revenue | | | | | | | | |
| Cost of goods sold | | | | | | | | |
| Salary expense | | | | | | | | |
| Rent expense | | | | | | | | |
| Depreciation expense | | | | | | | | |
| Insurance expense | | | | | | | | |
| Utilities expense | | | | | | | | |
| Supplies expense | | | | | | | | |
| Interest expense | | | | | | | | |
| | | | | | | | | |
| Net Income | | | | | | | | |

**DE7-2**

**DE7-3**

**DE7-5**

**DE7-7**

**DE7-9**

| Bank | | Books | |
|------|--|-------|--|
| | | | |
| | | | |
| | | | |
| | | | |
| | | | |
| | | | |
| | | | |
| | | | |

# DE7-11

| | | Journal | | | |
|---|---|---|---|---|---|
| DATE | | ACCOUNTS AND EXPLANATIONS | POST. REF. | DEBIT | CREDIT |
| | | | | | |
| | | | | | |
| | | | | | |
| | | | | | |
| | | | | | |
| | | | | | |
| | | | | | |
| | | | | | |
| | | | | | |
| | | | | | |
| | | | | | |

**DE7-13**

**DE7-14**

**DE7-16**

1.

2.

1) division of duties

1.
2.
3.
4.
5.
6.
7.

## Journal

| DATE | ACCOUNTS AND EXPLANATIONS | POST. REF. | DEBIT | CREDIT |
|------|---------------------------|------------|-------|--------|
|  |  |  |  |  |
|  |  |  |  |  |
|  |  |  |  |  |
|  |  |  |  |  |
|  |  |  |  |  |
|  |  |  |  |  |
|  |  |  |  |  |
|  |  |  |  |  |
|  |  |  |  |  |
|  |  |  |  |  |
|  |  |  |  |  |
|  |  |  |  |  |
|  |  |  |  |  |
|  |  |  |  |  |
|  |  |  |  |  |
|  |  |  |  |  |
|  |  |  |  |  |
|  |  |  |  |  |

# Journal

| DATE | | ACCOUNTS AND EXPLANATIONS | POST. REF. | DEBIT | CREDIT |
|------|---|---------------------------|-----------|-------|--------|
| | | | | | |
| | | | | | |
| | | | | | |
| | | | | | |
| | | | | | |
| | | | | | |
| | | | | | |
| | | | | | |
| | | | | | |
| | | | | | |
| | | | | | |
| | | | | | |
| | | | | | |
| | | | | | |
| | | | | | |

*eq. 1*

| | | Journal | | | | |
|---|---|---|---|---|---|---|
| DATE | | ACCOUNTS AND EXPLANATIONS | POST. REF. | DEBIT | CREDIT |
| | | | | | |
| | | | | | |
| | | | | | |
| | | | | | |
| | | | | | |
| | | | | | |
| | | | | | |
| | | | | | |
| | | | | | |
| | | | | | |
| | | | | | |
| | | | | | |
| | | | | | |
| | | | | | |

*Req. 2*

*Req. 3*

Req. 1

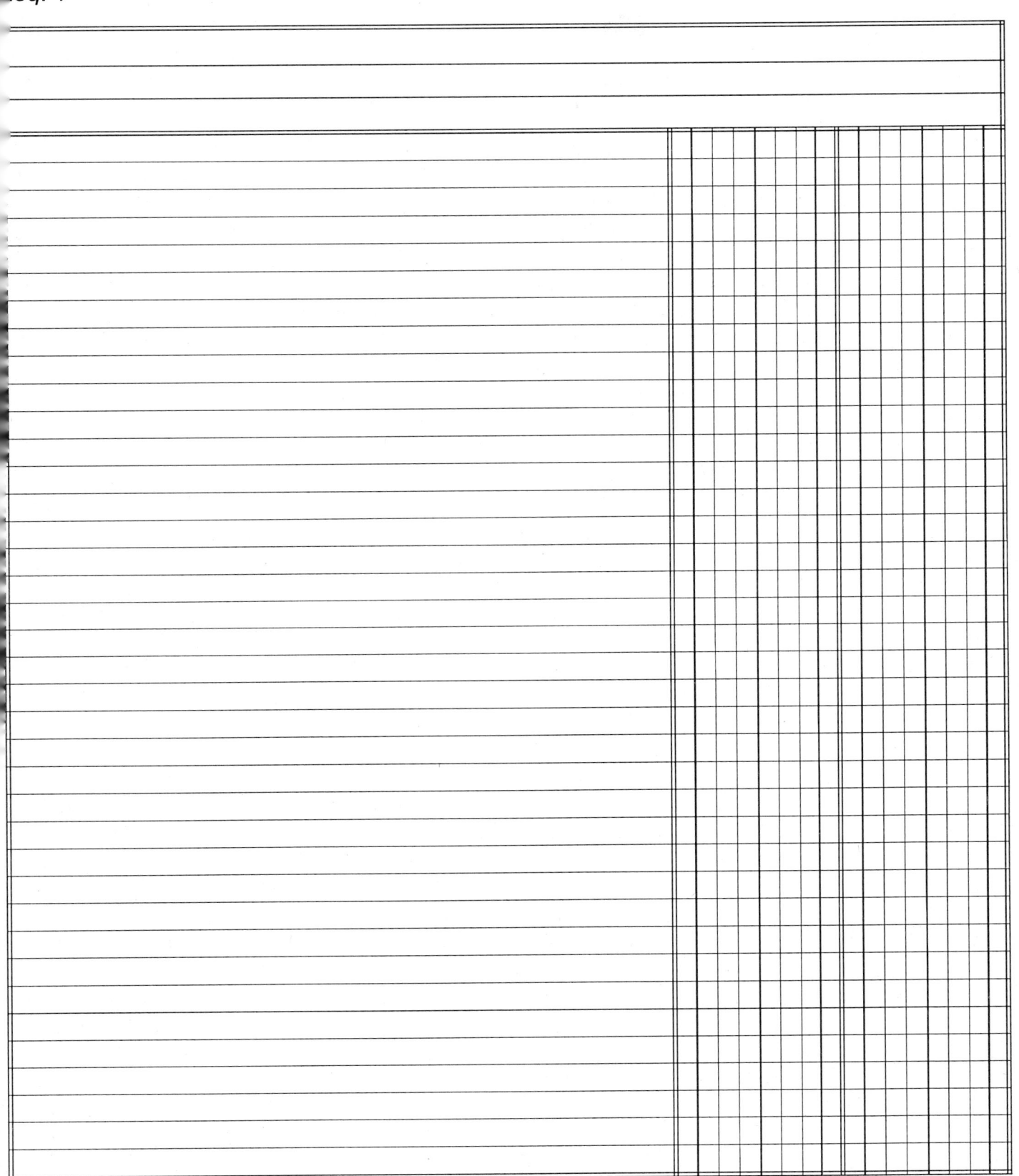

*Req. 2*

*Req. 1*

*Req. 2*

eq. 2 (Continued)

## Journal

| DATE | ACCOUNTS AND EXPLANATIONS | POST. REF. | DEBIT | CREDIT |
|------|---------------------------|-----------|-------|--------|
|  |  |  |  |  |
|  |  |  |  |  |
|  |  |  |  |  |
|  |  |  |  |  |
|  |  |  |  |  |
|  |  |  |  |  |
|  |  |  |  |  |
|  |  |  |  |  |
|  |  |  |  |  |
|  |  |  |  |  |
|  |  |  |  |  |
|  |  |  |  |  |
|  |  |  |  |  |
|  |  |  |  |  |
|  |  |  |  |  |
|  |  |  |  |  |
|  |  |  |  |  |
|  |  |  |  |  |
|  |  |  |  |  |
|  |  |  |  |  |
|  |  |  |  |  |
|  |  |  |  |  |
|  |  |  |  |  |
|  |  |  |  |  |
|  |  |  |  |  |
|  |  |  |  |  |
|  |  |  |  |  |
|  |  |  |  |  |
|  |  |  |  |  |

AME
ECTION
ATE

*eq. 1*

*Reqs. 2 & 3*

## Journal

| DATE | ACCOUNTS AND EXPLANATIONS | POST. REF. | DEBIT | CREDIT |
|------|---------------------------|-----------|-------|--------|
|      |                           |           |       |        |
|      |                           |           |       |        |
|      |                           |           |       |        |
|      |                           |           |       |        |
|      |                           |           |       |        |
|      |                           |           |       |        |
|      |                           |           |       |        |
|      |                           |           |       |        |
|      |                           |           |       |        |
|      |                           |           |       |        |
|      |                           |           |       |        |
|      |                           |           |       |        |
|      |                           |           |       |        |
|      |                           |           |       |        |
|      |                           |           |       |        |
|      |                           |           |       |        |
|      |                           |           |       |        |
|      |                           |           |       |        |
|      |                           |           |       |        |

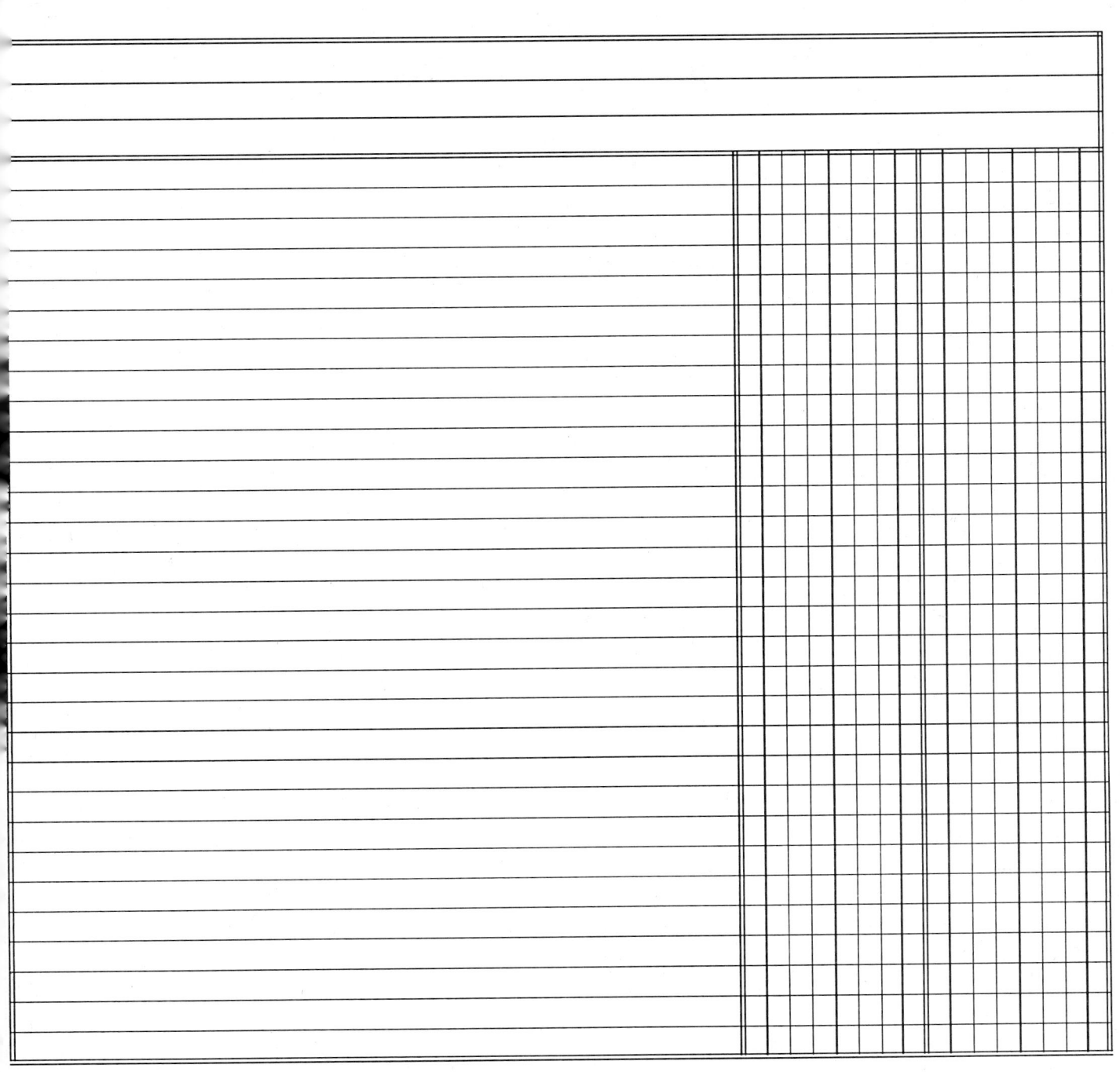

*Req. 2*

*Req. 1*

**MISSING INTERNAL
CONTROL
CHARACTERISTIC**

*Req. 2*

**POSSIBLE PROBLEM**

*Req. 3*

**SOLUTION**

AME
ECTION
ATE

*Req. 1*

*Req. 2 (Continued)*

## Journal

| DATE | | ACCOUNTS AND EXPLANATIONS | POST. REF. | DEBIT | CREDIT |
|------|--|---------------------------|------------|-------|--------|
| | | | | | |
| | | | | | |
| | | | | | |
| | | | | | |
| | | | | | |
| | | | | | |
| | | | | | |
| | | | | | |
| | | | | | |
| | | | | | |
| | | | | | |
| | | | | | |
| | | | | | |
| | | | | | |
| | | | | | |
| | | | | | |
| | | | | | |
| | | | | | |
| | | | | | |
| | | | | | |
| | | | | | |
| | | | | | |
| | | | | | |
| | | | | | |
| | | | | | |
| | | | | | |
| | | | | | |
| | | | | | |
| | | | | | |
| | | | | | |
| | | | | | |
| | | | | | |
| | | | | | |
| | | | | | |
| | | | | | |
| | | | | | |
| | | | | | |
| | | | | | |

*Req. 1*

*Reqs. 2 & 3*

| | | Journal | | | |
|---|---|---|---|---|---|
| DATE | | ACCOUNTS AND EXPLANATIONS | POST. REF. | DEBIT | CREDIT |
| | | | | | |
| | | | | | |
| | | | | | |
| | | | | | |
| | | | | | |
| | | | | | |
| | | | | | |
| | | | | | |
| | | | | | |
| | | | | | |
| | | | | | |
| | | | | | |
| | | | | | |
| | | | | | |
| | | | | | |
| | | | | | |
| | | | | | |
| | | | | | |
| | | | | | |
| | | | | | |
| | | | | | |
| | | | | | |

**Req. 2**

*Reqs. 1–5*

**DE8-2**

**DE8-3**

| DATE | ACCOUNTS AND EXPLANATIONS | POST. REF. | DEBIT | CREDIT |
|---|---|---|---|---|
|  |  |  |  |  |
|  |  |  |  |  |
|  |  |  |  |  |
|  |  |  |  |  |
|  |  |  |  |  |
|  |  |  |  |  |
|  |  |  |  |  |
|  |  |  |  |  |

# DE8-6

| DATE | ACCOUNTS AND EXPLANATIONS | POST. REF. | DEBIT | CREDIT |
|---|---|---|---|---|
|  |  |  |  |  |
|  |  |  |  |  |
|  |  |  |  |  |
|  |  |  |  |  |
|  |  |  |  |  |
|  |  |  |  |  |
|  |  |  |  |  |
|  |  |  |  |  |
|  |  |  |  |  |
|  |  |  |  |  |
|  |  |  |  |  |
|  |  |  |  |  |
|  |  |  |  |  |
|  |  |  |  |  |
|  |  |  |  |  |
|  |  |  |  |  |
|  |  |  |  |  |
|  |  |  |  |  |
|  |  |  |  |  |
|  |  |  |  |  |
|  |  |  |  |  |
|  |  |  |  |  |
|  |  |  |  |  |
|  |  |  |  |  |
|  |  |  |  |  |
|  |  |  |  |  |
|  |  |  |  |  |
|  |  |  |  |  |
|  |  |  |  |  |

1.

2.

3.

## Journal

| DATE | ACCOUNTS AND EXPLANATIONS | POST. REF. | DEBIT | CREDIT |
|---|---|---|---|---|
| | | | | |
| | | | | |
| | | | | |
| | | | | |
| | | | | |
| | | | | |
| | | | | |
| | | | | |
| | | | | |
| | | | | |
| | | | | |
| | | | | |
| | | | | |
| | | | | |
| | | | | |
| | | | | |
| | | | | |
| | | | | |
| | | | | |

*Req. 1*

1.

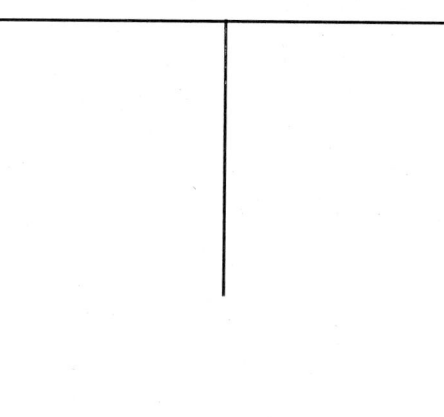

*Reqs. 2 & 3*

*Req. 1*

| DATE | ACCOUNTS AND EXPLANATIONS | POST. REF. | DEBIT | CREDIT |
|------|---------------------------|-----------|-------|--------|
|      |                           |           |       |        |
|      |                           |           |       |        |
|      |                           |           |       |        |
|      |                           |           |       |        |

*Req. 2*

*a + b*

## Journal

| DATE | ACCOUNTS AND EXPLANATIONS | POST. REF. | DEBIT | CREDIT |
|------|---------------------------|------------|-------|--------|
|      |                           |            |       |        |
|      |                           |            |       |        |
|      |                           |            |       |        |
|      |                           |            |       |        |
|      |                           |            |       |        |
|      |                           |            |       |        |
|      |                           |            |       |        |
|      |                           |            |       |        |
|      |                           |            |       |        |
|      |                           |            |       |        |
|      |                           |            |       |        |
|      |                           |            |       |        |
|      |                           |            |       |        |
|      |                           |            |       |        |
|      |                           |            |       |        |
|      |                           |            |       |        |

Req. 1

Req. 2

## Journal

| DATE | ACCOUNTS AND EXPLANATIONS | POST. REF. | DEBIT | CREDIT |
|------|---------------------------|------------|-------|--------|
|  |  |  |  |  |
|  |  |  |  |  |
|  |  |  |  |  |
|  |  |  |  |  |
|  |  |  |  |  |
|  |  |  |  |  |
|  |  |  |  |  |
|  |  |  |  |  |
|  |  |  |  |  |
|  |  |  |  |  |
|  |  |  |  |  |

# DE8-14

*Reqs. 1–3*

**DE8-16**

| | Journal | | | | |
|---|---|---|---|---|---|
| DATE | ACCOUNTS AND EXPLANATIONS | POST. REF. | DEBIT | CREDIT |
| | | | | |
| | | | | |
| | | | | |
| | | | | |
| | | | | |
| | | | | |
| | | | | |
| | | | | |
| | | | | |
| | | | | |
| | | | | |

## Journal

| DATE | ACCOUNTS AND EXPLANATIONS | POST. REF. | DEBIT | CREDIT |
|------|---------------------------|------------|-------|--------|
|      |                           |            |       |        |
|      |                           |            |       |        |
|      |                           |            |       |        |
|      |                           |            |       |        |
|      |                           |            |       |        |
|      |                           |            |       |        |
|      |                           |            |       |        |
|      |                           |            |       |        |
|      |                           |            |       |        |
|      |                           |            |       |        |
|      |                           |            |       |        |
|      |                           |            |       |        |
|      |                           |            |       |        |
|      |                           |            |       |        |
|      |                           |            |       |        |

**DE8-18**

*f*

## Journal

| DATE | ACCOUNTS AND EXPLANATIONS | POST. REF. | DEBIT | CREDIT |
|------|---------------------------|-----------|-------|--------|
|  |  |  |  |  |
|  |  |  |  |  |
|  |  |  |  |  |
|  |  |  |  |  |
|  |  |  |  |  |
|  |  |  |  |  |
|  |  |  |  |  |
|  |  |  |  |  |
|  |  |  |  |  |
|  |  |  |  |  |
|  |  |  |  |  |
|  |  |  |  |  |
|  |  |  |  |  |
|  |  |  |  |  |
|  |  |  |  |  |
|  |  |  |  |  |
|  |  |  |  |  |
|  |  |  |  |  |
|  |  |  |  |  |
|  |  |  |  |  |

| | | | | | | | | | | | | | | | | | | | | |
|---|---|---|---|---|---|---|---|---|---|---|---|---|---|---|---|---|---|---|---|---|
| | | | | | | | | | | | | | | | | | | | | |

*Req. 1*

# Income Statement Balance Shee⌐

| | Debit Balance | Credit Balance | Debit Balance | Credit Balanc |
|---|---|---|---|---|
| | | | | |
| | | | | |
| | | | | |
| | | | | |
| | | | | |
| | | | | |
| | | | | |
| | | | | |
| | | | | |
| | | | | |
| | | | | |
| | | | | |
| | | | | |
| | | | | |
| | | | | |

*Reqs. 2 and 3*

*eqs. a and b*

*Reqs. a–d*

*Req. 1*

| | | Journal | | | |
|---|---|---|---|---|---|
| DATE | | ACCOUNTS AND EXPLANATIONS | POST. REF. | DEBIT | CREDIT |
| | | | | | |
| | | | | | |
| | | | | | |
| | | | | | |
| | | | | | |
| | | | | | |
| | | | | | |
| | | | | | |
| | | | | | |
| | | | | | |
| | | | | | |
| | | | | | |
| | | | | | |
| | | | | | |
| | | | | | |

*Req. 2*

Acct Rec

Allow.

*Req. 3*

Req. 1

### Journal

| DATE | ACCOUNTS AND EXPLANATIONS | POST. REF. | DEBIT | CREDIT |
|------|---------------------------|------------|-------|--------|
|      |                           |            |       |        |
|      |                           |            |       |        |
|      |                           |            |       |        |
|      |                           |            |       |        |
|      |                           |            |       |        |

Req. 2

E8-5

Age of Acct

| Req. 1 Tot. Bal. | 1-30 | 31-60 | 61-90 | over 90 |
|------------------|------|-------|-------|---------|
| $269,000 | $107,000 | 78,000 | 69,000 | 15,000 |
| estimated % | .3% | 1.2% | 6.0% | 50% |
| Allow | $(321) | $936 | $4,140 | $7,500 |

### Journal

| DATE | ACCOUNTS AND EXPLANATIONS | POST. REF. | DEBIT | CREDIT |
|------|---------------------------|------------|-------|--------|
|      | Uncollect. Acct. Expense  |            | 8987  |        |
|      | Allow for Uncollect. Acct |            |       | 8987   |
|      |                           |            |       |        |
|      |                           |            |       |        |
|      |                           |            |       |        |
|      |                           |            |       |        |

_Req. 2_

a.

%

### Journal

| DATE | ACCOUNTS AND EXPLANATIONS | POST. REF. | DEBIT | CREDIT |
|---|---|---|---|---|
| | ADJ | | | |
| | Uncollect. Acct. Expense | | 3000 | |
| | Allow for U. A. | | | 3000 |
| | | | | |
| | | | | |

Rel    Allow for U. A.                                    bal

Bal                                                          4,000

600,000 × .001⅗ = 3,000  aditional
                              exp

                    ·ADJ

                                                           1,600
                                                           3,000  Write
                                                           4,600

b.

Aging

### Journal

| DATE | ACCOUNTS AND EXPLANATIONS | POST. REF. | DEBIT | CREDIT |
|---|---|---|---|---|
| | | | 5600 | |
| | Uncollect. Acct. Expense | | 5600 | |
| | Allow for U.A. | | | 5600 |
| | | | | |
| | | | | |

                          DR        CR

Bal                       4000                     Aging
                                                   3900
                            0

                    1700
Allow                       5600
                            3900

## Journal

| DATE | | ACCOUNTS AND EXPLANATIONS | POST. REF. | DEBIT | CREDIT |
|------|---|---------------------------|------------|-------|--------|
| Nov | 1 | Notes Rec | | 50000 | |
| | | Cash | | | 50000 |
| | | | | | |
| Dec | 3 | Notes Rec | | 3750 | |
| | | Sales Rev | | | 3750 |
| | | | | | |
| Dec | 16 | Notes Rec | | 2000 | |
| | | Acct. Rec. - E.M.C. | | | 2000 |
| | | | | | |
| | | ADJ | | | |
| Dec | 31 | Intrest Rec. | | 795 | |
| | | Intrest Rev. | | | 795 |

Accrue int. Rev.

1. 50,000 × 9% × $\frac{2}{12}$

750

2. 3,750 × 12% × $\frac{28}{360}$

.01

= 35

3. 2,000 × 12% × $\frac{.5}{12}$

= 40

Intrest = Princp × int. ra × period

Dec 31

28.

795

## Journal

| DATE | ACCOUNTS AND EXPLANATIONS | POST. REF. | DEBIT | CREDIT |
|---|---|---|---|---|
| 19X6 | | | | |
| Feb 12 | Cash | | 29400 | |
| | Credit Card Disc. Exp | | 600 | |
| | Sales Rev | | | 30000 |
| April 1 | Notes Rec | | 8000 | |
| | Cash | | | 8000 |
| Dec 31 | Intrest Rec. | | 600 | |
| | Intrest Rev. | | | 600 |
| 19X7 | | | | |
| April 1 | Cash | | 8800 | |
| | Notes Rec | | | 8000 |
| | Intrest Rec. | | | 600 |
| | Intrest Rev. | | | 200 |

Req. 1

**E8-9**

## Journal

| DATE | ACCOUNTS AND EXPLANATIONS | POST. REF. | DEBIT | CREDIT |
|---|---|---|---|---|
| 19X4 | | | | |
| Aug 29 | Accounts Rec. - V.M. | | 3900 | |
| | Sales Rev | | | 3900 |
| Dec 1 | Notes Rec. | | 3900 | |
| | Acct. Rec - V.M. | | | 3900 |
| Dec 1 | Cash | | 3600 | |
| | Intrest Exp / Loss on Sale of Note | | 300 | |
| | Notes Rec | | | 3900 |

Req. 2

*Reqs. 1 and 2*

_Reqs. 1 & 2_

# E8-13

*Req. 1*

| | | Journal | | | |
|---|---|---|---|---|---|
| DATE | | ACCOUNTS AND EXPLANATIONS | POST. REF. | DEBIT | CREDIT |
| | | | | | |
| | | | | | |
| | | | | | |
| | | | | | |
| | | | | | |
| | | | | | |

eq. 2

| | | Journal | | | | | | | |
|---|---|---|---|---|---|---|---|---|---|
| DATE | | ACCOUNTS AND EXPLANATIONS | | POST. REF. | | DEBIT | | CREDIT | |
| | | | | | | | | | |
| | | | | | | | | | |
| | | | | | | | | | |
| | | | | | | | | | |
| | | | | | | | | | |
| | | | | | | | | | |
| | | | | | | | | | |
| | | | | | | | | | |
| | | | | | | | | | |
| | | | | | | | | | |
| | | | | | | | | | |

*Req. 3*

*Req. 4*

AME
ECTION
ATE

Req.1

| | Journal | | | | |
|---|---|---|---|---|
| DATE | ACCOUNTS AND EXPLANATIONS | POST. REF. | DEBIT | CREDIT |
| | | | | |
| | | | | |
| | | | | |
| | | | | |
| | | | | |
| | | | | |
| | | | | |
| | | | | |
| | | | | |
| | | | | |
| | | | | |
| | | | | |
| | | | | |
| | | | | |
| | | | | |
| | | | | |
| | | | | |
| | | | | |
| | | | | |
| | | | | |
| | | | | |
| | | | | |
| | | | | |
| | | | | |
| | | | | |
| | | | | |
| | | | | |
| | | | | |
| | | | | |
| | | | | |
| | | | | |
| | | | | |
| | | | | |
| | | | | |
| | | | | |
| | | | | |
| | | | | |
| | | | | |
| | | | | |

*Req.1 (Continued)*

## Journal

| DATE | ACCOUNTS AND EXPLANATIONS | POST. REF. | DEBIT | CREDIT |
|------|---------------------------|------------|-------|--------|
|  |  |  |  |  |
|  |  |  |  |  |
|  |  |  |  |  |
|  |  |  |  |  |
|  |  |  |  |  |
|  |  |  |  |  |
|  |  |  |  |  |
|  |  |  |  |  |
|  |  |  |  |  |
|  |  |  |  |  |
|  |  |  |  |  |
|  |  |  |  |  |
|  |  |  |  |  |
|  |  |  |  |  |
|  |  |  |  |  |
|  |  |  |  |  |
|  |  |  |  |  |
|  |  |  |  |  |
|  |  |  |  |  |
|  |  |  |  |  |
|  |  |  |  |  |
|  |  |  |  |  |
|  |  |  |  |  |
|  |  |  |  |  |
|  |  |  |  |  |
|  |  |  |  |  |
|  |  |  |  |  |
|  |  |  |  |  |
|  |  |  |  |  |
|  |  |  |  |  |

Req. 1

|  | 19X4 | 19X3 |
|---|---|---|

A. CURRENT RATIO:

B. ACID TEST RATIO:

C. ONE DAY'S SALES:

D. DAYS' SALES IN AVERAGE
    RECEIVABLES:

*Req. 2*

*Req. 1*

*Req. 2*

NAME
SECTION
DATE

*Req. 1*

## Journal

| DATE | ACCOUNTS AND EXPLANATIONS | POST. REF. | DEBIT | CREDIT |
|------|---------------------------|------------|-------|--------|
|      |                           |            |       |        |
|      |                           |            |       |        |
|      |                           |            |       |        |
|      |                           |            |       |        |
|      |                           |            |       |        |
|      |                           |            |       |        |

*Req. 2*

## Journal

| DATE | ACCOUNTS AND EXPLANATIONS | POST. REF. | DEBIT | CREDIT |
|------|---------------------------|------------|-------|--------|
|      |                           |            |       |        |
|      |                           |            |       |        |
|      |                           |            |       |        |
|      |                           |            |       |        |
|      |                           |            |       |        |
|      |                           |            |       |        |
|      |                           |            |       |        |
|      |                           |            |       |        |
|      |                           |            |       |        |
|      |                           |            |       |        |
|      |                           |            |       |        |
|      |                           |            |       |        |
|      |                           |            |       |        |
|      |                           |            |       |        |
|      |                           |            |       |        |

NAME
SECTION
DATE



**P8-2B** *(Continued)*

*Req. 3*

*Req. 4*

*Req. 1*

| | | Journal | | | |
|---|---|---|---|---|---|
| DATE | | ACCOUNTS AND EXPLANATIONS | POST. REF. | DEBIT | CREDIT |
| | | | | | |
| | | | | | |
| | | | | | |
| | | | | | |
| | | | | | |
| | | | | | |
| | | | | | |
| | | | | | |
| | | | | | |
| | | | | | |
| | | | | | |
| | | | | | |
| | | | | | |
| | | | | | |
| | | | | | |
| | | | | | |
| | | | | | |
| | | | | | |
| | | | | | |
| | | | | | |
| | | | | | |
| | | | | | |

*eq. 2*

| ACCOUNT | | | | | ACCOUNT NO. | | |
|---------|------|-------|-------|--------|-------------|---|---|
| | | | | | BALANCE | | |
| DATE | ITEM | JRNL. REF. | DEBIT | CREDIT | DEBIT | CREDIT | |
| | | | | | | | |
| | | | | | | | |
| | | | | | | | |
| | | | | | | | |
| | | | | | | | |
| | | | | | | | |
| | | | | | | | |
| | | | | | | | |
| | | | | | | | |

Req. 3

| | | | | | | | | | | | | | | | | | | | | | |
|---|---|---|---|---|---|---|---|---|---|---|---|---|---|---|---|---|---|---|---|---|---|
| | | | | | | | | | | | | | | | | | | | | | |
| | | | | | | | | | | | | | | | | | | | | | |
| | | | | | | | | | | | | | | | | | | | | | |
| | | | | | | | | | | | | | | | | | | | | | |
| | | | | | | | | | | | | | | | | | | | | | |
| | | | | | | | | | | | | | | | | | | | | | |
| | | | | | | | | | | | | | | | | | | | | | |
| | | | | | | | | | | | | | | | | | | | | | |
| | | | | | | | | | | | | | | | | | | | | | |

Reqs. 1 and 2

| ACCOUNT | Uncollect Acct Exp | | | | ACCOUNT NO. | |
|---|---|---|---|---|---|---|
| | | JRNL. REF. | | | BALANCE | |
| DATE | ITEM | | DEBIT | CREDIT | DEBIT | CREDIT |
| 12 31 | ADJ | | 3000 | | 3000 | |
| 12 31 | Close | | | 3000 | | |
| 12 31 | ADJ | | 3600 | | 3600 | |
| 12 31 | close | | | 3600 | | |
| | | | | | | |
| | | | | | | |
| | | | | | | |
| | | | | | | |
| | | | | | | |
| | | | | | | |

| ACCOUNT | Allow for Uncollect acct. | | | | ACCOUNT NO. | |
|---|---|---|---|---|---|---|
| | | JRNL. REF. | | | BALANCE | |
| DATE | ITEM | | DEBIT | CREDIT | DEBIT | CREDIT |
| 12 31 | ADJ | | | 3000 | | 3000 |
| 1/1 | write off | | 1521 | | | 1479 |
| 10/19 | Reinstate | | | 1521 | | 3000 |
| 12/31 | write off | | 2701 | | | 299 |
| 12/31 | ADJ | | | 3600 | | 3899 |
| | | | | | | |
| | | | | | | |

*Reqs. 1 and 2 (Continued)*

| ACCOUNT | | | | | ACCOUNT NO. | |
|---|---|---|---|---|---|---|
| | | | | | BALANCE | |
| DATE | ITEM | JRNL. REF. | DEBIT | CREDIT | DEBIT | CREDIT |
| | | | | | | |
| | | | | | | |
| | | | | | | |
| | | | | | | |
| | | | | | | |
| | | | | | | |
| | | | | | | |
| | | | | | | |
| | | | | | | |
| | | | | | | |
| | | | | | | |
| | | | | | | |

| ACCOUNT | | | | | ACCOUNT NO. | |
|---|---|---|---|---|---|---|
| | | | | | BALANCE | |
| DATE | ITEM | JRNL. REF. | DEBIT | CREDIT | DEBIT | CREDIT |
| | | | | | | |
| | | | | | | |
| | | | | | | |
| | | | | | | |
| | | | | | | |
| | | | | | | |
| | | | | | | |
| | | | | | | |
| | | | | | | |
| | | | | | | |
| | | | | | | |
| | | | | | | |
| | | | | | | |

*Req. 2*

Sales on Acct $450,000
x % of sales   2/3 of 1%

exp. 3,000

## Journal

| DATE | | ACCOUNTS AND EXPLANATIONS | POST. REF. | DEBIT | CREDIT |
|---|---|---|---|---|---|
| Dec | 31 | Uncollect Acct Exp | | 3000 | |
| 19X1 | | Allow for U.A. | | | 3000 |
| 12 | 31 | Income Summary | | 3000 | |
| | | Uncollect Acct Exp | | | 3000 |
| 19X2 | | | | | |
| Feb | 4 | Acct. Rec. – G.C. | | 1521 | |
| | | Sales Rev. | | | 1521 |
| July | 1 | Allow for U.A. | | 1521 | |
| | | Acct. Rec – G.C. | | | 1521 |
| Oct | 19 | Acct Rec. – G.C. | | 1521 | |
| | | Allow for U.A. | | | 1521 |
| Oct | 19 | Cash | | 521 | |
| | | Acct. Rec. – G.C. | | | 521 |
| Nov | 15 | Cash | | 1000 | |
| | | Acct Rec. – G.C. | | | 1000 |
| Dec | 31 | Allow for U.A. | | 2701 | |
| | | Acct. Rec – K.M. | | | 899 |
| | | Acct Rec – M.M. | | | 530 |
| | | Acct Rec – G.F. | | | 1272 |
| Dec | 31 | Uncollect Acct Exp | | 3600 | |
| | | Allow for U.A. | | | 3600 |
| | 31 | Income Summary | | 3600 | |
| | | Uncollect acct Exp | | | 3600 |

Sales on Acct   540,000
x % of sale    2/3 of 1%
43,600

*Req. 2 (Continued)*

| | | | | | |
|---|---|---|---|---|---|
| | | **Journal** | | | |
| DATE | | ACCOUNTS AND EXPLANATIONS | POST. REF. | DEBIT | CREDIT |
| | | | | | |
| | | | | | |
| | | | | | |
| | | | | | |
| | | | | | |
| | | | | | |
| | | | | | |
| | | | | | |
| | | | | | |
| | | | | | |
| | | | | | |
| | | | | | |
| | | | | | |
| | | | | | |
| | | | | | |
| | | | | | |
| | | | | | |
| | | | | | |
| | | | | | |
| | | | | | |
| | | | | | |
| | | | | | |
| | | | | | |
| | | | | | |
| | | | | | |
| | | | | | |
| | | | | | |
| | | | | | |
| | | | | | |
| | | | | | |
| | | | | | |
| | | | | | |
| | | | | | |
| | | | | | |
| | | | | | |
| | | | | | |
| | | | | | |
| | | | | | |

*Req. 3*

*Req. 4a*

| | | Journal | | | | | | |
|---|---|---|---|---|---|---|---|---|
| DATE | | ACCOUNTS AND EXPLANATIONS | POST. REF. | | DEBIT | | CREDIT | |
| | | Uncollect. Acct. Expense | | | 3246 | | | |
| | | Allow for U.A. | | | | | 3246 | |
| | | | | | | | | |

```
         299
ADJ +3246
        3545
```

*Req. 4b*

*Req. 1*

| NOTE | DUE DATE | PRINCIPAL + INTEREST | | MATURITY VALUE |
|------|----------|----------------------|---|----------------|
| (1) | _____ | _____ | = | _____ |
| (2) | _____ | _____ | = | _____ |
| (3) | _____ | _____ | = | _____ |
| (4) | _____ | _____ | = | _____ |
| (5) | _____ | _____ | = | _____ |
| (6) | _____ | _____ | = | _____ |

*Req. 2*

| NOTE | MATURITY VALUE | DISCOUNT | PROCEEDS |
|------|----------------|----------|----------|
| (1) | _____ | _____ | _____ |
| (2) | _____ | _____ | _____ |
| (3) | _____ | _____ | _____ |

Reqs. 3–5

## Journal

| DATE | ACCOUNTS AND EXPLANATIONS | POST. REF. | DEBIT | CREDIT |
|------|---------------------------|------------|-------|--------|
| | | | | |
| | | | | |
| | | | | |
| | | | | |
| | | | | |
| | | | | |
| | | | | |
| | | | | |
| | | | | |
| | | | | |
| | | | | |
| | | | | |
| | | | | |
| | | | | |
| | | | | |
| | | | | |
| | | | | |
| | | | | |
| | | | | |
| | | | | |
| | | | | |
| | | | | |
| | | | | |
| | | | | |
| | | | | |
| | | | | |
| | | | | |
| | | | | |
| | | | | |
| | | | | |
| | | | | |
| | | | | |
| | | | | |
| | | | | |
| | | | | |
| | | | | |
| | | | | |
| | | | | |
| | | | | |
| | | | | |

Req.1

| | | Journal | | | |
|---|---|---|---|---|---|
| DATE | | ACCOUNTS AND EXPLANATIONS | POST. REF. | DEBIT | CREDIT |
| | | | | | |

*Req.1 (Continued)*

## Journal

| DATE | ACCOUNTS AND EXPLANATIONS | POST. REF. | DEBIT | CREDIT |
|------|---------------------------|------------|-------|--------|
| | | | | |

Req. 1

## Journal

| DATE | ACCOUNTS AND EXPLANATIONS | POST. REF. | DEBIT | CREDIT |
|------|---------------------------|------------|-------|--------|
|      |                           |            |       |        |
|      |                           |            |       |        |
|      |                           |            |       |        |
|      |                           |            |       |        |
|      |                           |            |       |        |
|      |                           |            |       |        |
|      |                           |            |       |        |
|      |                           |            |       |        |
|      |                           |            |       |        |
|      |                           |            |       |        |
|      |                           |            |       |        |
|      |                           |            |       |        |
|      |                           |            |       |        |
|      |                           |            |       |        |
|      |                           |            |       |        |
|      |                           |            |       |        |
|      |                           |            |       |        |
|      |                           |            |       |        |
|      |                           |            |       |        |
|      |                           |            |       |        |
|      |                           |            |       |        |
|      |                           |            |       |        |
|      |                           |            |       |        |
|      |                           |            |       |        |
|      |                           |            |       |        |
|      |                           |            |       |        |
|      |                           |            |       |        |
|      |                           |            |       |        |

*Req. 1 (Continued)*

## Journal

| DATE | ACCOUNTS AND EXPLANATIONS | POST. REF. | DEBIT | CREDIT |
|------|---------------------------|------------|-------|--------|
|      |                           |            |       |        |
|      |                           |            |       |        |
|      |                           |            |       |        |
|      |                           |            |       |        |
|      |                           |            |       |        |
|      |                           |            |       |        |
|      |                           |            |       |        |
|      |                           |            |       |        |
|      |                           |            |       |        |
|      |                           |            |       |        |
|      |                           |            |       |        |
|      |                           |            |       |        |
|      |                           |            |       |        |
|      |                           |            |       |        |
|      |                           |            |       |        |
|      |                           |            |       |        |
|      |                           |            |       |        |
|      |                           |            |       |        |
|      |                           |            |       |        |
|      |                           |            |       |        |
|      |                           |            |       |        |
|      |                           |            |       |        |
|      |                           |            |       |        |
|      |                           |            |       |        |
|      |                           |            |       |        |
|      |                           |            |       |        |
|      |                           |            |       |        |
|      |                           |            |       |        |
|      |                           |            |       |        |
|      |                           |            |       |        |
|      |                           |            |       |        |

*Req. 1*

**A. CURRENT RATIO:**                                    **19X4**                    **19X3**

**B. ACID TEST RATIO:**

**C. ONE DAY'S SALES:**

**D. DAYS' SALES IN AVERAGE
   RECEIVABLES:**

AME
ECTION
ATE

*Chapter 8*

**P8-8B** *(Continued)*

Req. 2

*Req. 1*

*Req. 2*

*Req. 1*

| | | |
|---|---|---|
| | | |

*Req. 2*

*Req. 1*

_____

_____

_____

_____

_____

_____

_____

_____

_____

*Req. 2*

*Req. 3*

_____

_____

_____

_____

_____

_____

_____

_____

_____

_____

**DE9-2**

## Journal

| DATE | ACCOUNTS AND EXPLANATIONS | POST. REF. | DEBIT | CREDIT |
|------|---------------------------|------------|-------|--------|
|      |                           |            |       |        |
|      |                           |            |       |        |
|      |                           |            |       |        |
|      |                           |            |       |        |
|      |                           |            |       |        |
|      |                           |            |       |        |
|      |                           |            |       |        |
|      |                           |            |       |        |

**DE9-6**

| | | | | |
|---|---|---|---|---|
| | | | | |

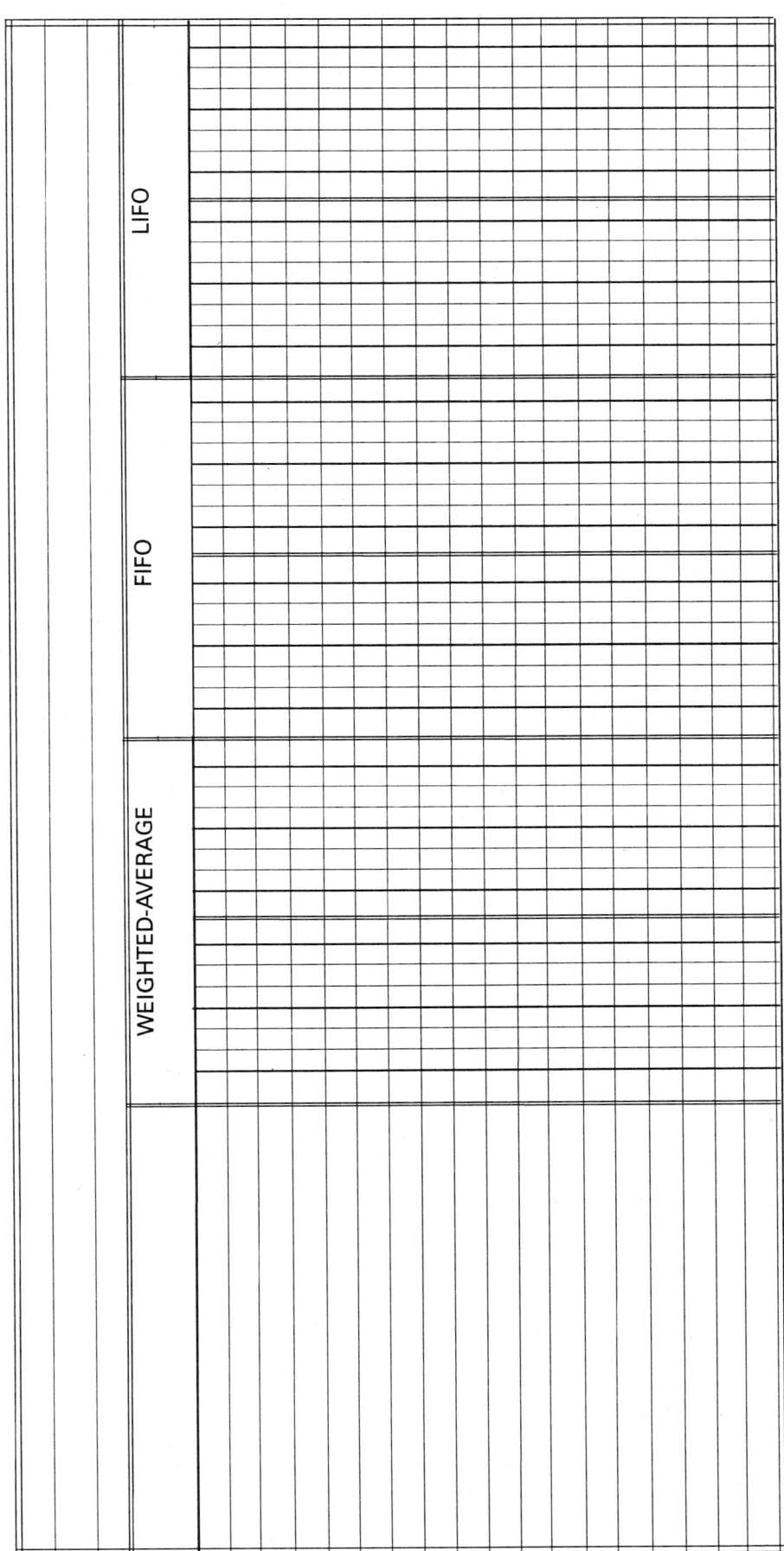

| | WEIGHTED-AVERAGE | FIFO | LIFO |
|---|---|---|---|

**DE9-13**

1.

| | Journal | | | | |
|---|---|---|---|---|---|
| DATE | ACCOUNTS AND EXPLANATIONS | POST. REF. | DEBIT | | CREDIT |
| | | | | | |
| | | | | | |
| | | | | | |
| | | | | | |
| | | | | | |
| | | | | | |
| | | | | | |

2.

eq. 1

## Journal

| DATE | ACCOUNTS AND EXPLANATIONS | POST. REF. | DEBIT | CREDIT |
|------|---------------------------|------------|-------|--------|
|      |                           |            |       |        |
|      |                           |            |       |        |
|      |                           |            |       |        |
|      |                           |            |       |        |
|      |                           |            |       |        |
|      |                           |            |       |        |
|      |                           |            |       |        |
|      |                           |            |       |        |
|      |                           |            |       |        |
|      |                           |            |       |        |
|      |                           |            |       |        |
|      |                           |            |       |        |
|      |                           |            |       |        |
|      |                           |            |       |        |
|      |                           |            |       |        |
|      |                           |            |       |        |
|      |                           |            |       |        |
|      |                           |            |       |        |
|      |                           |            |       |        |
|      |                           |            |       |        |
|      |                           |            |       |        |
|      |                           |            |       |        |
|      |                           |            |       |        |

*Req. 2*

Ave

Pace Maker Switches

| Date | | Units | | Cost/u | Total Cost |
|------|---|-------|---|--------|-----------|
| Oct 1 | S 1 | 7 | I | $160 | 1120 |
| 8 | S 1 | 4 | 17 35 | 160 | 640 |
| 15 | 8S 3I 1 | 11 | S | 170 | 1870 |
| 26 | I | 5 | S | 176 | 880 |
| | | 27 | | 4510 | |

oct 31      8 left

1.)  end Inv                                    cost of good sold

5 U @ $170 = $850               Avail       4510
3 U @ 160 = 480                 - end      -1330
              $1330                           $3180

2.)  ave.                ending inv,                    Cost of G.S.
4510                                                    Avail  4510
————  = $167      8 u @ 167 = $1336              ending -1336
2⊘u                                                     $3174*

Lifo  4)   Ending Inv                      Cost of Goods Sold
7 U @ 160 = 1120              Avail      4510
1 U @ 160 = 160              - endin   -1280
              $1280                        $3230

Fifo  3)   Ending inventory              Cost of Goods Sold
3 U @ 170 = 510                Avail for Sale
5 u @ 176 = 880              - ending inventory
              $1390                        4,510
                                           1390

                                           $3120

# Journal

| DATE | ACCOUNTS AND EXPLANATIONS | POST. REF. | DEBIT | CREDIT |
|------|---------------------------|-----------|-------|--------|
|      |                           |           |       |        |
|      |                           |           |       |        |
|      |                           |           |       |        |
|      |                           |           |       |        |
|      |                           |           |       |        |
|      |                           |           |       |        |
|      |                           |           |       |        |
|      |                           |           |       |        |
|      |                           |           |       |        |
|      |                           |           |       |        |
|      |                           |           |       |        |
|      |                           |           |       |        |
|      |                           |           |       |        |
|      |                           |           |       |        |
|      |                           |           |       |        |
|      |                           |           |       |        |
|      |                           |           |       |        |
|      |                           |           |       |        |
|      |                           |           |       |        |
|      |                           |           |       |        |
|      |                           |           |       |        |
|      |                           |           |       |        |
|      |                           |           |       |        |
|      |                           |           |       |        |
|      |                           |           |       |        |
|      |                           |           |       |        |
|      |                           |           |       |        |
|      |                           |           |       |        |

**E9-8**

# Perpetual Inventory Record

ITEM:

| DATE | RECEIVED | | | SOLD | | | BALANCE | | |
|---|---|---|---|---|---|---|---|---|---|
| | QTY. | UNIT COST | TOTAL COST | QTY. | UNIT COST | TOTAL COST | QTY. | UNIT COST | TOTAL COST |
| May 1 | | | | | | | 5 | 90 | 450 |
| May 6 | | | | 3 | 90 | 270 | 2 | 90 | 180 |
| May 8 | 11 | 95 | 1045 | | | | 2 | 90 | 180 |
| | | | | | | | 11 | 95 | 1045 |
| 17 | | | | 2 | 90 | 180 | | | |
| | | | | 2 | 95 | 190 | 9 | 95 | 855 |
| 30 | | | | 1 | 95 | 95 | 8 | 95 | 760 |
| | | | | | | | | | |

| A | B | C | D | E |
|---|---|---|---|---|
| | | | | |
| | **Walnut Lubricants** | | | |
| | **Estimated Income under FIFO and LIFO** | | | |
| | **March 19XX** | | | |
| | | | | |
| | **FIFO** | **LIFO** | **FIFO** | **LIFO** |
| **Sales** | $260,000 | $260,000 | $260,000 | $260,000 |
| **Cost of goods sold** | ———— | ———— | ———— | ———— |
| **10 Beginning inventory** | 63,000 | 63,000 | 63,000 | 63,000 |
| **11 Net purchases** | 159,000 | 159,000 | 182,000 | 182,000 |
| **12** | ———— | ———— | ———— | ———— |
| **13 Cost of goods available** | | | | |
| **14 Ending inventory** | 85,000 | 78,000 | 85,000 | 78,000 |
| **15** | ———— | ———— | ———— | ———— |
| **16 Cost of goods sold** | | | | |
| **17** | ———— | ———— | ———— | ———— |
| **18 Gross margin** | | | | |
| **19 Operating expenses** | 83,000 | 83,000 | 83,000 | 83,000 |
| **20** | ———— | ———— | ———— | ———— |
| **21 Net Income** | ════ | ════ | ════ | ════ |

| | | | | | | | |
|---|---|---|---|---|---|---|---|
| Hillis Corp. | | | | | | | |
| Income statement | | | | | | | |
| Year ended Dec 31, 19X1 | | | | | | | |
| Sales Rev | | | 2 | 2 | 5 | 0 | 0 | 0 |
| Cost of Goods Sold | | | 1 | 1 | 1 | 3 | 4 | 9 |
| Gross Margin | | | 1 | 1 | 3 | 6 | 5 | 1 |

| | | |
|---|---|---|
| Beg Inv | | 42,000 |
| Purchases | | 31,600 |
| Cost of Available | | 19,600 |
| Less Cost of G.S.: | | |
| est Cost | | |
| Sales Rev | 60,000 | |
| – Gross Mar (40%) | 24,000 | 36,000 ← Cost of G.S. |
| Loss from Fire (end Inv) | | (436,600) |

Inventory
$2,000

Purch.
$1,600

. and 2.

3.

*Req. 1*

| | Journal | | | | | |
|---|---|---|---|---|---|---|
| DATE | ACCOUNTS AND EXPLANATIONS | POST. REF. | DEBIT | | CREDIT | |
| | | | | | | |
| | | | | | | |
| | | | | | | |
| | | | | | | |
| | | | | | | |
| | | | | | | |
| | | | | | | |
| | | | | | | |
| | | | | | | |
| | | | | | | |
| | | | | | | |
| | | | | | | |
| | | | | | | |
| | | | | | | |
| | | | | | | |
| | | | | | | |

*Req. 2*

**P9-1A** *(Continued)*

*Req. 3*

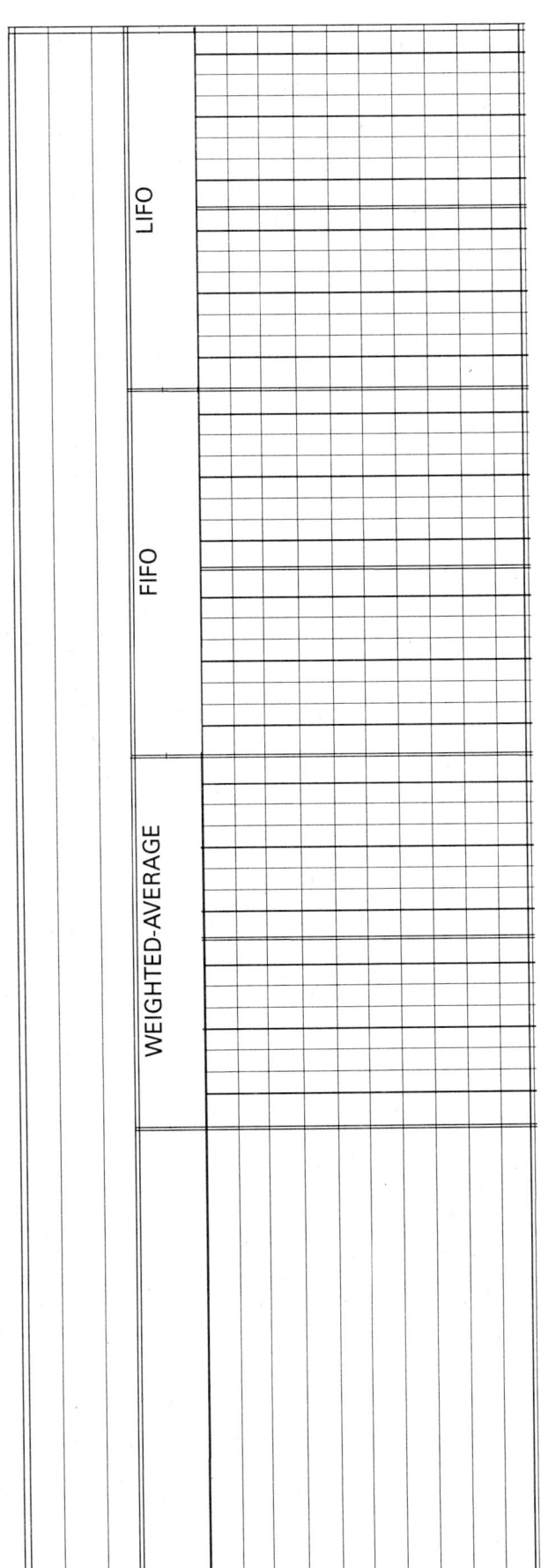

WEIGHTED-AVERAGE

FIFO

LIFO

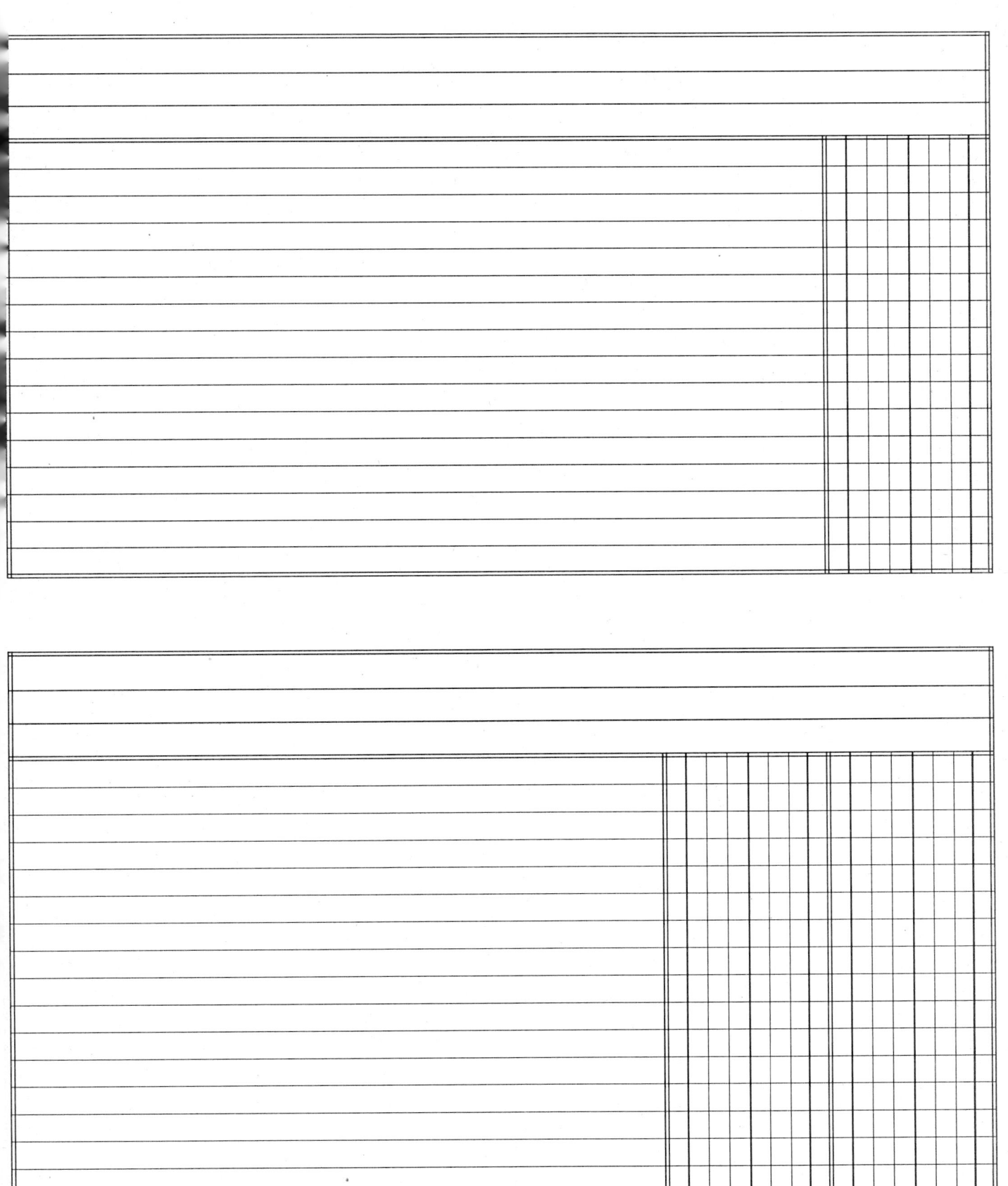

*Req. 1*

| | Journal | | | |
|---|---|---|---|---|
| DATE | ACCOUNTS AND EXPLANATIONS | POST. REF. | DEBIT | CREDIT |
| | | | | |
| | | | | |
| | | | | |
| | | | | |
| | | | | |
| | | | | |
| | | | | |
| | | | | |
| | | | | |
| | | | | |
| | | | | |
| | | | | |
| | | | | |
| | | | | |
| | | | | |
| | | | | |

*Req. 2*

Req. 3

Req. 1

Req. 2

**P9-3B**

*Req. 1*

*Req. 2*

| PERPETUAL SYSTEM | | PERIODIC SYSTEM | |
|---|---|---|---|
| | | | |

*Req. 3*

Req. 1

**P9-4B** *(Continued)*

*Req. 2*

| | WEIGHTED-AVERAGE | FIFO | LIFO |
|---|---|---|---|

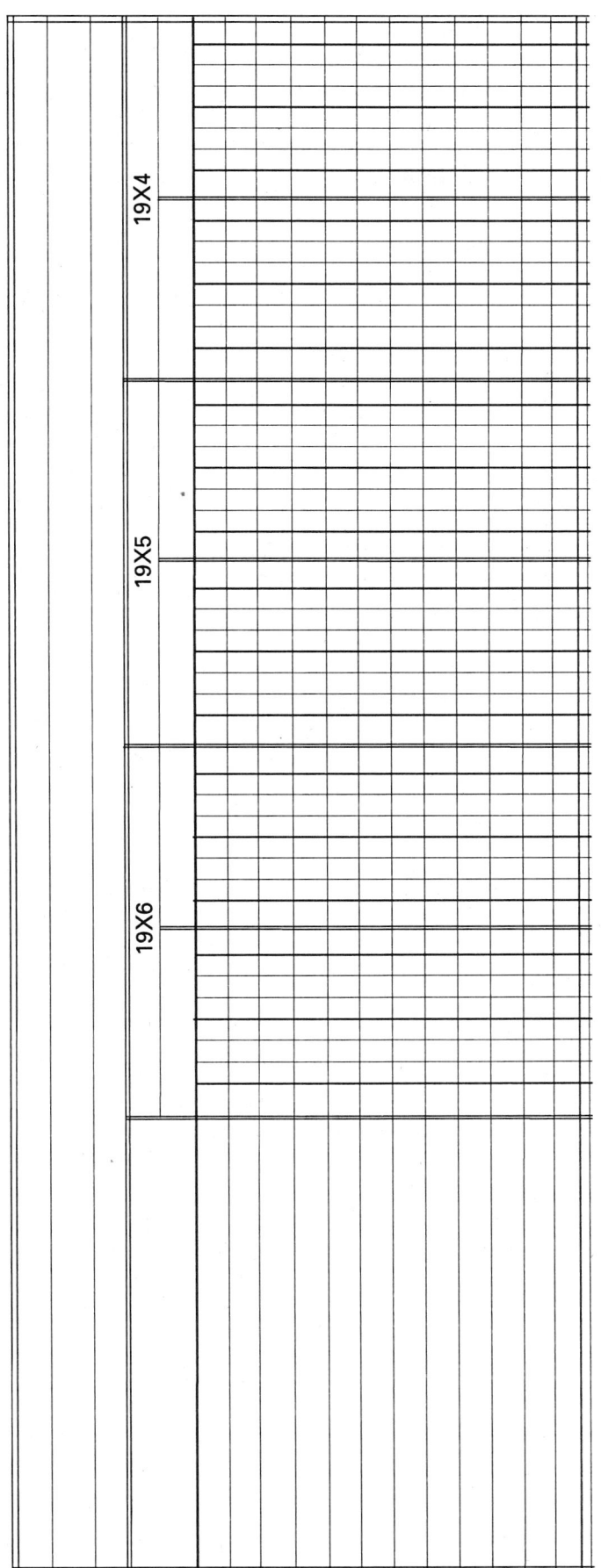

19X4

19X5

19X6

*Req. 1*

*Req. 2*

| | FIFO | LIFO |
|---|---|---|
| | | |
| | | |
| | | |
| | | |
| | | |
| | | |
| | | |
| | | |
| | | |
| | | |
| | | |
| | | |
| | | |
| | | |
| | | |
| | | |
| | | |
| | | |
| | | |
| | | |
| | | |
| | | |
| | | |

NAME
SECTION
DATE

Chapter 9

**Decision Case**
*(Continue*

*Req. 3*

*Req. 4*

*1. and 2.*

*3.*

**DE10-2**

**DE10-3**

**DE10-4**

*Req. 1*

| | | Journal | | | | | | | | | | | | | | | | | | | |
|---|---|---|---|---|---|---|---|---|---|---|---|---|---|---|---|---|---|---|---|---|---|
| DATE | | ACCOUNTS AND EXPLANATIONS | POST. REF. | | DEBIT | | | | | | CREDIT | | | | |
| | | | | | | | | | | | | | | | |
| | | | | | | | | | | | | | | | |
| | | | | | | | | | | | | | | | |
| | | | | | | | | | | | | | | | |
| | | | | | | | | | | | | | | | |
| | | | | | | | | | | | | | | | |
| | | | | | | | | | | | | | | | |

*Req. 2*

# DE10-6

## Journal

| DATE | ACCOUNTS AND EXPLANATIONS | POST. REF. | DEBIT | CREDIT |
|------|---------------------------|------------|-------|--------|
|  |  |  |  |  |
|  |  |  |  |  |
|  |  |  |  |  |
|  |  |  |  |  |
|  |  |  |  |  |

## Journal

| DATE | ACCOUNTS AND EXPLANATIONS | POST. REF. | DEBIT | CREDIT |
|------|---------------------------|------------|-------|--------|
|  |  |  |  |  |
|  |  |  |  |  |
|  |  |  |  |  |
|  |  |  |  |  |
|  |  |  |  |  |
|  |  |  |  |  |
|  |  |  |  |  |

eq. 1

**DE10-8**

2.

| | STRAIGHT-LINE | UNITS-OF-PRODUCUTION | DOUBLE-DECLIN-ING BALANCE |
|---|---|---|---|
| | | | |

NAME
SECTION
DATE

## Journal

| DATE | ACCOUNTS AND EXPLANATIONS | POST. REF. | DEBIT | CREDIT |
|------|---------------------------|------------|-------|--------|
|      |                           |            |       |        |
|      |                           |            |       |        |
|      |                           |            |       |        |
|      |                           |            |       |        |
|      |                           |            |       |        |

*Req. 1a and b*

| | | Journal | | | | |
|---|---|---|---|---|---|---|
| DATE | | ACCOUNTS AND EXPLANATIONS | POST. REF. | DEBIT | | CREDIT |
| | | | | | | |
| | | | | | | |
| | | | | | | |
| | | | | | | |
| | | | | | | |
| | | | | | | |
| | | | | | | |
| | | | | | | |
| | | | | | | |
| | | | | | | |
| | | | | | | |
| | | | | | | |

*Req. 2*

## Journal

| DATE | ACCOUNTS AND EXPLANATIONS | POST. REF. | DEBIT | CREDIT |
|------|---------------------------|-----------|-------|--------|
|  |  |  |  |  |
|  |  |  |  |  |
|  |  |  |  |  |
|  |  |  |  |  |
|  |  |  |  |  |

Req. 1

| | | |
|---|---|---|
| | | |

Req. 2

| | Journal | | | |
|---|---|---|---|---|
| DATE | ACCOUNTS AND EXPLANATIONS | POST. REF. | DEBIT | CREDIT |
| | | | | |
| | | | | |
| | | | | |
| | | | | |
| | | | | |

Req. 3

Req. 1

Req. 2

Req. 3a

Req. 3b

*Req. 1*

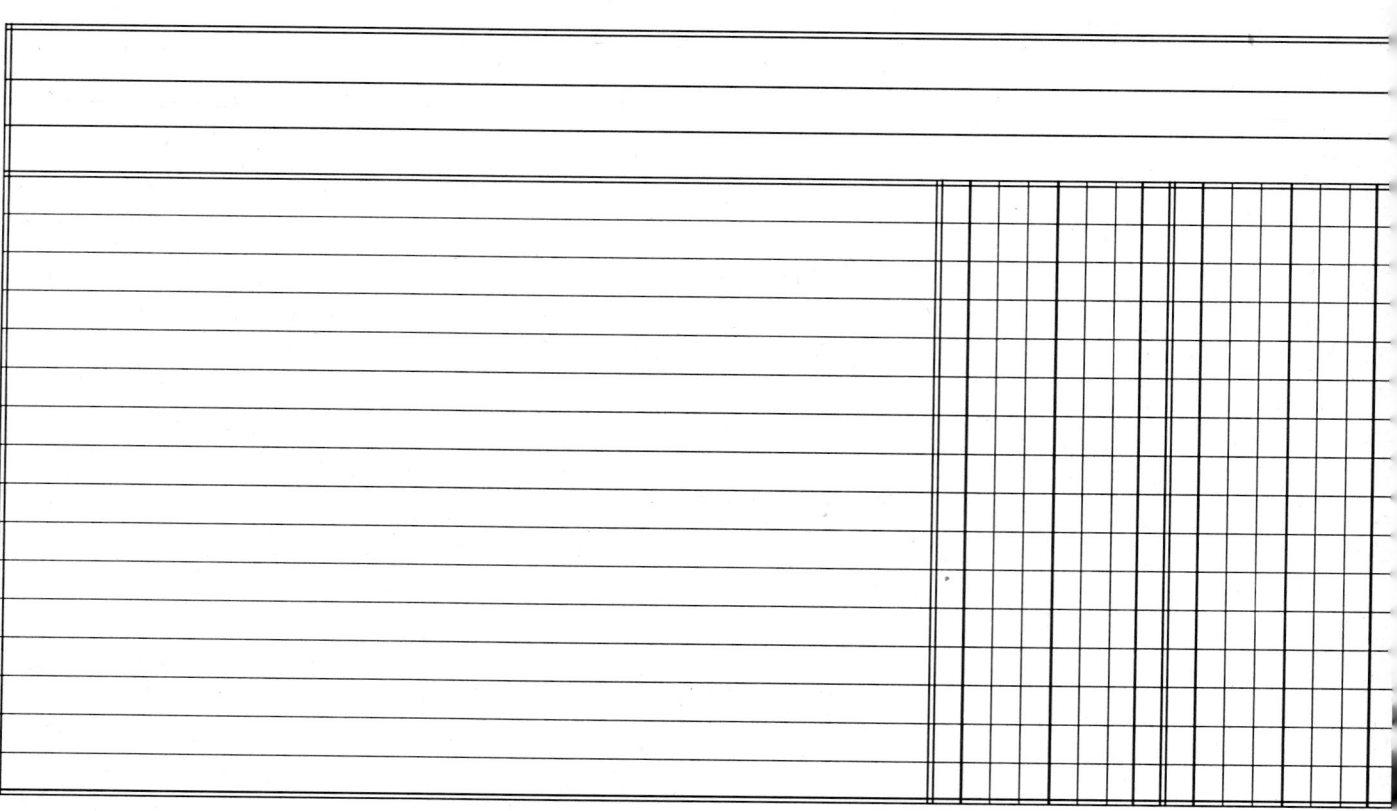

*Req. 2*

AME
CTION
ATE

Purchase of Land        90,000    120,000    Land

Cash or Note Pay    210,000

Prop. Tax    3,000

Building 810,000    2,500

Land Improv.   63,000 fence    5,400

    10,400 sign    219,900

    6,000

    79,400

**E10-2**

*Req. 1*

| | | |
|---|---|---|
| | | |
| | | |
| | | |
| | | |
| | | |
| | | |
| | | |
| | | |
| | | |
| | | |
| | | |
| | | |

*Req. 2*

| | | Journal | | | |
|---|---|---|---|---|---|
| DATE | | ACCOUNTS AND EXPLANATIONS | POST. REF. | DEBIT | CREDIT |
| | | | | | |
| | | | | | |
| | | | | | |
| | | | | | |
| | | | | | |
| | | | | | |
| | | | | | |
| | | | | | |
| | | | | | |
| | | | | | |
| | | | | | |
| | | | | | |
| | | | | | |

| Mach | Mkt Val | Cost | |
|---|---|---|---|
| 1 | 14,000 | 11,680 | $\frac{14}{48} = 29.2\%$ |
| 2 | 18,000 | 15,000 | $\frac{18}{48} = 37.5\%$ |
| 3 | 16,000 | 13,320 | $\frac{16}{48} = 33.3\%$ |
| | 48,000 | 40,000 | |

| | | Journal | | | | | | | | | | | | |
|---|---|---|---|---|---|---|---|---|---|---|---|---|---|---|
| DATE | | ACCOUNTS AND EXPLANATIONS | POST. REF. | | DEBIT | | | | | CREDIT | | | | | |
| | | Machinery (1, 2, 3) | | 4 | 0 | 0 | 0 | 0 | | | | | | |
| | | Cash | | | | | | | | 2 | 0 | 0 | 0 | 0 |
| | | Note Pay | | | | | | | | 2 | 0 | 0 | 0 | 0 |
| | | | | | | | | | | | | | | |
| | | | | | | | | | | | | | | |
| | | | | | | | | | | | | | | |

a – Cap
b – Cap
c – Cap
d – Cap
e – expense
f – cap
g – expense
h – Cap
i – expense
j – cap
k – expense

## Journal

| DATE | ACCOUNTS AND EXPLANATIONS | POST. REF. | DEBIT | CREDIT |
|------|---------------------------|------------|-------|--------|
|      |                           |            |       |        |
|      |                           |            |       |        |
|      |                           |            |       |        |
|      |                           |            |       |        |
|      |                           |            |       |        |
|      |                           |            |       |        |
|      |                           |            |       |        |
|      |                           |            |       |        |
|      |                           |            |       |        |
|      |                           |            |       |        |
|      |                           |            |       |        |
|      |                           |            |       |        |
|      |                           |            |       |        |
|      |                           |            |       |        |
|      |                           |            |       |        |
|      |                           |            |       |        |
|      |                           |            |       |        |
|      |                           |            |       |        |
|      |                           |            |       |        |

## Journal

| DATE | | ACCOUNTS AND EXPLANATIONS | POST. REF. | DEBIT | CREDIT |
|------|---|---------------------------|-----------|-------|--------|
| Jan | 2 | Store Fixtures | | 8700 | |
| | | Cash | | | 8700 |
| Dec | 31 | Deprec Exp | | 3480 | |
| | | Accum Dep - S.F. | | | 3480 |
| Sep | 30 X8 | Deprec Exp | | 1566 | |
| | | Accum Dep - S.F. | | | 1566 |
| Sep | 30 | Accum Deprec | | 5046 | |
| | | CASH | | 4950 | |
| | | GAIN on sale | | | 1296 |
| | | STORE Fixtures | | | 8700 |
| | | | | | |
| | | | | | |
| | | | | | |
| | | | | | |

**COMPUTATIONS:**

$$Dep \ Exp/yr = BV \times \frac{2}{life}$$

$$= 8,700 \times \frac{2}{5}$$

① $= 3,480$

$$= 5,220 \times \frac{2}{5}$$

② $= 2088 \times \frac{9}{12}$

$$= 1,566$$

Store Fix     A/D - S.F.
8700 |        | 3980
  ①           | 1566
            ② | 5046

Cost  8700
A/D   5046
      3654

③ SP  4950

④ GAIN 1296

*eq. 1*

*Reqs. 2 and 3*

## Journal

| DATE | | ACCOUNTS AND EXPLANATIONS | POST. REF. | DEBIT | CREDIT |
|---|---|---|---|---|---|
| | | | | | |
| | | | | | |
| | | | | | |
| | | | | | |
| | | | | | |
| | | | | | |
| | | | | | |
| | | | | | |
| | | | | | |
| | | | | | |
| | | | | | |
| | | | | | |

Asset 14
Lib 11
UrAs. 3
Paid 12
Goodwill 9

NAME
SECTION
DATE

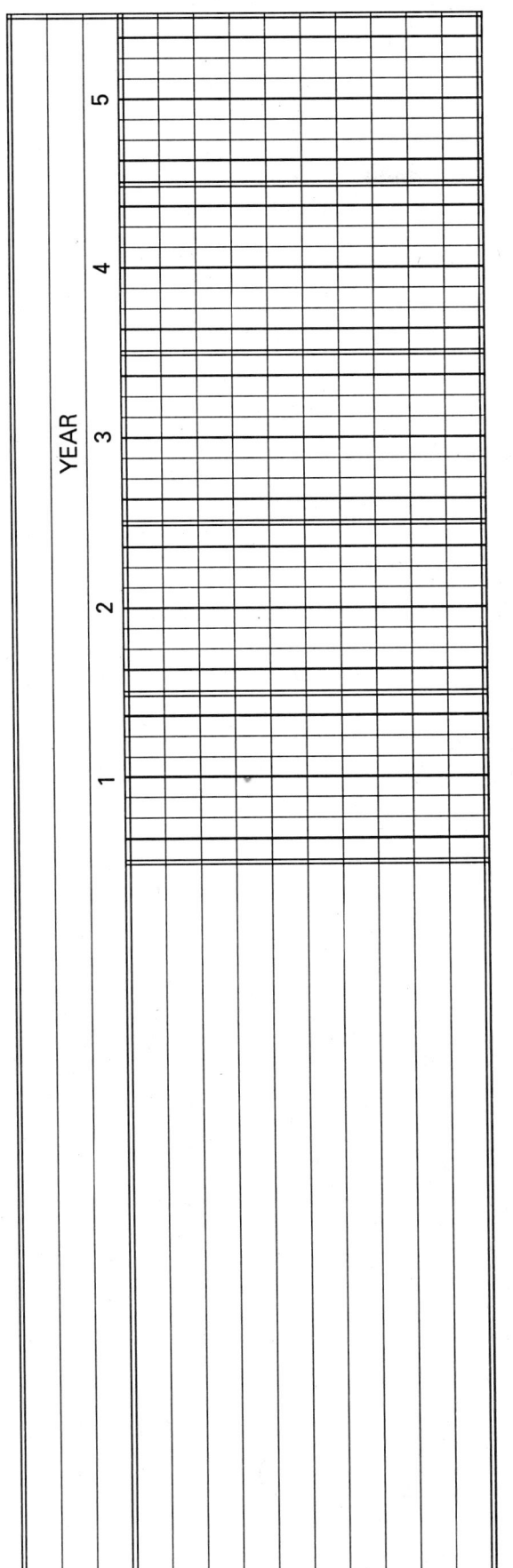

YEAR

1  2  3  4  5

**COMPUTATIONS:**

*Req. 1*

*Req. 2*

*Req. 3*

*Reqs. 1 & 2*

Req. 1

Req. 2

Req. 3

*Req. 1*

| ITEM | LAND | LAND IMPROVEMENTS | OFFICE BUILDING | STORAGE BUILDING | FURNITURE |
|------|------|-------------------|-----------------|------------------|-----------|
|  |  |  |  |  |  |
|  |  |  |  |  |  |
|  |  |  |  |  |  |
|  |  |  |  |  |  |
|  |  |  |  |  |  |
|  |  |  |  |  |  |
|  |  |  |  |  |  |
|  |  |  |  |  |  |
|  |  |  |  |  |  |
|  |  |  |  |  |  |
|  |  |  |  |  |  |
|  |  |  |  |  |  |
|  |  |  |  |  |  |
|  |  |  |  |  |  |
|  |  |  |  |  |  |
|  |  |  |  |  |  |
|  |  |  |  |  |  |

**COMPUTATIONS:**

*eq. 2*

| | | Journal | | | |
|---|---|---|---|---|---|
| DATE | | ACCOUNTS AND EXPLANATIONS | POST. REF. | DEBIT | CREDIT |
| | | | | | |
| | | | | | |
| | | | | | |
| | | | | | |
| | | | | | |
| | | | | | |
| | | | | | |
| | | | | | |
| | | | | | |
| | | | | | |
| | | | | | |
| | | | | | |
| | | | | | |
| | | | | | |
| | | | | | |
| | | | | | |
| | | | | | |
| | | | | | |
| | | | | | |
| | | | | | |
| | | | | | |
| | | | | | |

## Journal

| DATE | ACCOUNTS AND EXPLANATIONS | POST. REF. | DEBIT | CREDIT |
|------|---------------------------|-----------|-------|--------|
| | | | | |
| | | | | |
| | | | | |
| | | | | |
| | | | | |
| | | | | |
| | | | | |
| | | | | |
| | | | | |
| | | | | |
| | | | | |
| | | | | |
| | | | | |
| | | | | |
| | | | | |
| | | | | |
| | | | | |
| | | | | |
| | | | | |
| | | | | |
| | | | | |
| | | | | |
| | | | | |
| | | | | |
| | | | | |
| | | | | |
| | | | | |
| | | | | |
| | | | | |
| | | | | |
| | | | | |
| | | | | |
| | | | | |
| | | | | |
| | | | | |
| | | | | |
| | | | | |
| | | | | |
| | | | | |
| | | | | |

Req. 2 (Continued)

## Journal

| DATE | ACCOUNTS AND EXPLANATIONS | POST. REF. | DEBIT | CREDIT |
|------|---------------------------|------------|-------|--------|
| | | | | |
| | | | | |
| | | | | |
| | | | | |
| | | | | |
| | | | | |
| | | | | |
| | | | | |
| | | | | |
| | | | | |
| | | | | |
| | | | | |
| | | | | |
| | | | | |
| | | | | |
| | | | | |
| | | | | |
| | | | | |
| | | | | |
| | | | | |
| | | | | |
| | | | | |
| | | | | |
| | | | | |
| | | | | |
| | | | | |
| | | | | |
| | | | | |
| | | | | |
| | | | | |
| | | | | |
| | | | | |
| | | | | |
| | | | | |
| | | | | |
| | | | | |
| | | | | |
| | | | | |
| | | | | |

Req. 1

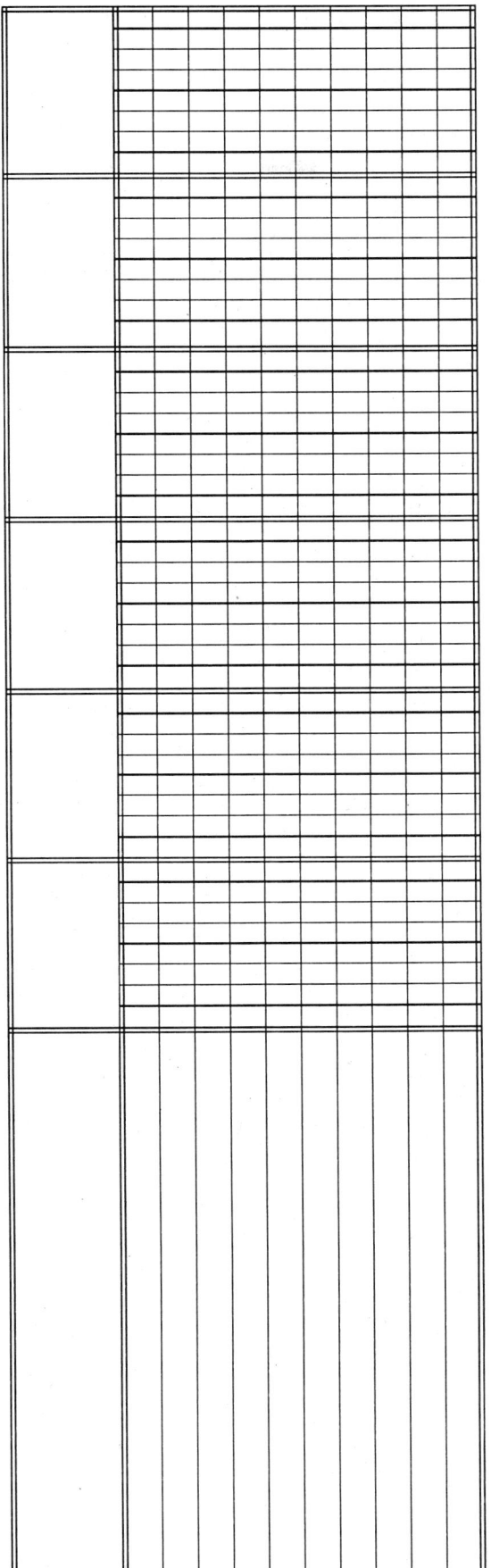

**COMPUTATIONS:**

NAME
SECTION
DATE

**P10-4B** *(Continued)*

*Req. 1 (Continued)*

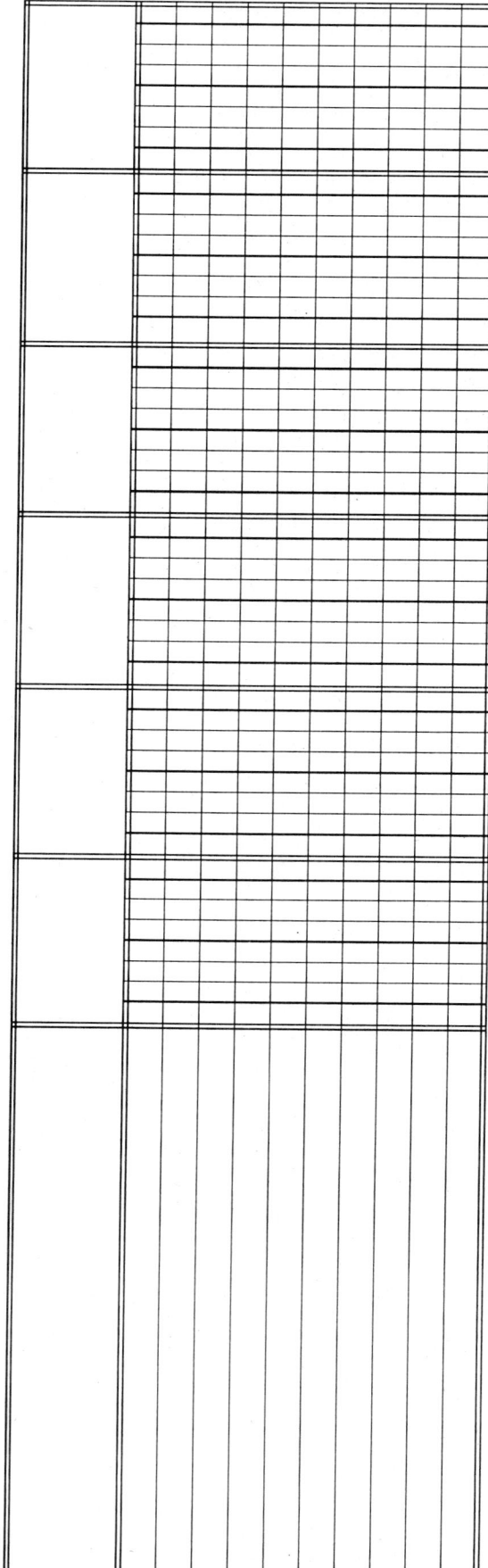

**COMPUTATIONS:**

*Req. 1 (Continued)*

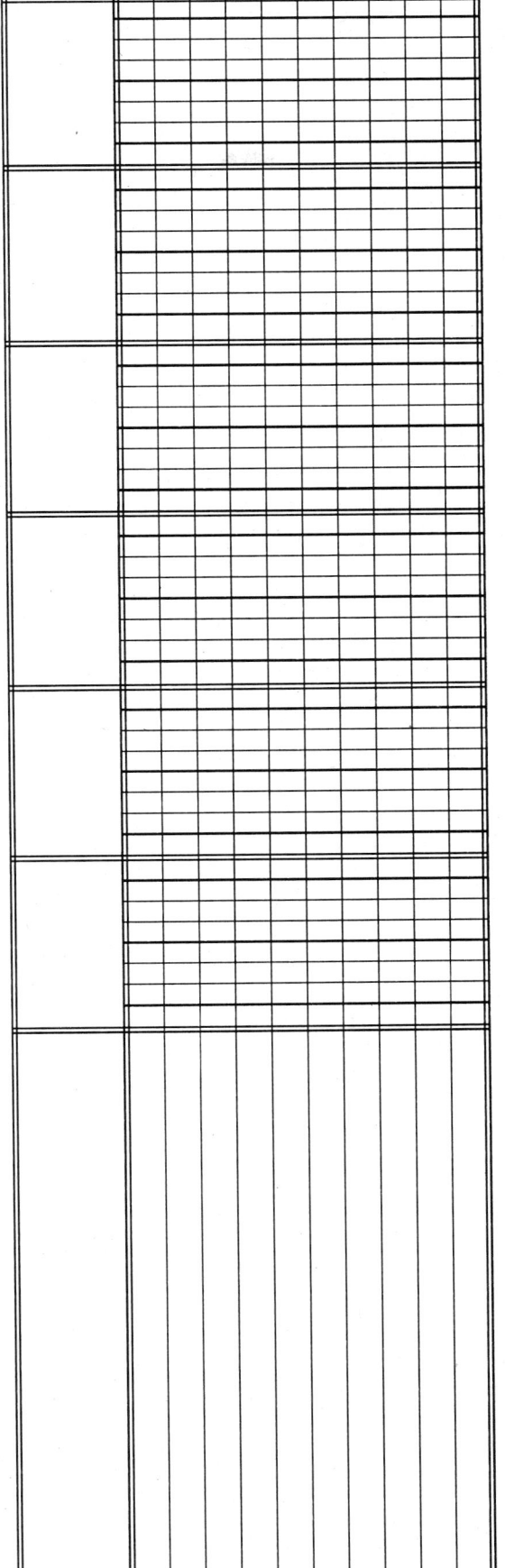

**COMPUTATIONS:**

*Req. 2*

*Req. 3*

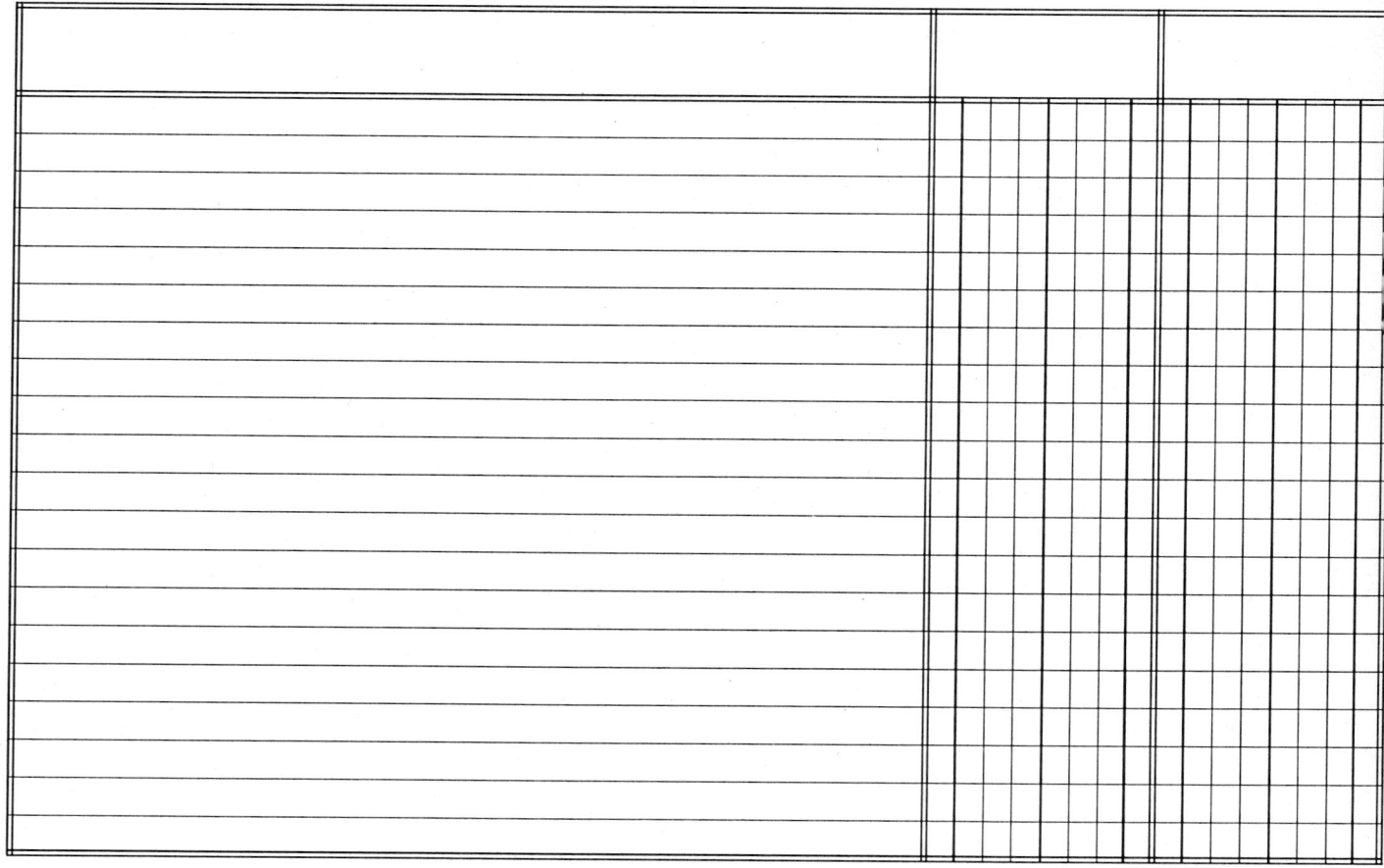

AME
ECTION
ATE

eq. 1

eq. 2

Req. 3

*Req. 4*

*Req. 5*

AME
ECTION
ATE

*Chapter 10*

**P10-6B**

eq. 1

| | | Journal | | | |
|---|---|---|---|---|---|
| DATE | | ACCOUNTS AND EXPLANATIONS | POST. REF. | DEBIT | CREDIT |
| | | | | | |
| | | | | | |
| | | | | | |
| | | | | | |
| | | | | | |
| | | | | | |
| | | | | | |
| | | | | | |
| | | | | | |
| | | | | | |
| | | | | | |
| | | | | | |
| | | | | | |
| | | | | | |
| | | | | | |
| | | | | | |
| | | | | | |
| | | | | | |
| | | | | | |
| | | | | | |
| | | | | | |
| | | | | | |
| | | | | | |
| | | | | | |
| | | | | | |
| | | | | | |
| | | | | | |
| | | | | | |
| | | | | | |
| | | | | | |
| | | | | | |
| | | | | | |
| | | | | | |
| | | | | | |
| | | | | | |
| | | | | | |

*Req. 2*

AME
ECTION
ATE

Chapter 10

**P10-6B***(Continued)*

Part 2

*Req. 1*

_____

_____

_____

_____

*Reqs. 2 & 3*

| | | | | | |
|---|---|---|---|---|---|
| **Journal** | | | | | |
| DATE | ACCOUNTS AND EXPLANATIONS | POST. REF. | DEBIT | CREDIT | |
| | | | | | |
| | | | | | |
| | | | | | |
| | | | | | |
| | | | | | |
| | | | | | |
| | | | | | |
| | | | | | |
| | | | | | |
| | | | | | |
| | | | | | |
| | | | | | |
| | | | | | |
| | | | | | |
| | | | | | |

*Req. 1*

*Req. 2*

*Req. 3*

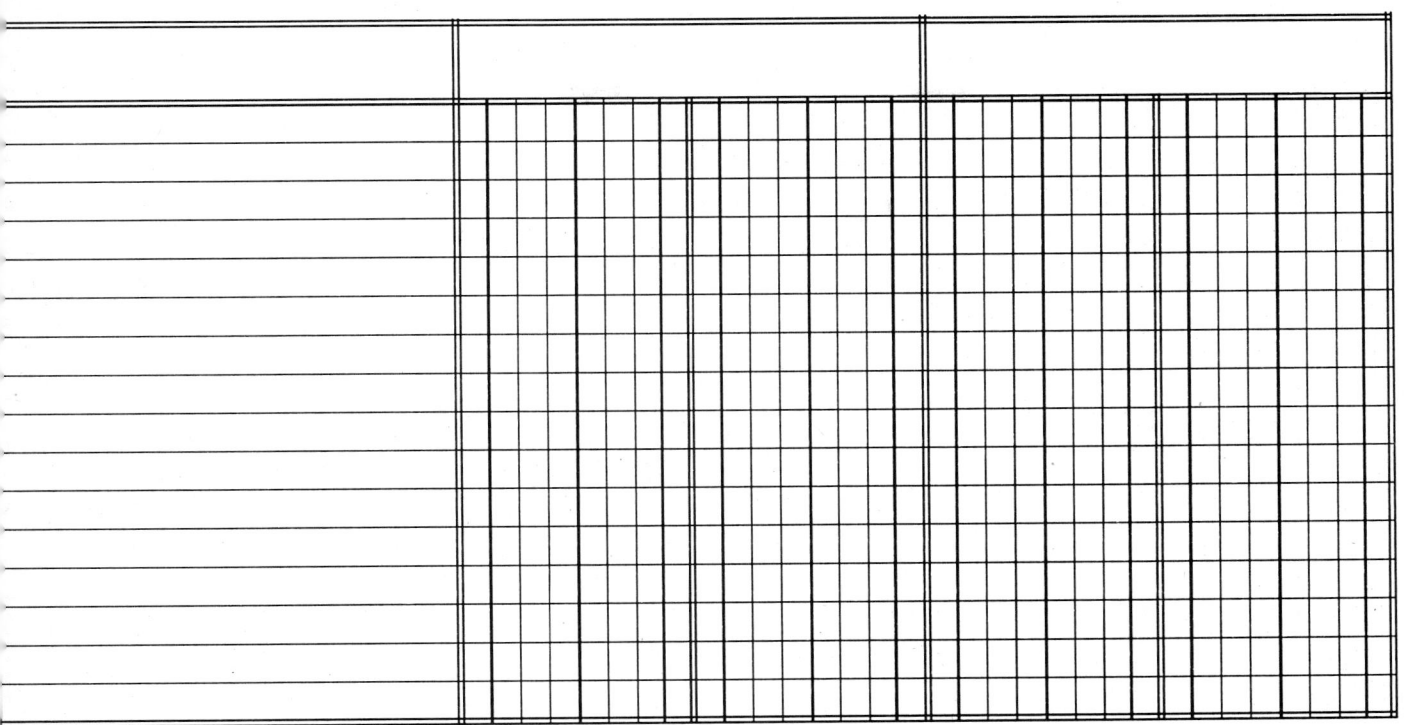

**COMPUTATIONS:**

*Req. 2*

AME
ECTION
ATE

*eqs. 1–5*

Chapter 10 **Financial Statement
Case 1**

Reqs. 1–5

*Chapter 10*  **Solution to Internet Exercise**

# DE11-2

AME
ECTION
ATE

## Journal

| DATE | ACCOUNTS AND EXPLANATIONS | POST. REF. | DEBIT | CREDIT |
|------|---------------------------|------------|-------|--------|
|  |  |  |  |  |
|  |  |  |  |  |
|  |  |  |  |  |
|  |  |  |  |  |
|  |  |  |  |  |
|  |  |  |  |  |
|  |  |  |  |  |
|  |  |  |  |  |
|  |  |  |  |  |
|  |  |  |  |  |
|  |  |  |  |  |
|  |  |  |  |  |
|  |  |  |  |  |
|  |  |  |  |  |
|  |  |  |  |  |
|  |  |  |  |  |

**Req. 1**

**Req. 2**

NAME
SECTION
DATE

*Req. 1a*

*Reqs. b and d*

| | | Journal | | | | | | | | | | | | | | |
|---|---|---|---|---|---|---|---|---|---|---|---|---|---|---|---|---|
| DATE | | ACCOUNTS AND EXPLANATIONS | POST. REF. | | DEBIT | | | | | | | CREDIT | | | | |
| | | | | | | | | | | | | | | | | |
| | | | | | | | | | | | | | | | | |
| | | | | | | | | | | | | | | | | |
| | | | | | | | | | | | | | | | | |
| | | | | | | | | | | | | | | | | |
| | | | | | | | | | | | | | | | | |
| | | | | | | | | | | | | | | | | |
| | | | | | | | | | | | | | | | | |
| | | | | | | | | | | | | | | | | |
| | | | | | | | | | | | | | | | | |
| | | | | | | | | | | | | | | | | |

*Req. c*

Req. 1

| | | Journal | | | |
|---|---|---|---|---|---|
| DATE | | ACCOUNTS AND EXPLANATIONS | POST. REF. | DEBIT | CREDIT |
| | | | | | |
| | | | | | |
| | | | | | |
| | | | | | |
| | | | | | |
| | | | | | |
| | | | | | |
| | | | | | |
| | | | | | |
| | | | | | |
| | | | | | |
| | | | | | |
| | | | | | |
| | | | | | |
| | | | | | |
| | | | | | |
| | | | | | |

Req. 2

NAME
SECTION
DATE

*Req. 1*

| | | Journal | | | | |
|---|---|---|---|---|---|---|
| DATE | | ACCOUNTS AND EXPLANATIONS | POST. REF. | DEBIT | | CREDIT |
| | | | | | | |
| | | | | | | |
| | | | | | | |
| | | | | | | |
| | | | | | | |
| | | | | | | |
| | | | | | | |
| | | | | | | |
| | | | | | | |
| | | | | | | |
| | | | | | | |
| | | | | | | |
| | | | | | | |
| | | | | | | |
| | | | | | | |
| | | | | | | |
| | | | | | | |
| | | | | | | |

*Req. 2*

**DE11-8**

| | | | | | | | | | | | | | | | |
|---|---|---|---|---|---|---|---|---|---|---|---|---|---|---|---|
| | | | | | | | | | | | | | | | |
| | | | | | | | | | | | | | | | |
| | | | | | | | | | | | | | | | |
| | | | | | | | | | | | | | | | |
| | | | | | | | | | | | | | | | |
| | | | | | | | | | | | | | | | |
| | | | | | | | | | | | | | | | |
| | | | | | | | | | | | | | | | |
| | | | | | | | | | | | | | | | |
| | | | | | | | | | | | | | | | |
| | | | | | | | | | | | | | | | |
| | | | | | | | | | | | | | | | |
| | | | | | | | | | | | | | | | |
| | | | | | | | | | | | | | | | |
| | | | | | | | | | | | | | | | |
| | | | | | | | | | | | | | | | |
| | | | | | | | | | | | | | | | |
| | | | | | | | | | | | | | | | |
| | | | | | | | | | | | | | | | |

## Journal

| DATE | ACCOUNTS AND EXPLANATIONS | POST. REF. | DEBIT | CREDIT |
|------|---------------------------|------------|-------|--------|
|      |                           |            |       |        |

| DATE | ACCOUNTS AND EXPLANATIONS | POST. REF. | DEBIT | CREDIT |
|---|---|---|---|---|
| | | | | |
| | | | | |
| | | | | |
| | | | | |
| | | | | |
| | | | | |
| | | | | |
| | | | | |
| | | | | |
| | | | | |
| | | | | |
| | | | | |
| | | | | |
| | | | | |
| | | | | |
| | | | | |
| | | | | |
| | | | | |

## Journal

*eqs. 1 & 2*

## Journal

| DATE | ACCOUNTS AND EXPLANATIONS | POST. REF. | DEBIT | CREDIT |
|------|---------------------------|------------|-------|--------|
| Mar 31 | Cash | | 105000 | |
| | Sales Rev | | | 100000 |
| | Sales Tax Pay. | | | 5000 |
| April 6 | Sales Tax Pay | | 5000 | |
| | Cash | | | 5000 |
| | | | | |
| | | | | |
| | | | | |
| | | | | |
| | | | | |
| | | | | |
| | | | | |
| | | | | |
| | | | | |
| | | | | |
| | | | | |
| | | | | |
| | | | | |

AME
ECTION
ATE

eq. 1

| | Journal | | | | | |
|---|---|---|---|---|---|---|
| DATE 1998 | ACCOUNTS AND EXPLANATIONS | POST. REF. | DEBIT | | CREDIT | |
| | Cash & Acct. Rec. | | 161 000 | | | |
| | Sales Rev. | | | | 161 000 | |
| | Est. War. Pay. | | 10 400 | | | |
| | Cash / Parts Inv. | | | | 10 400 | |
| | ADJ        161000 x 5% | | | | | |
| | War. Exp. | | 8050 | | | |
| | Est. War. Pay. | | | | 8050 | |

Req. 2

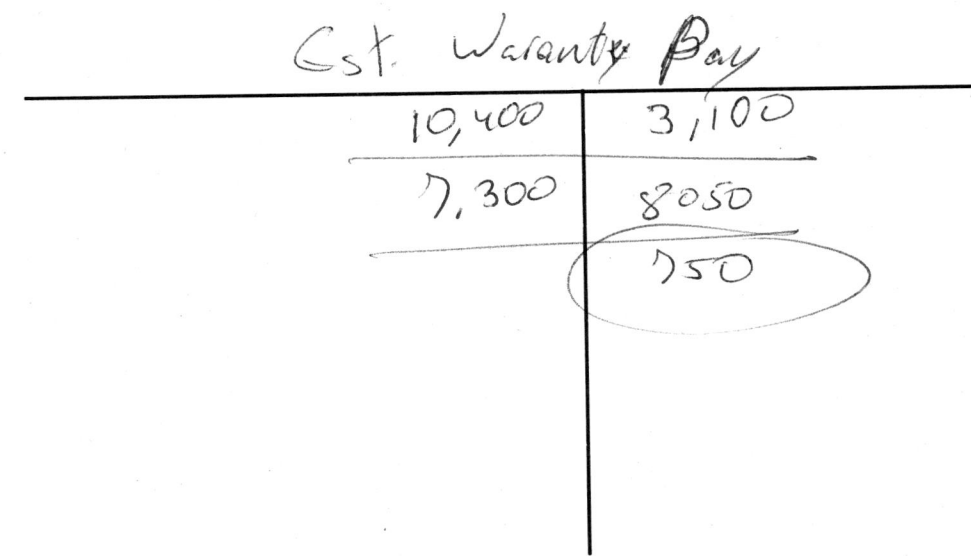

Est. Warantx Pay

| 10,400 | 3,100 |
|---|---|
| 7,300 | 8050 |
| | 750 |

NAME
SECTION
DATE

Chapter 11

E11-3

## Journal

| DATE 1982 | | ACCOUNTS AND EXPLANATIONS | POST. REF. | DEBIT | CREDIT |
|---|---|---|---|---|---|
| April | 1 | Equip | | 10000 | |
| | | Note Pay | | | 10000 |
| Dec | 31 | Intrest Exp | | 600 | |
| | | Intrest Pay | | | 600 |
| 1983 | | | | | |
| April | 1 | Notes Pay | | 10000 | |
| | | ~~Intrest Exp~~ Intrest Exp | | 200 | |
| | | Intrest Pay | | 600 | |
| | | Cash | | | 10800 |

NAME
SECTION
DATE

Req. 1

## Journal

| DATE | ACCOUNTS AND EXPLANATIONS | POST. REF. | DEBIT | CREDIT |
|---|---|---|---|---|
| | Cash | | 11580 | |
| | ~~Note pay~~ Disc on note pay | | 420 | 1200 |
| | Note pay | | | 12000 |
| | | | | |

Req. 2

Balance Sheet

| | | | | | |
|---|---|---|---|---|---|
| | | | | | |

## Journal

| DATE | ACCOUNTS AND EXPLANATIONS | POST. REF. | DEBIT | CREDIT |
|---|---|---|---|---|
| | | | | |
| | | | | |
| | | | | |

_____

_____

_____

_____

_____

_____

_____

_____

_____

_____

E11-8

Reqs. 1 & 2

*Reqs. 1 & 2*

*Reqs. 1 - 3*

*Req. 1*

## SUPPLY MISSING PAYROLL AMOUNTS

Employee Earnings:

(1) Straight-time employee earnings _____

(2) Overtime pay ............................... 5,109

(3) Total employee earnings .............. _____

Deductions and Net Pay:

(4) Withheld income tax .................... 9,293

(5) FICA tax ........................................ 6,052

(6) Charitable contributions ............. 885

(7) Medical insurance.................................. $1,373

(8) Total deductions .................................._____

(9) Net pay .................................................. 64,813

(10) Salary Expense ...................................... 31,278

(11) Wage Expense.........................................._____

(12) Sales Commision Expense.................... 27,931

**Computations:**

*Req. 2*

| | | Journal | | | |
|---|---|---|---|---|---|
| DATE | | ACCOUNTS AND EXPLANATIONS | POST. REF. | DEBIT | CREDIT |
| | | | | | |
| | | | | | |
| | | | | | |
| | | | | | |
| | | | | | |
| | | | | | |
| | | | | | |
| | | | | | |
| | | | | | |
| | | | | | |
| | | | | | |
| | | | | | |
| | | | | | |
| | | | | | |
| | | | | | |
| | | | | | |
| | | | | | |
| | | | | | |
| | | | | | |
| | | | | | |

*Req. 1*

**P11-4A**

*Req. 2*

*Req. 3*

## Journal

| DATE | ACCOUNTS AND EXPLANATIONS | POST. REF. | DEBIT | CREDIT |
|------|---------------------------|------------|-------|--------|
|  |  |  |  |  |
|  |  |  |  |  |
|  |  |  |  |  |
|  |  |  |  |  |
|  |  |  |  |  |
|  |  |  |  |  |
|  |  |  |  |  |
|  |  |  |  |  |
|  |  |  |  |  |
|  |  |  |  |  |
|  |  |  |  |  |
|  |  |  |  |  |
|  |  |  |  |  |
|  |  |  |  |  |
|  |  |  |  |  |
|  |  |  |  |  |
|  |  |  |  |  |
|  |  |  |  |  |
|  |  |  |  |  |
|  |  |  |  |  |
|  |  |  |  |  |
|  |  |  |  |  |
|  |  |  |  |  |
|  |  |  |  |  |
|  |  |  |  |  |
|  |  |  |  |  |
|  |  |  |  |  |
|  |  |  |  |  |
|  |  |  |  |  |
|  |  |  |  |  |
|  |  |  |  |  |
|  |  |  |  |  |
|  |  |  |  |  |
|  |  |  |  |  |
|  |  |  |  |  |
|  |  |  |  |  |
|  |  |  |  |  |
|  |  |  |  |  |
|  |  |  |  |  |

**Reqs. 1 & 2** (Continued)

| ACCOUNT | | | | | | ACCOUNT NO. | |
|---|---|---|---|---|---|---|---|
| DATE | ITEM | JRNL. REF. | DEBIT | CREDIT | BALANCE | |
| | | | | | DEBIT | CREDIT |
| | | | | | | |
| | | | | | | |
| | | | | | | |

| ACCOUNT | | | | | | ACCOUNT NO. | |
|---|---|---|---|---|---|---|---|
| DATE | ITEM | JRNL. REF. | DEBIT | CREDIT | BALANCE | |
| | | | | | DEBIT | CREDIT |
| | | | | | | |
| | | | | | | |
| | | | | | | |

| ACCOUNT | | | | | | ACCOUNT NO. | |
|---|---|---|---|---|---|---|---|
| DATE | ITEM | JRNL. REF. | DEBIT | CREDIT | BALANCE | |
| | | | | | DEBIT | CREDIT |
| | | | | | | |
| | | | | | | |
| | | | | | | |

| ACCOUNT | | | | | | ACCOUNT NO. | |
|---|---|---|---|---|---|---|---|
| DATE | ITEM | JRNL. REF. | DEBIT | CREDIT | BALANCE | |
| | | | | | DEBIT | CREDIT |
| | | | | | | |
| | | | | | | |
| | | | | | | |

*Reqs. 1 & 2 (Continued)*

| ACCOUNT | | | | | | ACCOUNT NO. | |
| --- | --- | --- | --- | --- | --- | --- | --- |
| | | | | | | BALANCE | |
| DATE | | ITEM | JRNL. REF. | DEBIT | CREDIT | DEBIT | CREDIT |
| | | | | | | | |
| | | | | | | | |
| | | | | | | | |
| | | | | | | | |

| ACCOUNT | | | | | | ACCOUNT NO. | |
| --- | --- | --- | --- | --- | --- | --- | --- |
| | | | | | | BALANCE | |
| DATE | | ITEM | JRNL. REF. | DEBIT | CREDIT | DEBIT | CREDIT |
| | | | | | | | |
| | | | | | | | |
| | | | | | | | |
| | | | | | | | |

| ACCOUNT | | | | | | ACCOUNT NO. | |
| --- | --- | --- | --- | --- | --- | --- | --- |
| | | | | | | BALANCE | |
| DATE | | ITEM | JRNL. REF. | DEBIT | CREDIT | DEBIT | CREDIT |
| | | | | | | | |
| | | | | | | | |
| | | | | | | | |
| | | | | | | | |

| ACCOUNT | | | | | | ACCOUNT NO. | |
| --- | --- | --- | --- | --- | --- | --- | --- |
| | | | | | | BALANCE | |
| DATE | | ITEM | JRNL. REF. | DEBIT | CREDIT | DEBIT | CREDIT |
| | | | | | | | |
| | | | | | | | |
| | | | | | | | |
| | | | | | | | |

*Reqs. 1 & 2 (Continued)*

| ACCOUNT | | | | | ACCOUNT NO. | |
| --- | --- | --- | --- | --- | --- | --- |
| | | JRNL. | | | BALANCE | |
| DATE | ITEM | REF. | DEBIT | CREDIT | DEBIT | CREDIT |
| | | | | | | |
| | | | | | | |
| | | | | | | |
| | | | | | | |

| ACCOUNT | | | | | ACCOUNT NO. | |
| --- | --- | --- | --- | --- | --- | --- |
| | | JRNL. | | | BALANCE | |
| DATE | ITEM | REF. | DEBIT | CREDIT | DEBIT | CREDIT |
| | | | | | | |
| | | | | | | |
| | | | | | | |
| | | | | | | |

| ACCOUNT | | | | | ACCOUNT NO. | |
| --- | --- | --- | --- | --- | --- | --- |
| | | JRNL. | | | BALANCE | |
| DATE | ITEM | REF. | DEBIT | CREDIT | DEBIT | CREDIT |
| | | | | | | |
| | | | | | | |
| | | | | | | |
| | | | | | | |

| ACCOUNT | | | | | ACCOUNT NO. | |
| --- | --- | --- | --- | --- | --- | --- |
| | | JRNL. | | | BALANCE | |
| DATE | ITEM | REF. | DEBIT | CREDIT | DEBIT | CREDIT |
| | | | | | | |
| | | | | | | |
| | | | | | | |

*Req. 2*

| | | | | | | | | | | |
|---|---|---|---|---|---|---|---|---|---|---|
| **Journal** | | | | | | | | | | |
| DATE | | ACCOUNTS AND EXPLANATIONS | POST. REF. | | DEBIT | | | CREDIT | | |
| | | | | | | | | | | |
| | | | | | | | | | | |
| | | | | | | | | | | |
| | | | | | | | | | | |
| | | | | | | | | | | |
| | | | | | | | | | | |
| | | | | | | | | | | |
| | | | | | | | | | | |
| | | | | | | | | | | |
| | | | | | | | | | | |
| | | | | | | | | | | |
| | | | | | | | | | | |
| | | | | | | | | | | |
| | | | | | | | | | | |
| | | | | | | | | | | |
| | | | | | | | | | | |
| | | | | | | | | | | |
| | | | | | | | | | | |
| | | | | | | | | | | |
| | | | | | | | | | | |
| | | | | | | | | | | |
| | | | | | | | | | | |
| | | | | | | | | | | |
| | | | | | | | | | | |
| | | | | | | | | | | |
| | | | | | | | | | | |
| | | | | | | | | | | |

*Reqs. 1 & 3*

The foldout worksheet to solve this problem can be found in the back of the book.

| | | Journal | | | | |
|---|---|---|---|---|---|---|
| DATE | | ACCOUNTS AND EXPLANATIONS | POST. REF. | DEBIT | CREDIT | |
| | | | | | | |
| | | | | | | |
| | | | | | | |
| | | | | | | |
| | | | | | | |
| | | | | | | |
| | | | | | | |
| | | | | | | |
| | | | | | | |
| | | | | | | |
| | | | | | | |
| | | | | | | |
| | | | | | | |
| | | | | | | |
| | | | | | | |
| | | | | | | |
| | | | | | | |
| | | | | | | |
| | | | | | | |
| | | | | | | |
| | | | | | | |
| | | | | | | |
| | | | | | | |
| | | | | | | |
| | | | | | | |
| | | | | | | |
| | | | | | | |
| | | | | | | |
| | | | | | | |
| | | | | | | |
| | | | | | | |
| | | | | | | |
| | | | | | | |
| | | | | | | |
| | | | | | | |
| | | | | | | |

## Journal

| DATE | ACCOUNTS AND EXPLANATIONS | POST. REF. | DEBIT | CREDIT |
|------|---------------------------|------------|-------|--------|
|      |                           |            |       |        |
|      |                           |            |       |        |
|      |                           |            |       |        |
|      |                           |            |       |        |
|      |                           |            |       |        |
|      |                           |            |       |        |
|      |                           |            |       |        |
|      |                           |            |       |        |
|      |                           |            |       |        |
|      |                           |            |       |        |
|      |                           |            |       |        |
|      |                           |            |       |        |
|      |                           |            |       |        |
|      |                           |            |       |        |
|      |                           |            |       |        |
|      |                           |            |       |        |
|      |                           |            |       |        |
|      |                           |            |       |        |
|      |                           |            |       |        |
|      |                           |            |       |        |
|      |                           |            |       |        |
|      |                           |            |       |        |
|      |                           |            |       |        |
|      |                           |            |       |        |
|      |                           |            |       |        |
|      |                           |            |       |        |
|      |                           |            |       |        |
|      |                           |            |       |        |
|      |                           |            |       |        |
|      |                           |            |       |        |
|      |                           |            |       |        |
|      |                           |            |       |        |

*Req. 1*

### SUPPLY MISSING PAYROLL AMOUNTS

Employee Earnings:

| | | | | |
|---|---|---|---|---|
| (1) Straight-time employee earnings | $16,431 | (7) | Medical insurance | $668 |
| (2) Overtime pay | _____ | (8) | Total deductions | 5,409 |
| (3) Total employee earnings | _____ | (9) | Net pay | 17,936 |
| (4) Withheld income tax | 2,403 | (10) | Salary Expense | _____ |
| (5) FICA tax | _____ | (11) | Wage Expense | 8,573 |
| (6) Charitable contributions | 340 | (12) | Sales Commision Expense | 2,077 |

**Computations:**

AME
ECTION
ATE

*Req. 2*

| | Journal | | | |
|---|---|---|---|---|
| DATE | ACCOUNTS AND EXPLANATIONS | POST. REF. | DEBIT | CREDIT |
| | | | | |
| | | | | |
| | | | | |
| | | | | |
| | | | | |
| | | | | |
| | | | | |
| | | | | |
| | | | | |
| | | | | |
| | | | | |
| | | | | |
| | | | | |
| | | | | |

*Req. 1*

**P11-4B**

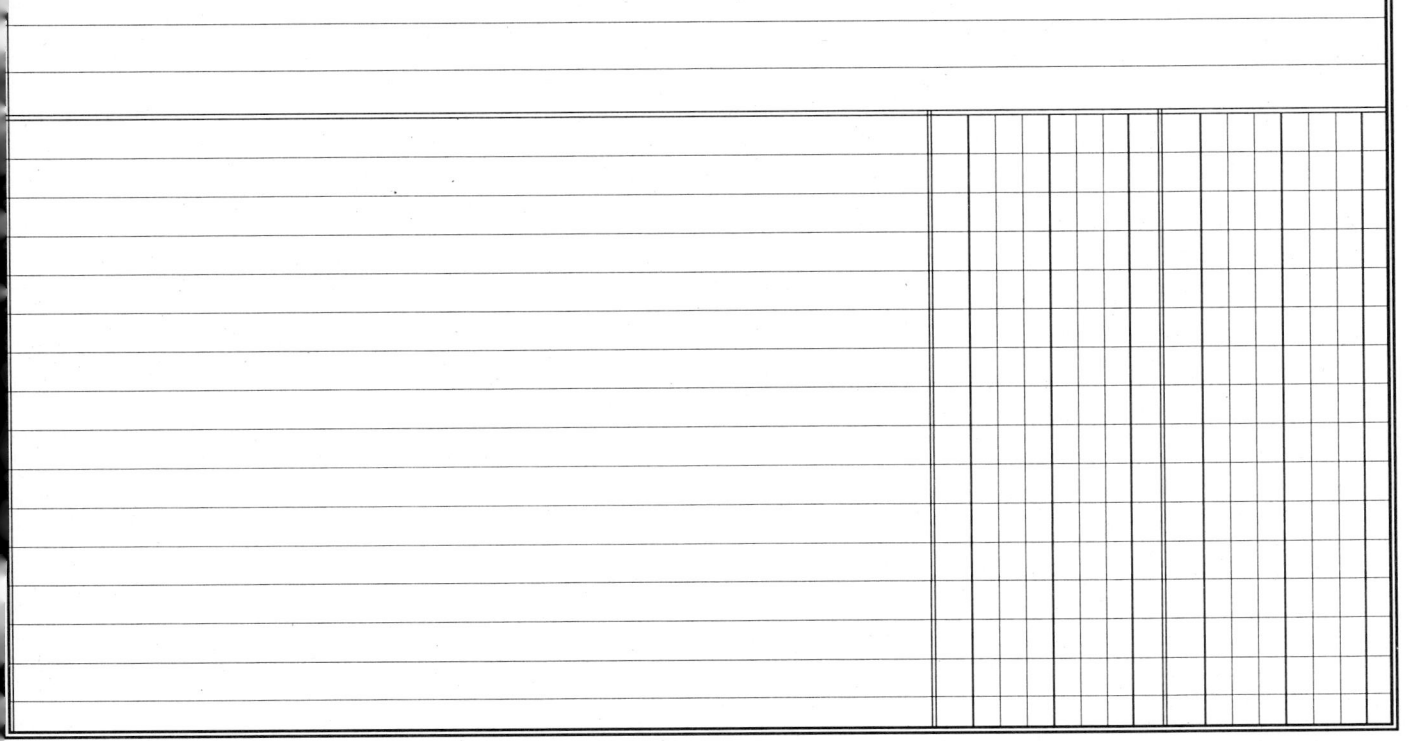

*Req. 2*

## Journal

| DATE | ACCOUNTS AND EXPLANATIONS | POST. REF. | DEBIT | CREDIT |
|------|---------------------------|-----------|-------|--------|
|  |  |  |  |  |
|  |  |  |  |  |
|  |  |  |  |  |
|  |  |  |  |  |
|  |  |  |  |  |
|  |  |  |  |  |
|  |  |  |  |  |
|  |  |  |  |  |
|  |  |  |  |  |
|  |  |  |  |  |
|  |  |  |  |  |
|  |  |  |  |  |
|  |  |  |  |  |
|  |  |  |  |  |
|  |  |  |  |  |
|  |  |  |  |  |
|  |  |  |  |  |
|  |  |  |  |  |
|  |  |  |  |  |
|  |  |  |  |  |
|  |  |  |  |  |
|  |  |  |  |  |
|  |  |  |  |  |
|  |  |  |  |  |
|  |  |  |  |  |
|  |  |  |  |  |
|  |  |  |  |  |
|  |  |  |  |  |
|  |  |  |  |  |
|  |  |  |  |  |
|  |  |  |  |  |
|  |  |  |  |  |

Reqs. 1 & 2 (Continued)

| ACCOUNT | | | | | ACCOUNT NO. | |
|---|---|---|---|---|---|---|
| | | | | | BALANCE | |
| DATE | ITEM | JRNL. REF. | DEBIT | CREDIT | DEBIT | CREDIT |
| | | | | | | |
| | | | | | | |
| | | | | | | |
| | | | | | | |

| ACCOUNT | | | | | ACCOUNT NO. | |
|---|---|---|---|---|---|---|
| | | | | | BALANCE | |
| DATE | ITEM | JRNL. REF. | DEBIT | CREDIT | DEBIT | CREDIT |
| | | | | | | |
| | | | | | | |
| | | | | | | |
| | | | | | | |

| ACCOUNT | | | | | ACCOUNT NO. | |
|---|---|---|---|---|---|---|
| | | | | | BALANCE | |
| DATE | ITEM | JRNL. REF. | DEBIT | CREDIT | DEBIT | CREDIT |
| | | | | | | |
| | | | | | | |
| | | | | | | |
| | | | | | | |

| ACCOUNT | | | | | ACCOUNT NO. | |
|---|---|---|---|---|---|---|
| | | | | | BALANCE | |
| DATE | ITEM | JRNL. REF. | DEBIT | CREDIT | DEBIT | CREDIT |
| | | | | | | |
| | | | | | | |
| | | | | | | |
| | | | | | | |

*Reqs. 1 & 2 (Continued)*

| ACCOUNT | | | | | ACCOUNT NO. | |
| --- | --- | --- | --- | --- | --- | --- |
| | | | | | BALANCE | |
| DATE | ITEM | JRNL. REF. | DEBIT | CREDIT | DEBIT | CREDIT |
| | | | | | | |
| | | | | | | |
| | | | | | | |
| | | | | | | |

| ACCOUNT | | | | | ACCOUNT NO. | |
| --- | --- | --- | --- | --- | --- | --- |
| | | | | | BALANCE | |
| DATE | ITEM | JRNL. REF. | DEBIT | CREDIT | DEBIT | CREDIT |
| | | | | | | |
| | | | | | | |
| | | | | | | |
| | | | | | | |

| ACCOUNT | | | | | ACCOUNT NO. | |
| --- | --- | --- | --- | --- | --- | --- |
| | | | | | BALANCE | |
| DATE | ITEM | JRNL. REF. | DEBIT | CREDIT | DEBIT | CREDIT |
| | | | | | | |
| | | | | | | |
| | | | | | | |
| | | | | | | |

| ACCOUNT | | | | | ACCOUNT NO. | |
| --- | --- | --- | --- | --- | --- | --- |
| | | | | | BALANCE | |
| DATE | ITEM | JRNL. REF. | DEBIT | CREDIT | DEBIT | CREDIT |
| | | | | | | |
| | | | | | | |
| | | | | | | |

*Reqs. 1 & 2 (Continued)*

| ACCOUNT | | | | | ACCOUNT NO. | |
|---|---|---|---|---|---|---|
| | | | | | BALANCE | |
| DATE | ITEM | JRNL. REF. | DEBIT | CREDIT | DEBIT | CREDIT |
| | | | | | | |
| | | | | | | |
| | | | | | | |
| | | | | | | |

| ACCOUNT | | | | | ACCOUNT NO. | |
|---|---|---|---|---|---|---|
| | | | | | BALANCE | |
| DATE | ITEM | JRNL. REF. | DEBIT | CREDIT | DEBIT | CREDIT |
| | | | | | | |
| | | | | | | |
| | | | | | | |
| | | | | | | |

| ACCOUNT | | | | | ACCOUNT NO. | |
|---|---|---|---|---|---|---|
| | | | | | BALANCE | |
| DATE | ITEM | JRNL. REF. | DEBIT | CREDIT | DEBIT | CREDIT |
| | | | | | | |
| | | | | | | |
| | | | | | | |
| | | | | | | |

| ACCOUNT | | | | | ACCOUNT NO. | |
|---|---|---|---|---|---|---|
| | | | | | BALANCE | |
| DATE | ITEM | JRNL. REF. | DEBIT | CREDIT | DEBIT | CREDIT |
| | | | | | | |
| | | | | | | |
| | | | | | | |
| | | | | | | |

AME
ECTION
ATE

*Req. 2*

## Journal

| DATE | ACCOUNTS AND EXPLANATIONS | POST. REF. | DEBIT | CREDIT |
|------|----------------------------|------------|-------|--------|
|  |  |  |  |  |
|  |  |  |  |  |
|  |  |  |  |  |
|  |  |  |  |  |
|  |  |  |  |  |
|  |  |  |  |  |
|  |  |  |  |  |
|  |  |  |  |  |
|  |  |  |  |  |
|  |  |  |  |  |
|  |  |  |  |  |
|  |  |  |  |  |
|  |  |  |  |  |
|  |  |  |  |  |
|  |  |  |  |  |
|  |  |  |  |  |
|  |  |  |  |  |
|  |  |  |  |  |
|  |  |  |  |  |
|  |  |  |  |  |
|  |  |  |  |  |
|  |  |  |  |  |
|  |  |  |  |  |
|  |  |  |  |  |
|  |  |  |  |  |

*Req. 3*

*Reqs. 1 & 3*

The foldout worksheet to solve this problem can be found in the back of the book.

*Reqs. 2 - 3*

| | Journal | | | | |
|---|---|---|---|---|---|
| DATE | ACCOUNTS AND EXPLANATIONS | POST. REF. | DEBIT | | CREDIT |
| | | | | | |
| | | | | | |
| | | | | | |
| | | | | | |
| | | | | | |
| | | | | | |
| | | | | | |
| | | | | | |
| | | | | | |
| | | | | | |
| | | | | | |
| | | | | | |
| | | | | | |
| | | | | | |
| | | | | | |
| | | | | | |
| | | | | | |
| | | | | | |
| | | | | | |
| | | | | | |
| | | | | | |
| | | | | | |
| | | | | | |
| | | | | | |
| | | | | | |
| | | | | | |
| | | | | | |
| | | | | | |
| | | | | | |
| | | | | | |
| | | | | | |
| | | | | | |
| | | | | | |
| | | | | | |

*Reqs. 1 - 3*

*Req. 1*

*Req. 2*

*Req. 3*

*Req. 4*

# Comprehensive Problem
# for Part 2

Req. 1

*Req. 2*

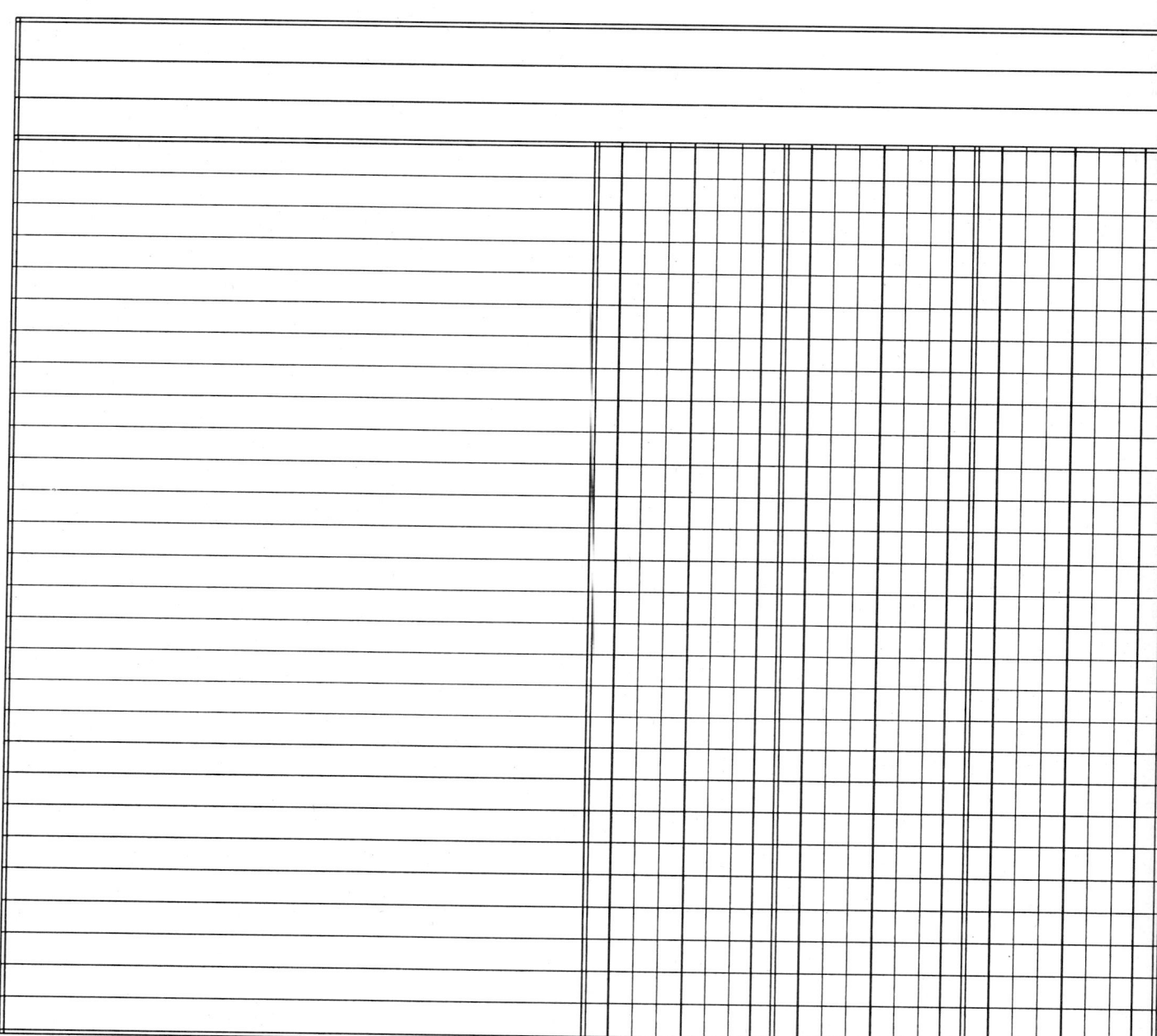

Chapter 11 **Comprehensive Problem
for Part 2**

**DE12-2**

## Journal

| DATE | ACCOUNTS AND EXPLANATIONS | POST. REF. | DEBIT | CREDIT |
|------|---------------------------|-----------|-------|--------|
|      |                           |           |       |        |
|      |                           |           |       |        |
|      |                           |           |       |        |
|      |                           |           |       |        |
|      |                           |           |       |        |
|      |                           |           |       |        |

1.

2.

| | | Journal | | | |
|---|---|---|---|---|---|
| DATE | | ACCOUNTS AND EXPLANATIONS | POST. REF. | DEBIT | CREDIT |
| | | | | | |
| | | | | | |
| | | | | | |
| | | | | | |
| | | | | | |
| | | | | | |
| | | | | | |

3.

1.

_____

_____

_____

_____

2.

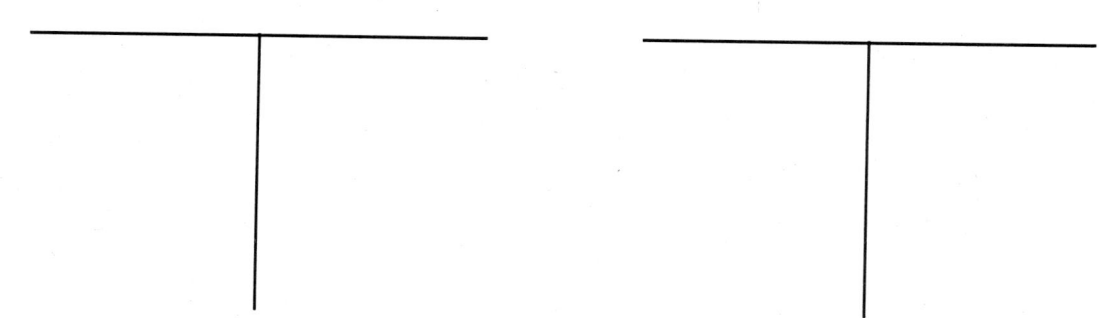

## Journal

| DATE | ACCOUNTS AND EXPLANATIONS | POST. REF. | DEBIT | CREDIT |
|------|---------------------------|------------|-------|--------|
| | | | | |
| | | | | |
| | | | | |
| | | | | |
| | | | | |
| | | | | |
| | | | | |
| | | | | |
| | | | | |
| | | | | |
| | | | | |
| | | | | |
| | | | | |
| | | | | |
| | | | | |
| | | | | |
| | | | | |
| | | | | |
| | | | | |
| | | | | |
| | | | | |
| | | | | |
| | | | | |
| | | | | |
| | | | | |
| | | | | |
| | | | | |
| | | | | |
| | | | | |
| | | | | |
| | | | | |
| | | | | |
| | | | | |
| | | | | |
| | | | | |
| | | | | |
| | | | | |

2.

NAME
SECTION
DATE

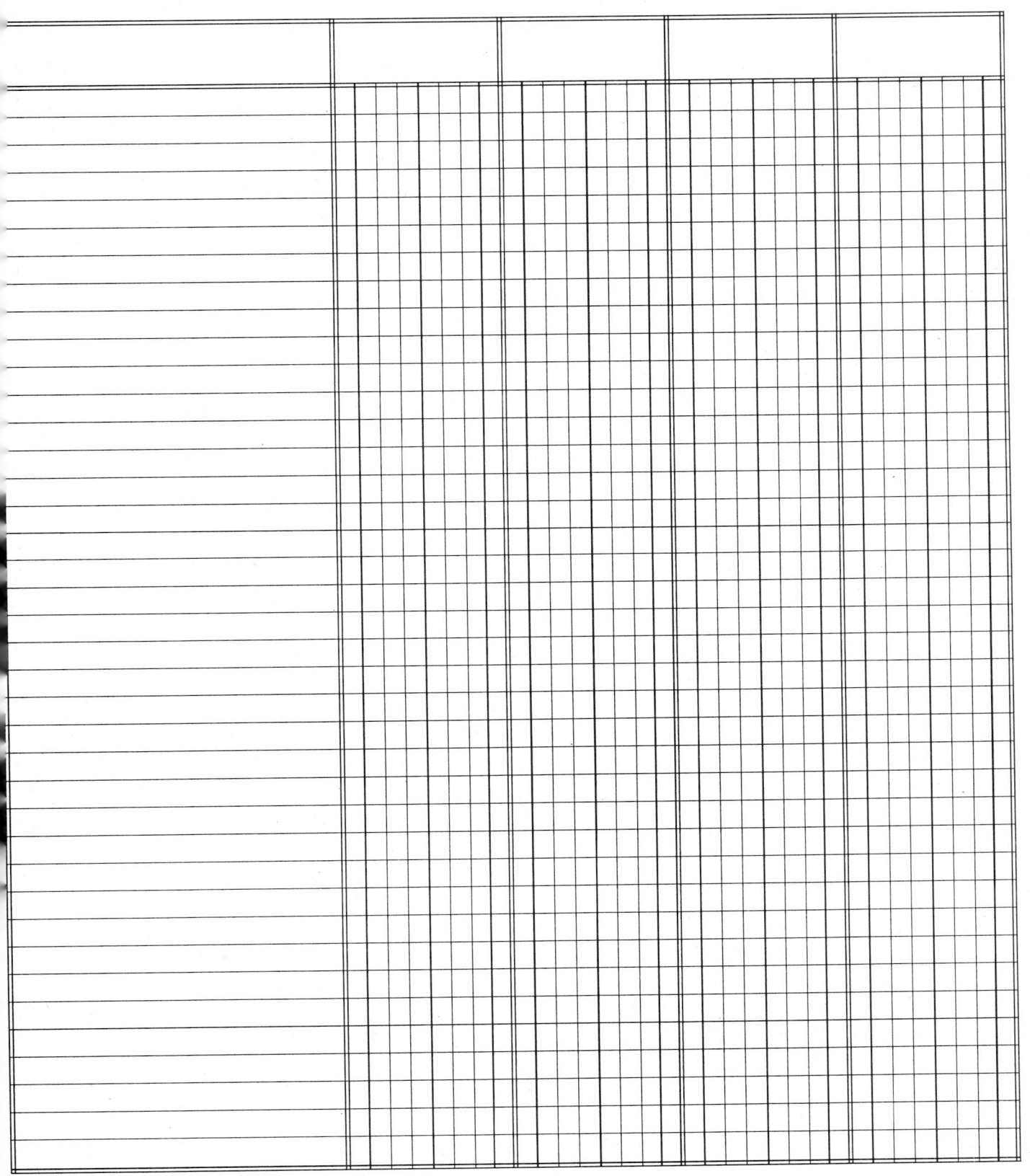

## Journal

| DATE | ACCOUNTS AND EXPLANATIONS | POST. REF. | DEBIT | CREDIT |
|---|---|---|---|---|
| | | | | |
| | | | | |
| | | | | |
| | | | | |
| | | | | |

# DE12-10

1.

2.

## Journal

| DATE | ACCOUNTS AND EXPLANATIONS | POST. REF. | DEBIT | CREDIT |
|---|---|---|---|---|
| | | | | |
| | | | | |
| | | | | |
| | | | | |
| | | | | |

## Journal

| DATE | | ACCOUNTS AND EXPLANATIONS | POST. REF. | DEBIT | CREDIT |
|------|---|---------------------------|-----------|-------|--------|
| | | | | | |
| | | | | | |
| | | | | | |
| | | | | | |
| | | | | | |
| | | | | | |
| | | | | | |
| | | | | | |
| | | | | | |
| | | | | | |

| | | |
|---|---|---|
| | | |
| | | |
| | | |
| | | |
| | | |
| | | |
| | | |
| | | |
| | | |
| | | |
| | | |
| | | |

## Journal

| DATE | ACCOUNTS AND EXPLANATIONS | POST. REF. | DEBIT | CREDIT |
|------|---------------------------|------------|-------|--------|
|      |                           |            |       |        |
|      |                           |            |       |        |
|      |                           |            |       |        |
|      |                           |            |       |        |
|      |                           |            |       |        |
|      |                           |            |       |        |
|      |                           |            |       |        |

## Journal

| DATE | ACCOUNTS AND EXPLANATIONS | POST. REF. | DEBIT | CREDIT |
|------|---------------------------|------------|-------|--------|
| | | | | |
| | | | | |
| | | | | |
| | | | | |
| | | | | |
| | | | | |
| | | | | |
| | | | | |
| | | | | |
| | | | | |
| | | | | |
| | | | | |
| | | | | |
| | | | | |
| | | | | |
| | | | | |
| | | | | |
| | | | | |
| | | | | |
| | | | | |
| | | | | |
| | | | | |
| | | | | |
| | | | | |
| | | | | |
| | | | | |
| | | | | |
| | | | | |
| | | | | |
| | | | | |
| | | | | |
| | | | | |

## Journal

| DATE | ACCOUNTS AND EXPLANATIONS | POST. REF. | DEBIT | CREDIT |
|------|---------------------------|------------|-------|--------|
|      |                           |            |       |        |
|      |                           |            |       |        |
|      |                           |            |       |        |
|      |                           |            |       |        |
|      |                           |            |       |        |
|      |                           |            |       |        |
|      |                           |            |       |        |

Chapter 12

NAME
SECTION
DATE

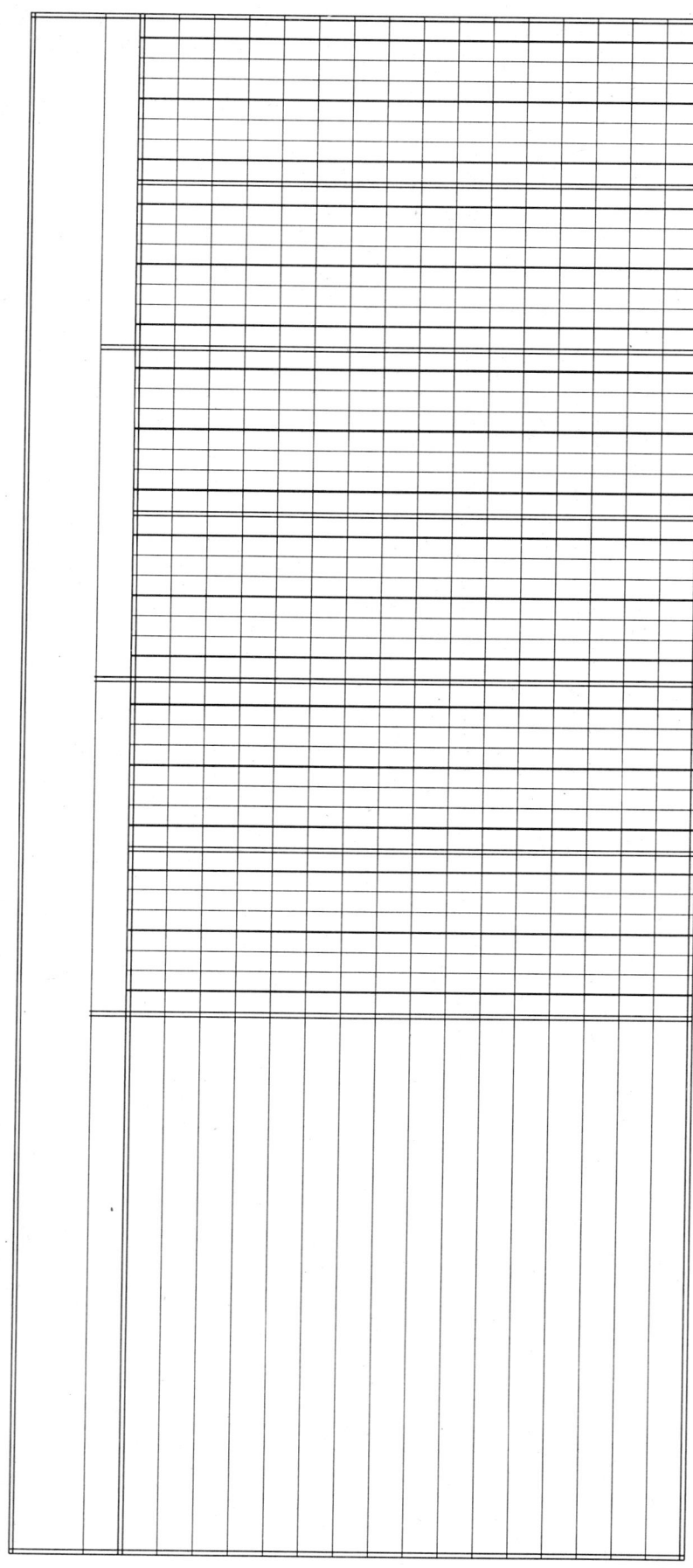

## Journal

| DATE | ACCOUNTS AND EXPLANATIONS | POST. REF. | DEBIT | CREDIT |
|------|---------------------------|------------|-------|--------|
|  |  |  |  |  |
|  |  |  |  |  |
|  |  |  |  |  |
|  |  |  |  |  |
|  |  |  |  |  |
|  |  |  |  |  |
|  |  |  |  |  |
|  |  |  |  |  |
|  |  |  |  |  |
|  |  |  |  |  |
|  |  |  |  |  |
|  |  |  |  |  |
|  |  |  |  |  |
|  |  |  |  |  |
|  |  |  |  |  |
|  |  |  |  |  |
|  |  |  |  |  |
|  |  |  |  |  |
|  |  |  |  |  |
|  |  |  |  |  |
|  |  |  |  |  |
|  |  |  |  |  |
|  |  |  |  |  |
|  |  |  |  |  |
|  |  |  |  |  |
|  |  |  |  |  |
|  |  |  |  |  |
|  |  |  |  |  |
|  |  |  |  |  |
|  |  |  |  |  |

**E12-2**

| | | |
|---|---|---|
| | | |
| | | |
| | | |
| | | |
| | | |
| | | |
| | | |
| | | |
| | | |
| | | |
| | | |
| | | |
| | | |
| | | |
| | | |
| | | |
| | | |

Req. 2

| | Journal | | | | | | |
|---|---|---|---|---|---|---|---|
| DATE | ACCOUNTS AND EXPLANATIONS | POST. REF. | | DEBIT | | CREDIT | |
| | | | | | | | |
| | | | | | | | |
| | | | | | | | |
| | | | | | | | |
| | | | | | | | |
| | | | | | | | |
| | | | | | | | |
| | | | | | | | |
| | | | | | | | |
| | | | | | | | |
| | | | | | | | |
| | | | | | | | |
| | | | | | | | |
| | | | | | | | |
| | | | | | | | |
| | | | | | | | |
| | | | | | | | |
| | | | | | | | |
| | | | | | | | |
| | | | | | | | |
| | | | | | | | |

## Journal

| DATE | ACCOUNTS AND EXPLANATIONS | POST. REF. | DEBIT | CREDIT |
|------|---------------------------|------------|-------|--------|
|  |  |  |  |  |
|  |  |  |  |  |
|  |  |  |  |  |
|  |  |  |  |  |
|  |  |  |  |  |
|  |  |  |  |  |
|  |  |  |  |  |
|  |  |  |  |  |
|  |  |  |  |  |
|  |  |  |  |  |
|  |  |  |  |  |
|  |  |  |  |  |
|  |  |  |  |  |
|  |  |  |  |  |
|  |  |  |  |  |
|  |  |  |  |  |
|  |  |  |  |  |
|  |  |  |  |  |

## Journal

| DATE | ACCOUNTS AND EXPLANATIONS | POST. REF. | DEBIT | CREDIT |
|------|---------------------------|------------|-------|--------|
|  |  |  |  |  |
|  |  |  |  |  |
|  |  |  |  |  |
|  |  |  |  |  |
|  |  |  |  |  |
|  |  |  |  |  |
|  |  |  |  |  |
|  |  |  |  |  |
|  |  |  |  |  |
|  |  |  |  |  |
|  |  |  |  |  |
|  |  |  |  |  |
|  |  |  |  |  |
|  |  |  |  |  |
|  |  |  |  |  |
|  |  |  |  |  |
|  |  |  |  |  |
|  |  |  |  |  |
|  |  |  |  |  |
|  |  |  |  |  |
|  |  |  |  |  |
|  |  |  |  |  |
|  |  |  |  |  |
|  |  |  |  |  |
|  |  |  |  |  |
|  |  |  |  |  |
|  |  |  |  |  |
|  |  |  |  |  |
|  |  |  |  |  |
|  |  |  |  |  |
|  |  |  |  |  |
|  |  |  |  |  |
|  |  |  |  |  |
|  |  |  |  |  |
|  |  |  |  |  |
|  |  |  |  |  |

Chapter 12

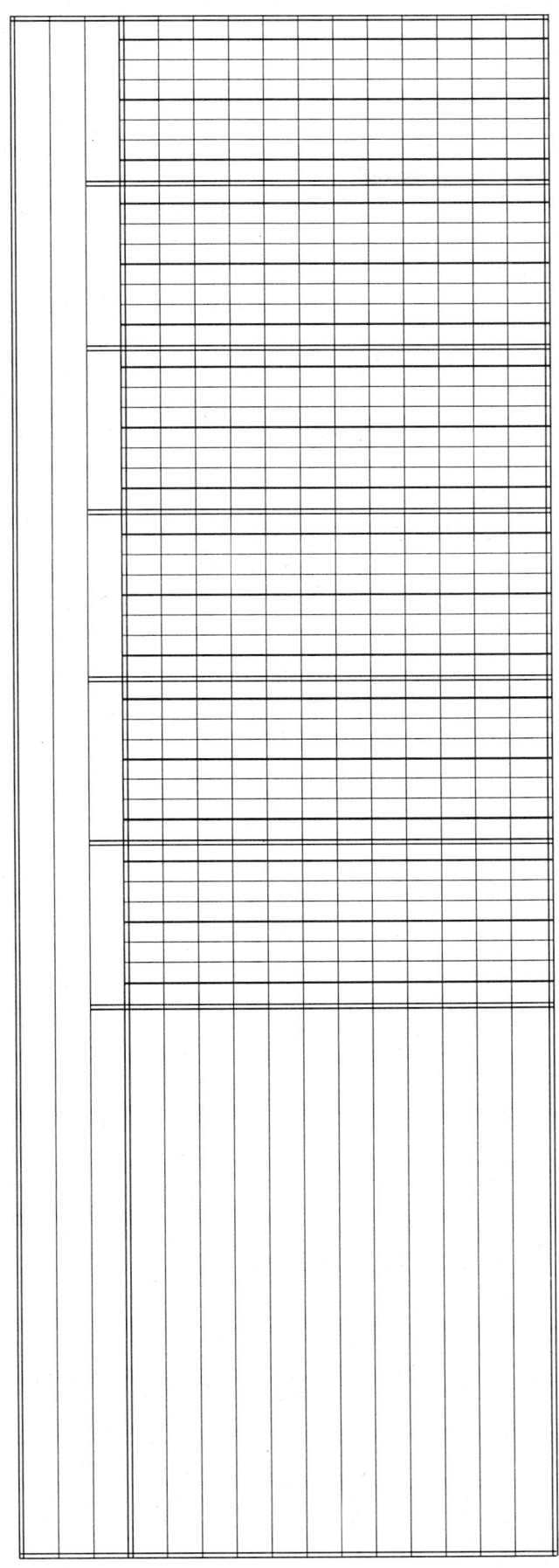

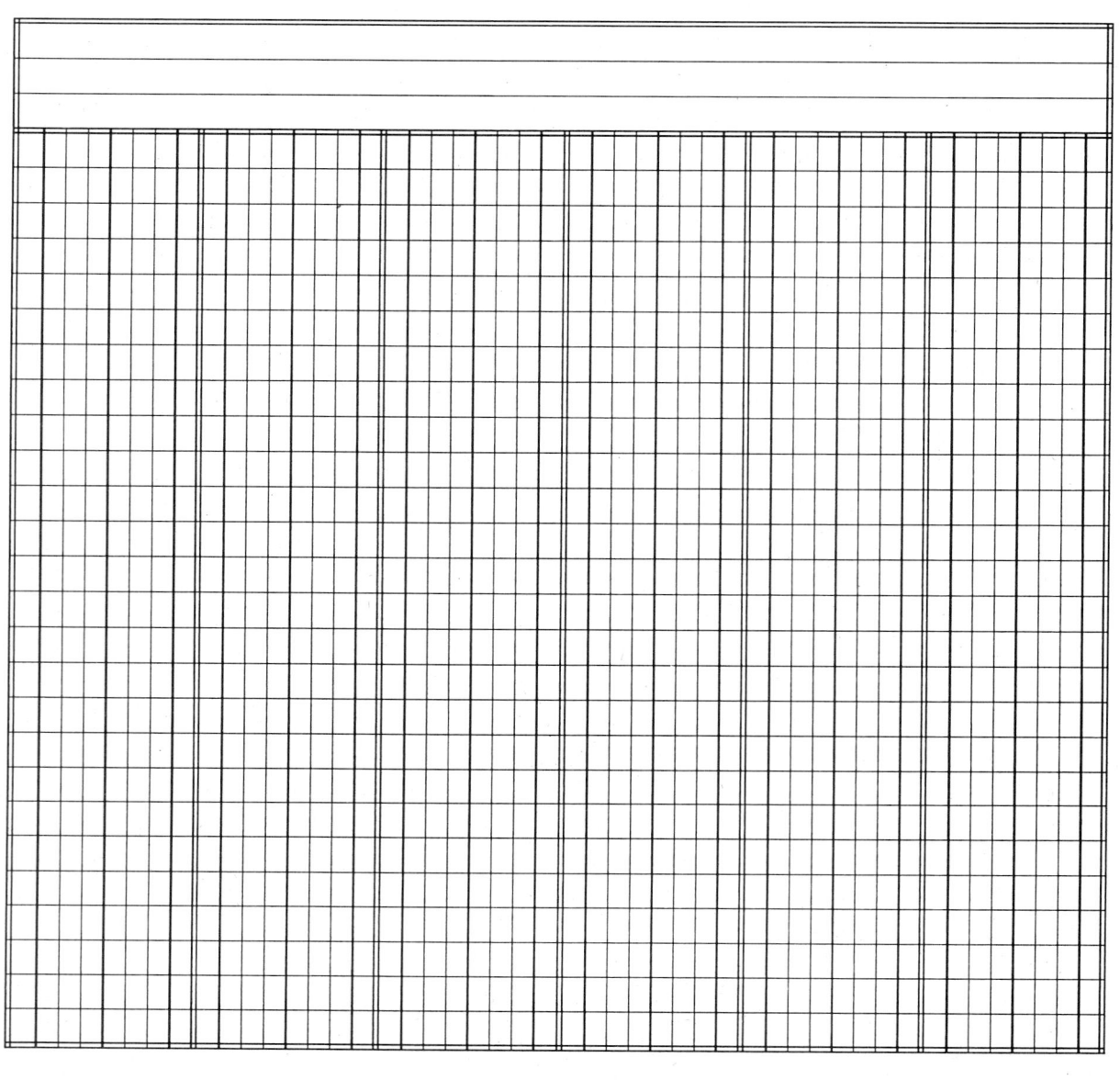

**Computations:**

# Ethical Issue

*Req. 1*

| | | General Journal | | |
|---|---|---|---|---|
| DATE | | DESCRIPTION | DEBIT | CREDIT |
| | | | | |
| | | | | |
| | | | | |
| | | | | |
| | | | | |

*Req. 2*

Reqs. 1 & 3

| | | Journal | | | |
|---|---|---|---|---|---|
| DATE | | ACCOUNTS AND EXPLANATIONS | POST. REF. | DEBIT | CREDIT |
| | | | | | |
| | | | | | |
| | | | | | |
| | | | | | |
| | | | | | |
| | | | | | |
| | | | | | |
| | | | | | |
| | | | | | |
| | | | | | |
| | | | | | |
| | | | | | |
| | | | | | |
| | | | | | |
| | | | | | |
| | | | | | |
| | | | | | |
| | | | | | |
| | | | | | |
| | | | | | |
| | | | | | |
| | | | | | |
| | | | | | |
| | | | | | |
| | | | | | |
| | | | | | |
| | | | | | |
| | | | | | |
| | | | | | |
| | | | | | |
| | | | | | |
| | | | | | |
| | | | | | |
| | | | | | |
| | | | | | |
| | | | | | |
| | | | | | |

Req. 2

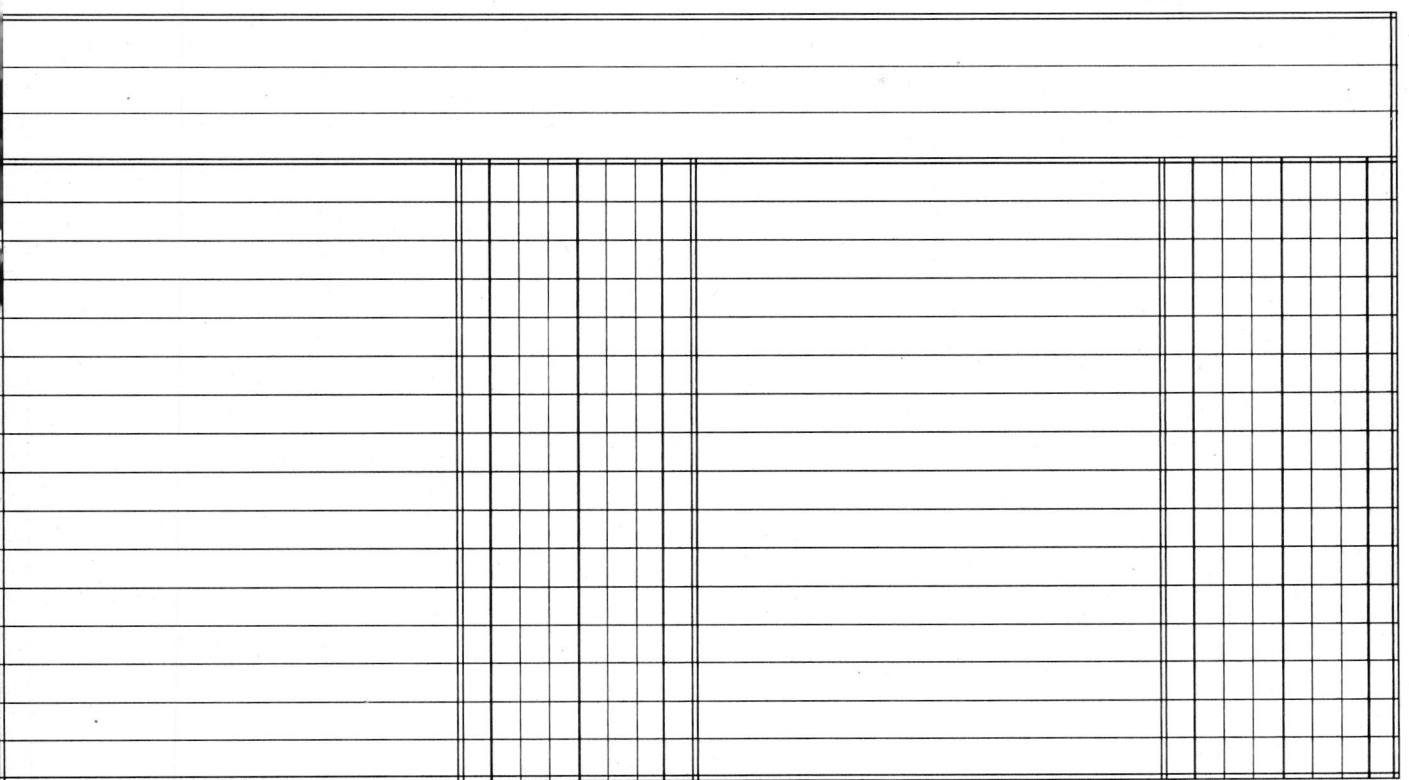

Reqs. 1 & 2

| | Journal | | | |
|---|---|---|---|---|
| DATE | ACCOUNTS AND EXPLANATIONS | POST. REF. | DEBIT | CREDIT |
| | | | | |
| | | | | |
| | | | | |
| | | | | |
| | | | | |
| | | | | |
| | | | | |
| | | | | |
| | | | | |
| | | | | |
| | | | | |
| | | | | |
| | | | | |
| | | | | |
| | | | | |
| | | | | |
| | | | | |
| | | | | |
| | | | | |
| | | | | |
| | | | | |
| | | | | |
| | | | | |
| | | | | |
| | | | | |
| | | | | |
| | | | | |
| | | | | |
| | | | | |
| | | | | |
| | | | | |
| | | | | |
| | | | | |
| | | | | |
| | | | | |
| | | | | |
| | | | | |
| | | | | |
| | | | | |
| | | | | |
| | | | | |

*Reqs. 3 & 4*

## Journal

| DATE | ACCOUNTS AND EXPLANATIONS | POST. REF. | DEBIT | CREDIT |
|------|---------------------------|------------|-------|--------|
|      |                           |            |       |        |
|      |                           |            |       |        |
|      |                           |            |       |        |
|      |                           |            |       |        |
|      |                           |            |       |        |
|      |                           |            |       |        |
|      |                           |            |       |        |
|      |                           |            |       |        |
|      |                           |            |       |        |
|      |                           |            |       |        |
|      |                           |            |       |        |
|      |                           |            |       |        |
|      |                           |            |       |        |
|      |                           |            |       |        |
|      |                           |            |       |        |
|      |                           |            |       |        |
|      |                           |            |       |        |
|      |                           |            |       |        |
|      |                           |            |       |        |
|      |                           |            |       |        |
|      |                           |            |       |        |
|      |                           |            |       |        |
|      |                           |            |       |        |
|      |                           |            |       |        |
|      |                           |            |       |        |
|      |                           |            |       |        |
|      |                           |            |       |        |
|      |                           |            |       |        |
|      |                           |            |       |        |
|      |                           |            |       |        |

Req. 1

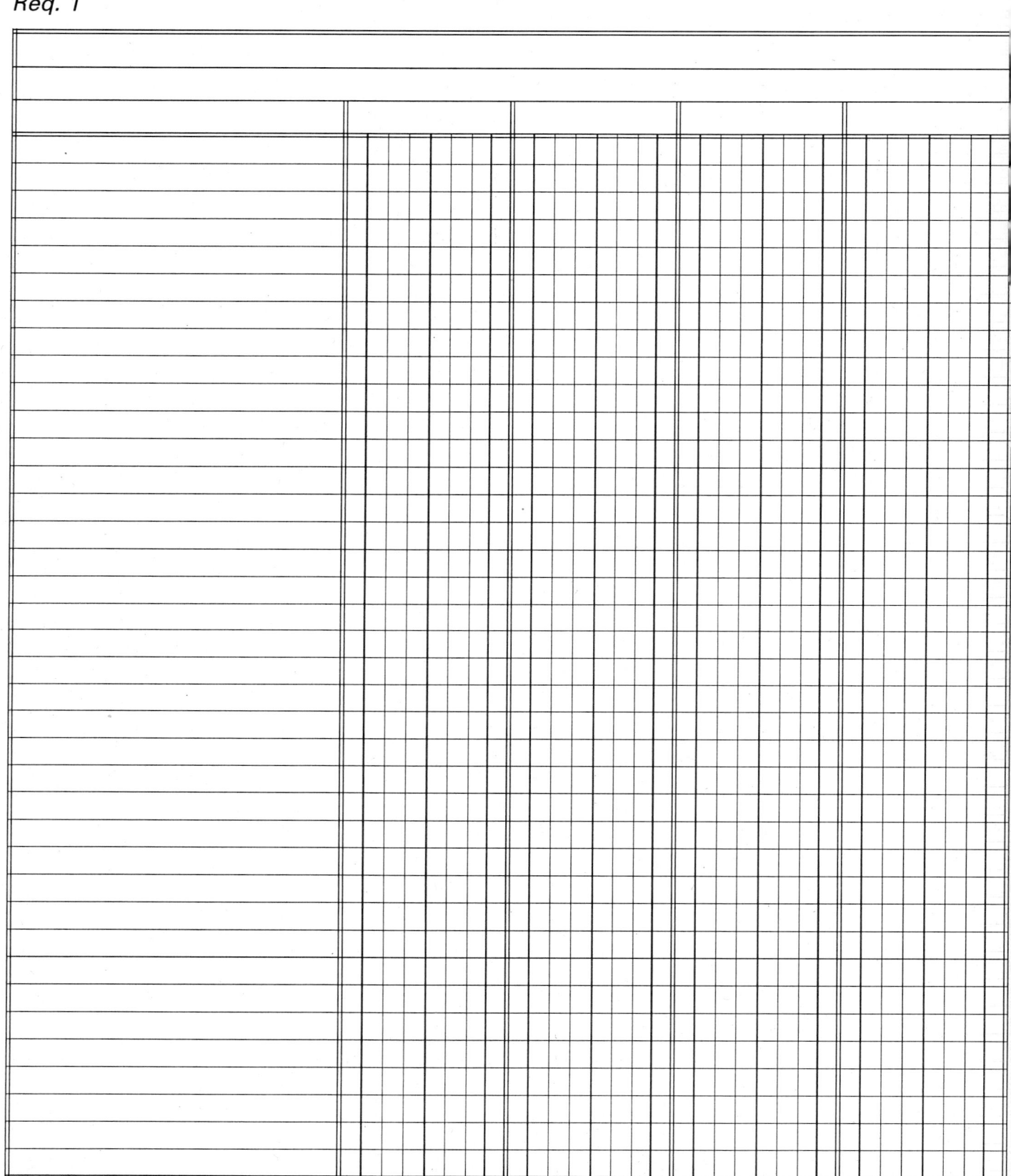

*Req. 1 (Continued)*

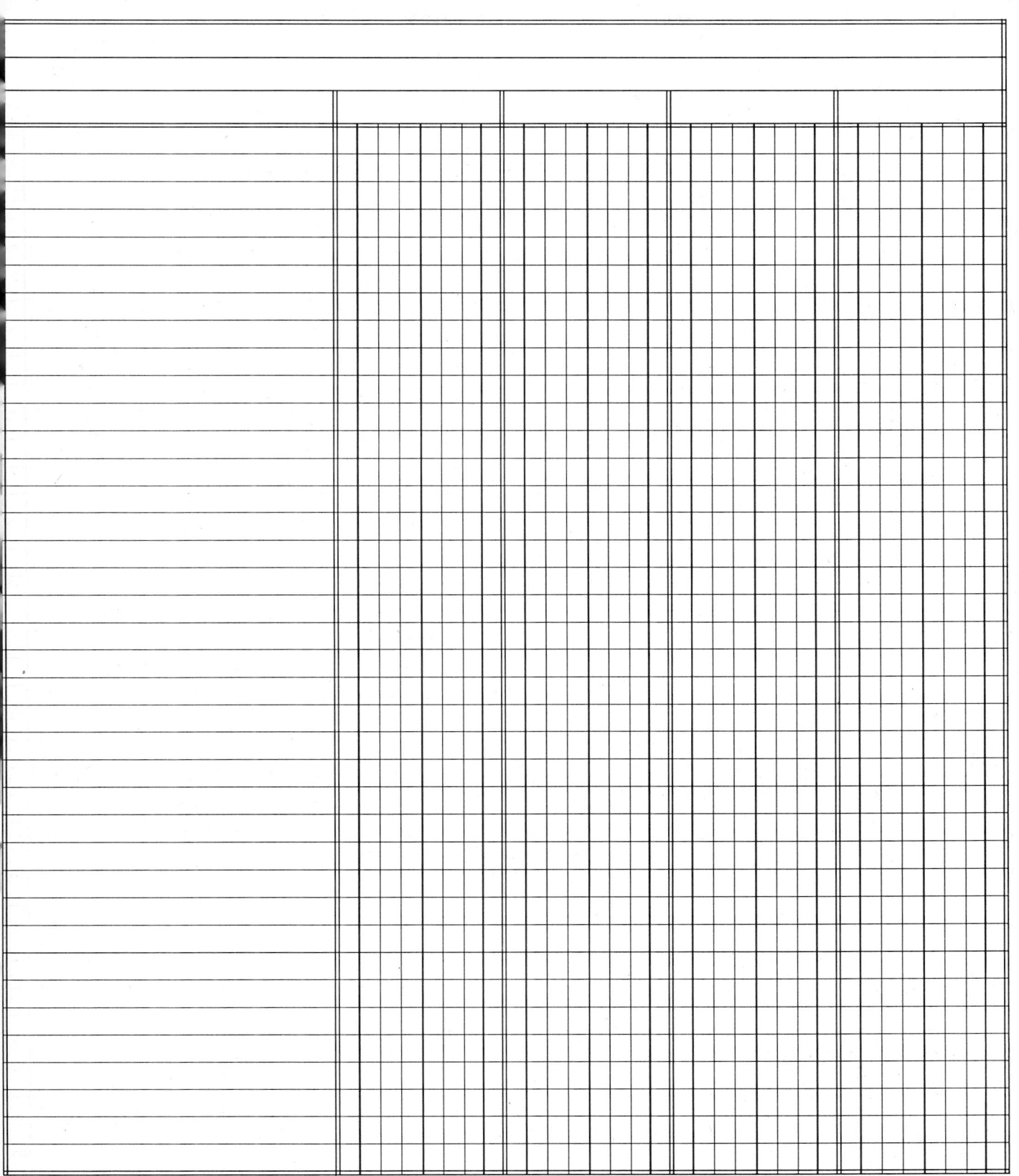

*Req. 1 (Continued)*

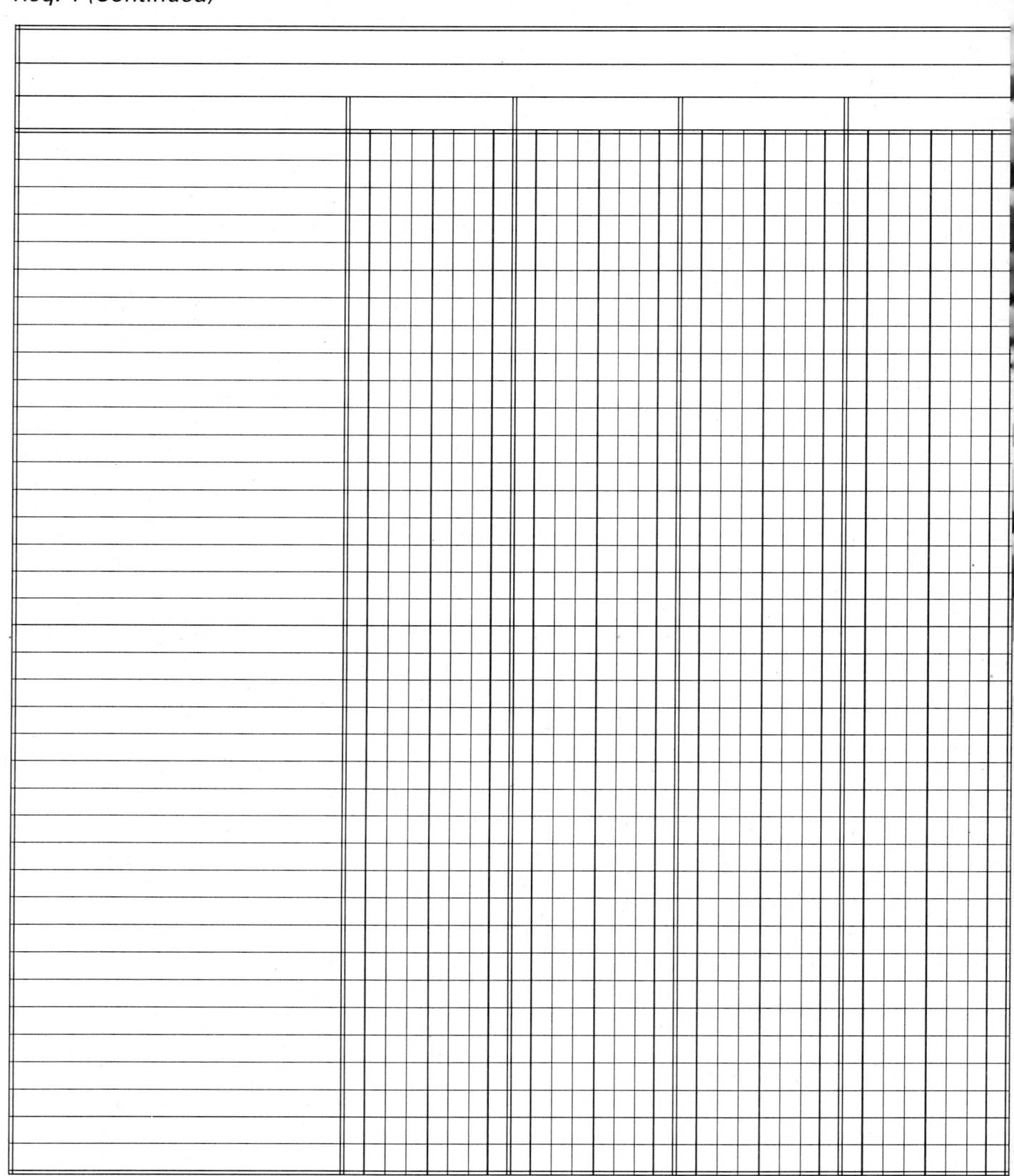

*Req. 2*

Reqs. 1–5

## Journal

| DATE | ACCOUNTS AND EXPLANATIONS | POST. REF. | DEBIT | CREDIT |
|------|---------------------------|-----------|-------|--------|
|  |  |  |  |  |
|  |  |  |  |  |
|  |  |  |  |  |
|  |  |  |  |  |
|  |  |  |  |  |
|  |  |  |  |  |
|  |  |  |  |  |
|  |  |  |  |  |
|  |  |  |  |  |
|  |  |  |  |  |
|  |  |  |  |  |
|  |  |  |  |  |
|  |  |  |  |  |
|  |  |  |  |  |
|  |  |  |  |  |
|  |  |  |  |  |
|  |  |  |  |  |
|  |  |  |  |  |
|  |  |  |  |  |
|  |  |  |  |  |
|  |  |  |  |  |
|  |  |  |  |  |
|  |  |  |  |  |
|  |  |  |  |  |
|  |  |  |  |  |
|  |  |  |  |  |
|  |  |  |  |  |
|  |  |  |  |  |
|  |  |  |  |  |
|  |  |  |  |  |
|  |  |  |  |  |
|  |  |  |  |  |
|  |  |  |  |  |
|  |  |  |  |  |
|  |  |  |  |  |
|  |  |  |  |  |
|  |  |  |  |  |
|  |  |  |  |  |

*Reqs. 1–5 (Continued)*

## Journal

| DATE | ACCOUNTS AND EXPLANATIONS | POST. REF. | DEBIT | CREDIT |
|------|---------------------------|-----------|-------|--------|
|  |  |  |  |  |
|  |  |  |  |  |
|  |  |  |  |  |
|  |  |  |  |  |
|  |  |  |  |  |
|  |  |  |  |  |
|  |  |  |  |  |
|  |  |  |  |  |
|  |  |  |  |  |
|  |  |  |  |  |
|  |  |  |  |  |
|  |  |  |  |  |
|  |  |  |  |  |
|  |  |  |  |  |
|  |  |  |  |  |
|  |  |  |  |  |
|  |  |  |  |  |
|  |  |  |  |  |
|  |  |  |  |  |
|  |  |  |  |  |
|  |  |  |  |  |
|  |  |  |  |  |
|  |  |  |  |  |

Chapter 12

Req. 1A

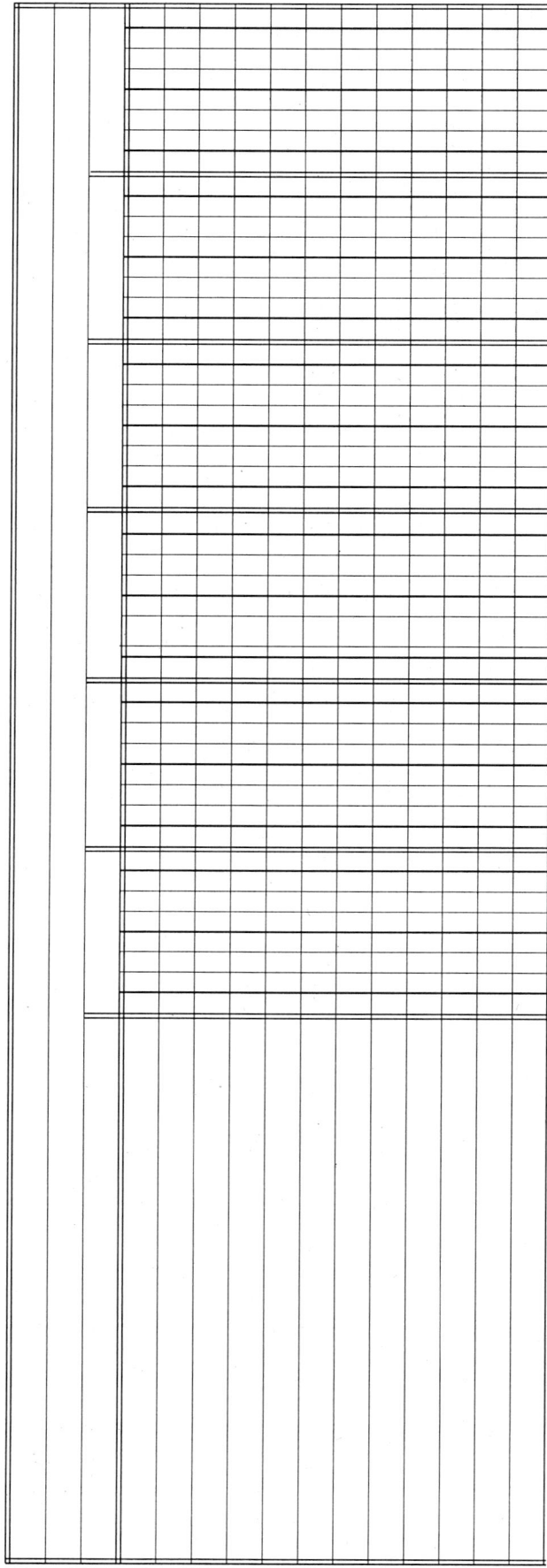

**P12-6A**(Continued)

Req. 1b

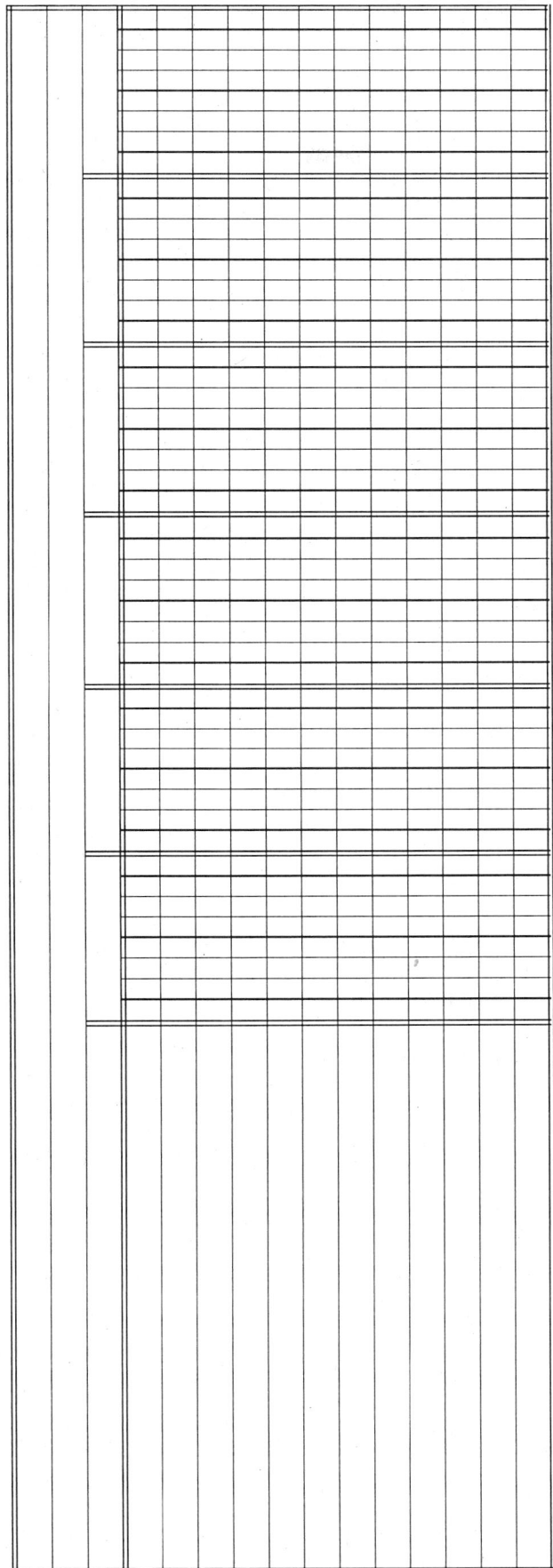

*Req. 2*

## Journal

| DATE | | ACCOUNTS AND EXPLANATIONS | POST. REF. | DEBIT | CREDIT |
|---|---|---|---|---|---|
| | | | | | |
| | | | | | |
| | | | | | |
| | | | | | |
| | | | | | |
| | | | | | |
| | | | | | |
| | | | | | |
| | | | | | |
| | | | | | |
| | | | | | |
| | | | | | |
| | | | | | |
| | | | | | |
| | | | | | |
| | | | | | |
| | | | | | |
| | | | | | |
| | | | | | |
| | | | | | |
| | | | | | |
| | | | | | |
| | | | | | |
| | | | | | |
| | | | | | |
| | | | | | |
| | | | | | |
| | | | | | |
| | | | | | |
| | | | | | |
| | | | | | |
| | | | | | |
| | | | | | |
| | | | | | |

*Reqs. 1 & 3*

## Journal

| DATE | ACCOUNTS AND EXPLANATIONS | POST. REF. | DEBIT | CREDIT |
|---|---|---|---|---|
| | | | | |
| | | | | |
| | | | | |
| | | | | |
| | | | | |
| | | | | |
| | | | | |
| | | | | |
| | | | | |
| | | | | |
| | | | | |
| | | | | |
| | | | | |
| | | | | |
| | | | | |
| | | | | |
| | | | | |
| | | | | |
| | | | | |
| | | | | |
| | | | | |
| | | | | |
| | | | | |
| | | | | |
| | | | | |
| | | | | |
| | | | | |
| | | | | |
| | | | | |
| | | | | |
| | | | | |
| | | | | |
| | | | | |
| | | | | |
| | | | | |
| | | | | |
| | | | | |
| | | | | |

*Req. 2*

P12-7A (Continued)

NAME
SECTION
DATE

Req. 3

*Reqs. 1 & 3*

| | | Journal | | | |
|---|---|---|---|---|---|
| DATE | | ACCOUNTS AND EXPLANATIONS | POST. REF. | DEBIT | CREDIT |
| | | | | | |
| | | | | | |
| | | | | | |
| | | | | | |
| | | | | | |
| | | | | | |
| | | | | | |
| | | | | | |
| | | | | | |
| | | | | | |
| | | | | | |
| | | | | | |
| | | | | | |
| | | | | | |
| | | | | | |
| | | | | | |
| | | | | | |
| | | | | | |
| | | | | | |
| | | | | | |
| | | | | | |
| | | | | | |
| | | | | | |
| | | | | | |
| | | | | | |
| | | | | | |
| | | | | | |
| | | | | | |
| | | | | | |
| | | | | | |
| | | | | | |
| | | | | | |
| | | | | | |
| | | | | | |
| | | | | | |
| | | | | | |
| | | | | | |
| | | | | | |
| | | | | | |
| | | | | | |

*Req. 2*

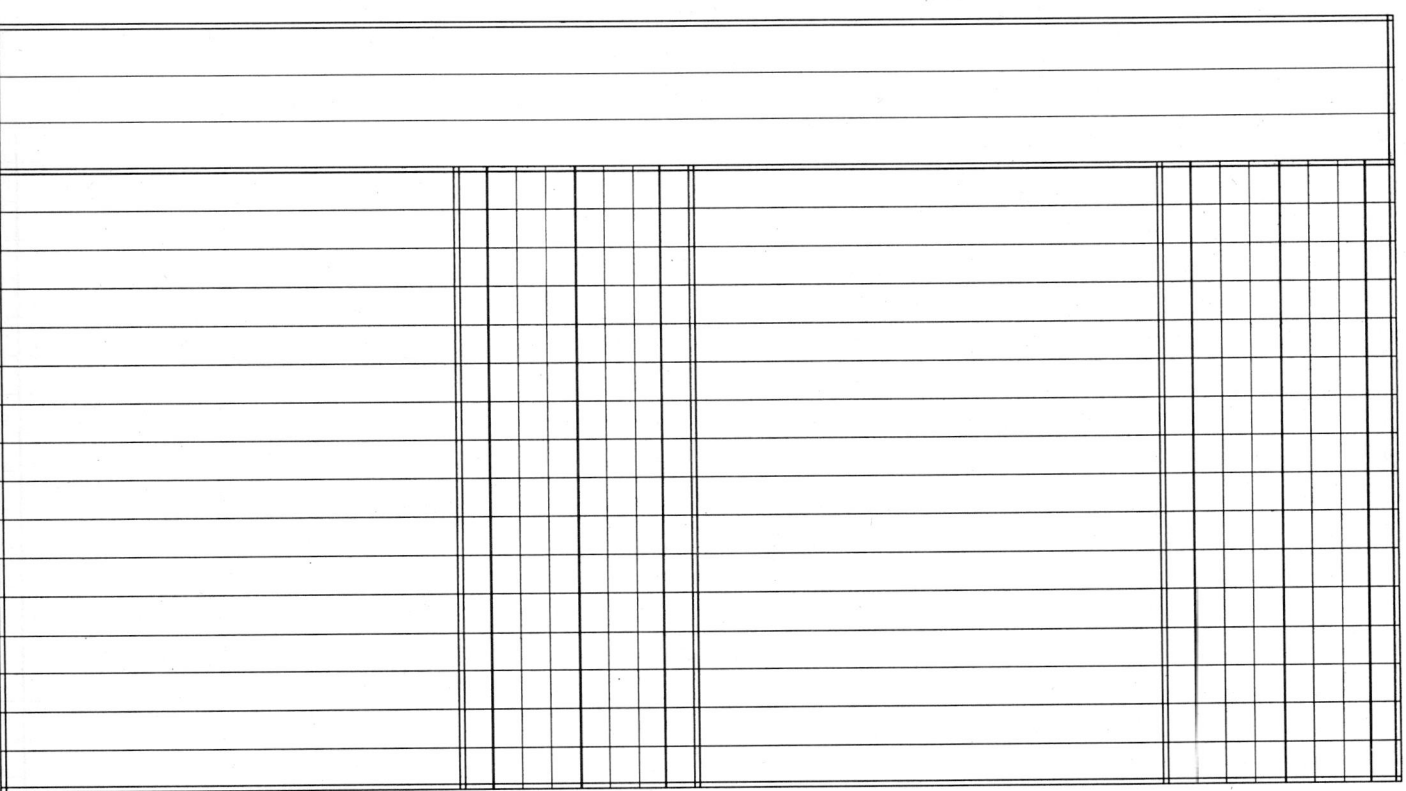

*Reqs. 1 & 2*

| | Journal | | | |
|---|---|---|---|---|
| DATE | ACCOUNTS AND EXPLANATIONS | POST. REF. | DEBIT | CREDIT |
| | | | | |
| | | | | |
| | | | | |
| | | | | |
| | | | | |
| | | | | |
| | | | | |
| | | | | |
| | | | | |
| | | | | |
| | | | | |
| | | | | |
| | | | | |
| | | | | |
| | | | | |
| | | | | |
| | | | | |
| | | | | |
| | | | | |
| | | | | |
| | | | | |
| | | | | |
| | | | | |
| | | | | |
| | | | | |
| | | | | |
| | | | | |
| | | | | |
| | | | | |
| | | | | |
| | | | | |
| | | | | |
| | | | | |
| | | | | |
| | | | | |
| | | | | |
| | | | | |
| | | | | |
| | | | | |

*Reqs. 3 & 4*

## Journal

| DATE | ACCOUNTS AND EXPLANATIONS | POST. REF. | DEBIT | CREDIT |
|------|---------------------------|------------|-------|--------|
| | | | | |
| | | | | |
| | | | | |
| | | | | |
| | | | | |
| | | | | |
| | | | | |
| | | | | |
| | | | | |
| | | | | |
| | | | | |
| | | | | |
| | | | | |
| | | | | |
| | | | | |
| | | | | |
| | | | | |
| | | | | |
| | | | | |
| | | | | |
| | | | | |
| | | | | |
| | | | | |
| | | | | |
| | | | | |
| | | | | |
| | | | | |
| | | | | |
| | | | | |
| | | | | |
| | | | | |
| | | | | |
| | | | | |
| | | | | |
| | | | | |
| | | | | |
| | | | | |
| | | | | |
| | | | | |
| | | | | |

*Req. 1*

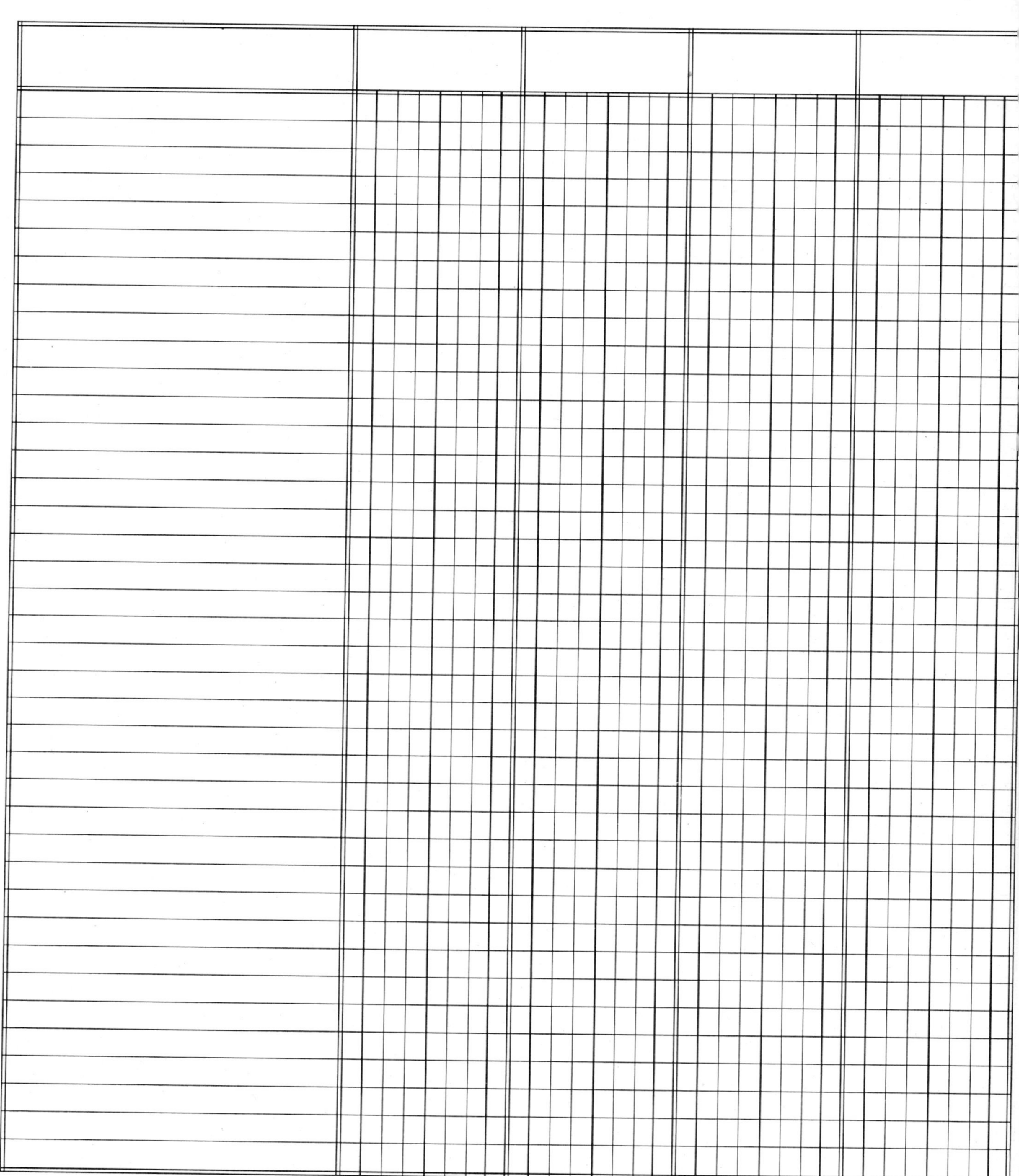

*Req. 1 (Continued)*

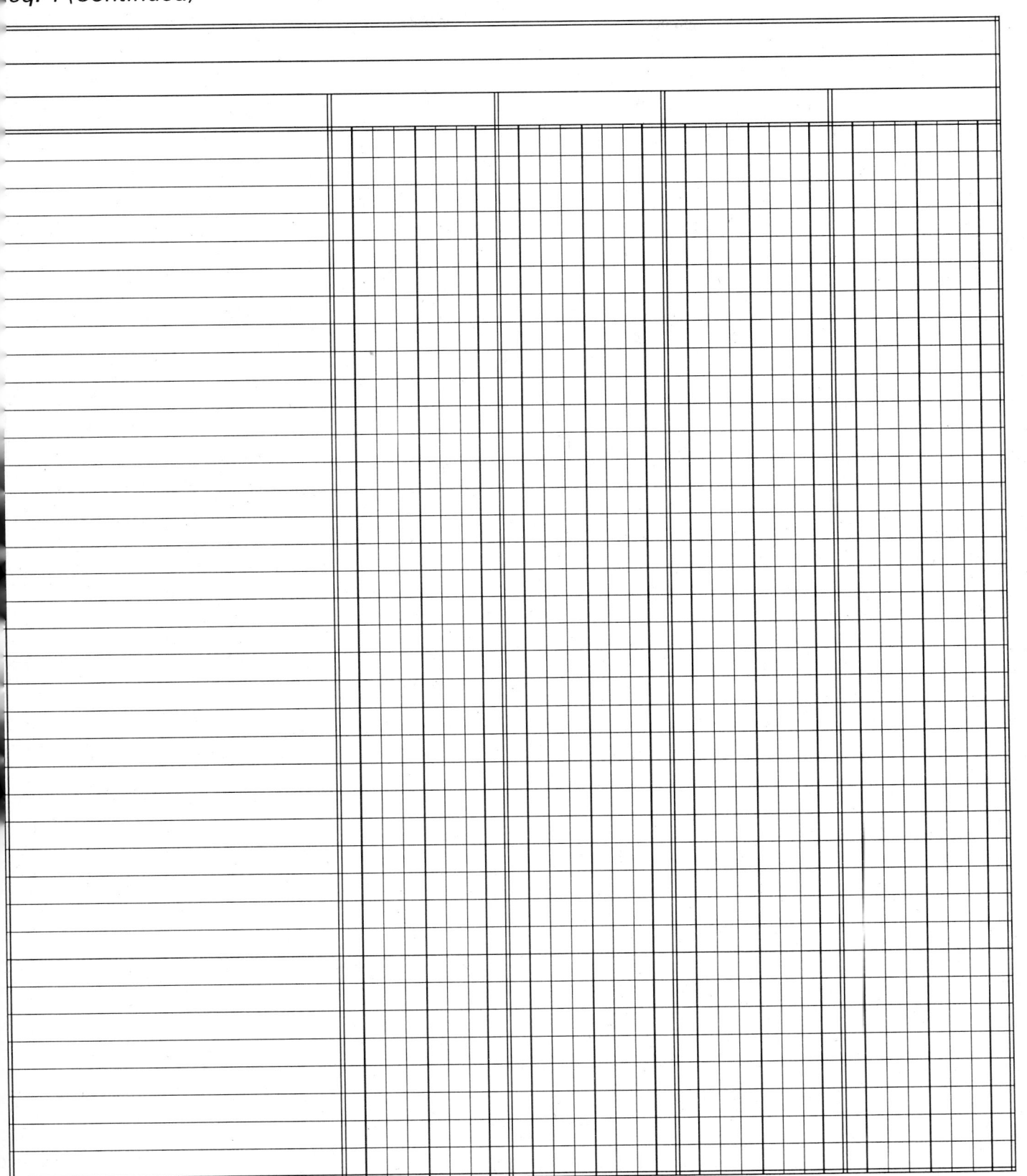

*Req. 1 (Continued)*

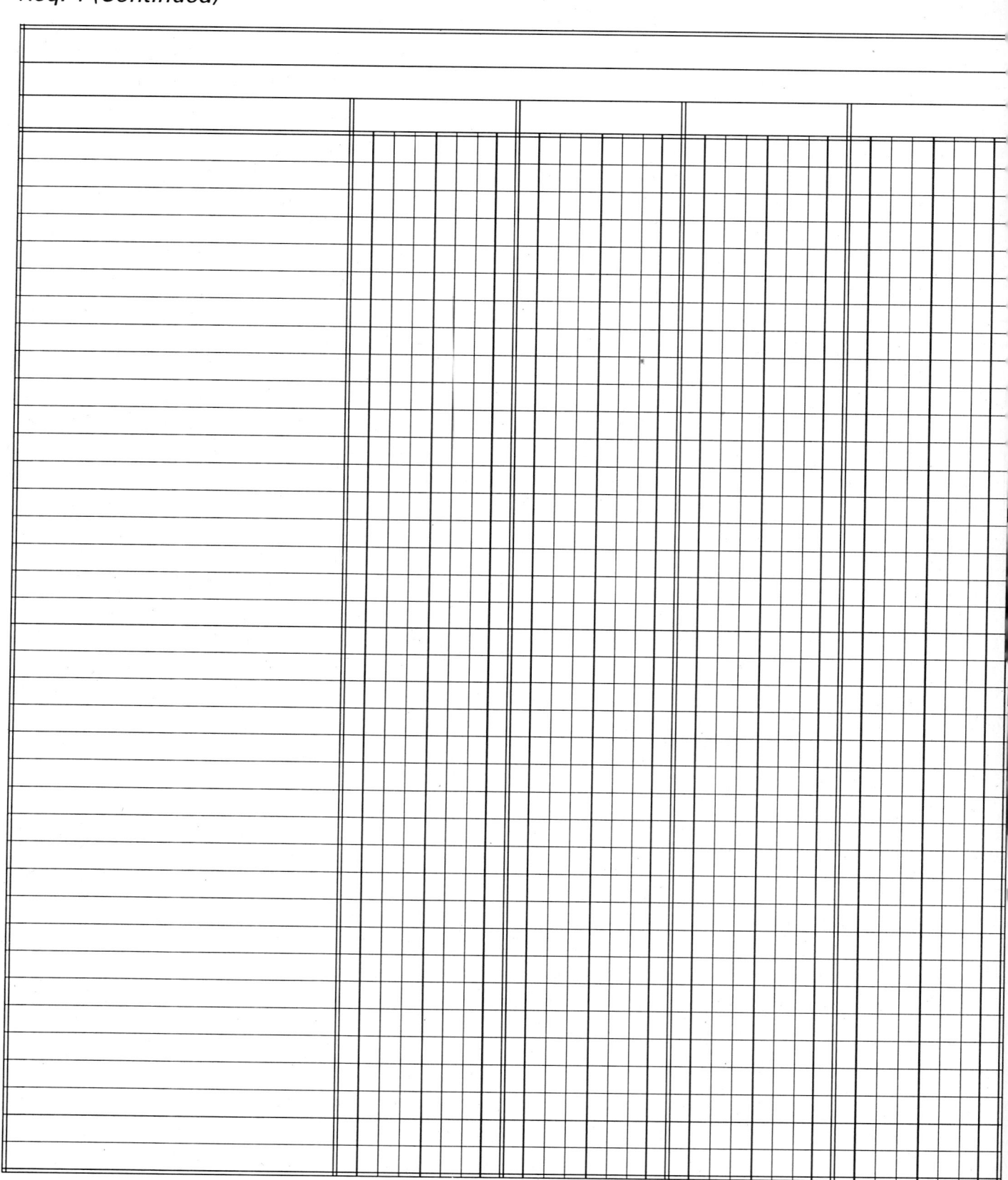

*Req. 2*

Reqs. 1–5

## Journal

| DATE | ACCOUNTS AND EXPLANATIONS | POST. REF. | DEBIT | CREDIT |
|------|---------------------------|------------|-------|--------|
|      |                           |            |       |        |
|      |                           |            |       |        |
|      |                           |            |       |        |
|      |                           |            |       |        |
|      |                           |            |       |        |
|      |                           |            |       |        |
|      |                           |            |       |        |
|      |                           |            |       |        |
|      |                           |            |       |        |
|      |                           |            |       |        |
|      |                           |            |       |        |
|      |                           |            |       |        |
|      |                           |            |       |        |
|      |                           |            |       |        |
|      |                           |            |       |        |
|      |                           |            |       |        |
|      |                           |            |       |        |
|      |                           |            |       |        |
|      |                           |            |       |        |
|      |                           |            |       |        |
|      |                           |            |       |        |
|      |                           |            |       |        |
|      |                           |            |       |        |
|      |                           |            |       |        |
|      |                           |            |       |        |
|      |                           |            |       |        |
|      |                           |            |       |        |
|      |                           |            |       |        |
|      |                           |            |       |        |
|      |                           |            |       |        |

NAME
SECTION
DATE

*Reqs. 1–5 (Continued)*

## Journal

| DATE | ACCOUNTS AND EXPLANATIONS | POST. REF. | DEBIT | CREDIT |
|------|---------------------------|-----------|-------|--------|
|      |                           |           |       |        |
|      |                           |           |       |        |
|      |                           |           |       |        |
|      |                           |           |       |        |
|      |                           |           |       |        |
|      |                           |           |       |        |
|      |                           |           |       |        |
|      |                           |           |       |        |
|      |                           |           |       |        |
|      |                           |           |       |        |
|      |                           |           |       |        |
|      |                           |           |       |        |
|      |                           |           |       |        |
|      |                           |           |       |        |
|      |                           |           |       |        |
|      |                           |           |       |        |
|      |                           |           |       |        |
|      |                           |           |       |        |
|      |                           |           |       |        |

Chapter 12

NAME
SECTION
DATE

Req. 1A

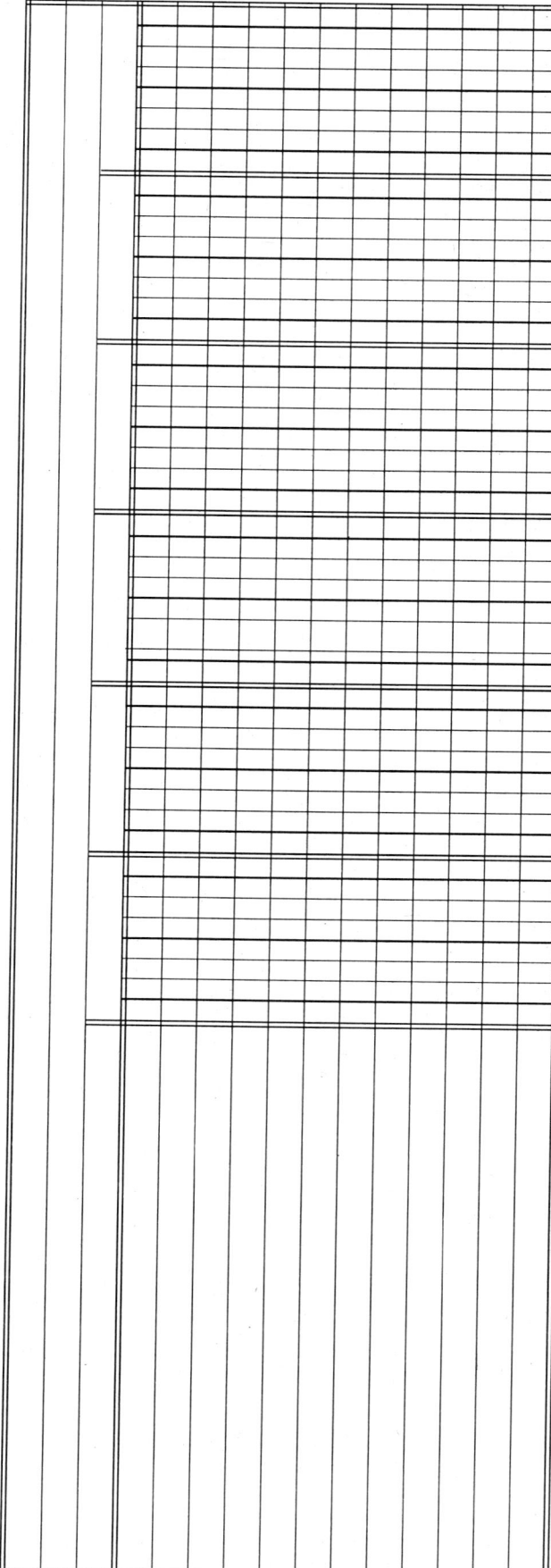

P12-6B *(Continued)*

NAME
SECTION
DATE

Req. 1b

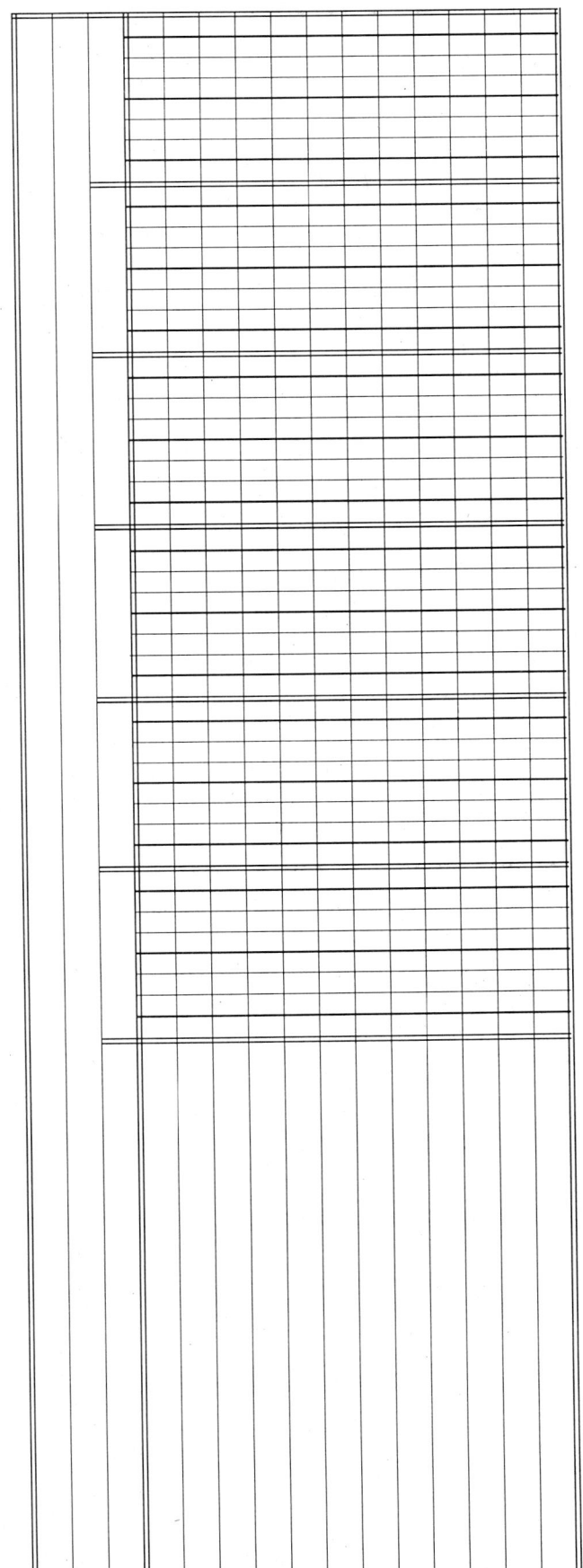

*Req. 2*

## Journal

| DATE | ACCOUNTS AND EXPLANATIONS | POST. REF. | DEBIT | CREDIT |
|------|---------------------------|-----------|-------|--------|
|      |                           |           |       |        |
|      |                           |           |       |        |
|      |                           |           |       |        |
|      |                           |           |       |        |
|      |                           |           |       |        |
|      |                           |           |       |        |
|      |                           |           |       |        |
|      |                           |           |       |        |
|      |                           |           |       |        |
|      |                           |           |       |        |
|      |                           |           |       |        |
|      |                           |           |       |        |
|      |                           |           |       |        |
|      |                           |           |       |        |
|      |                           |           |       |        |
|      |                           |           |       |        |
|      |                           |           |       |        |
|      |                           |           |       |        |
|      |                           |           |       |        |
|      |                           |           |       |        |
|      |                           |           |       |        |
|      |                           |           |       |        |
|      |                           |           |       |        |
|      |                           |           |       |        |
|      |                           |           |       |        |
|      |                           |           |       |        |
|      |                           |           |       |        |
|      |                           |           |       |        |
|      |                           |           |       |        |

*Reqs. 1 & 3*

## Journal

| DATE | | ACCOUNTS AND EXPLANATIONS | POST. REF. | DEBIT | CREDIT |
|---|---|---|---|---|---|
| | | | | | |
| | | | | | |
| | | | | | |
| | | | | | |
| | | | | | |
| | | | | | |
| | | | | | |
| | | | | | |
| | | | | | |
| | | | | | |
| | | | | | |
| | | | | | |
| | | | | | |
| | | | | | |
| | | | | | |
| | | | | | |
| | | | | | |
| | | | | | |
| | | | | | |
| | | | | | |
| | | | | | |
| | | | | | |
| | | | | | |
| | | | | | |
| | | | | | |
| | | | | | |
| | | | | | |
| | | | | | |
| | | | | | |
| | | | | | |
| | | | | | |
| | | | | | |
| | | | | | |
| | | | | | |
| | | | | | |
| | | | | | |

*Req. 2*

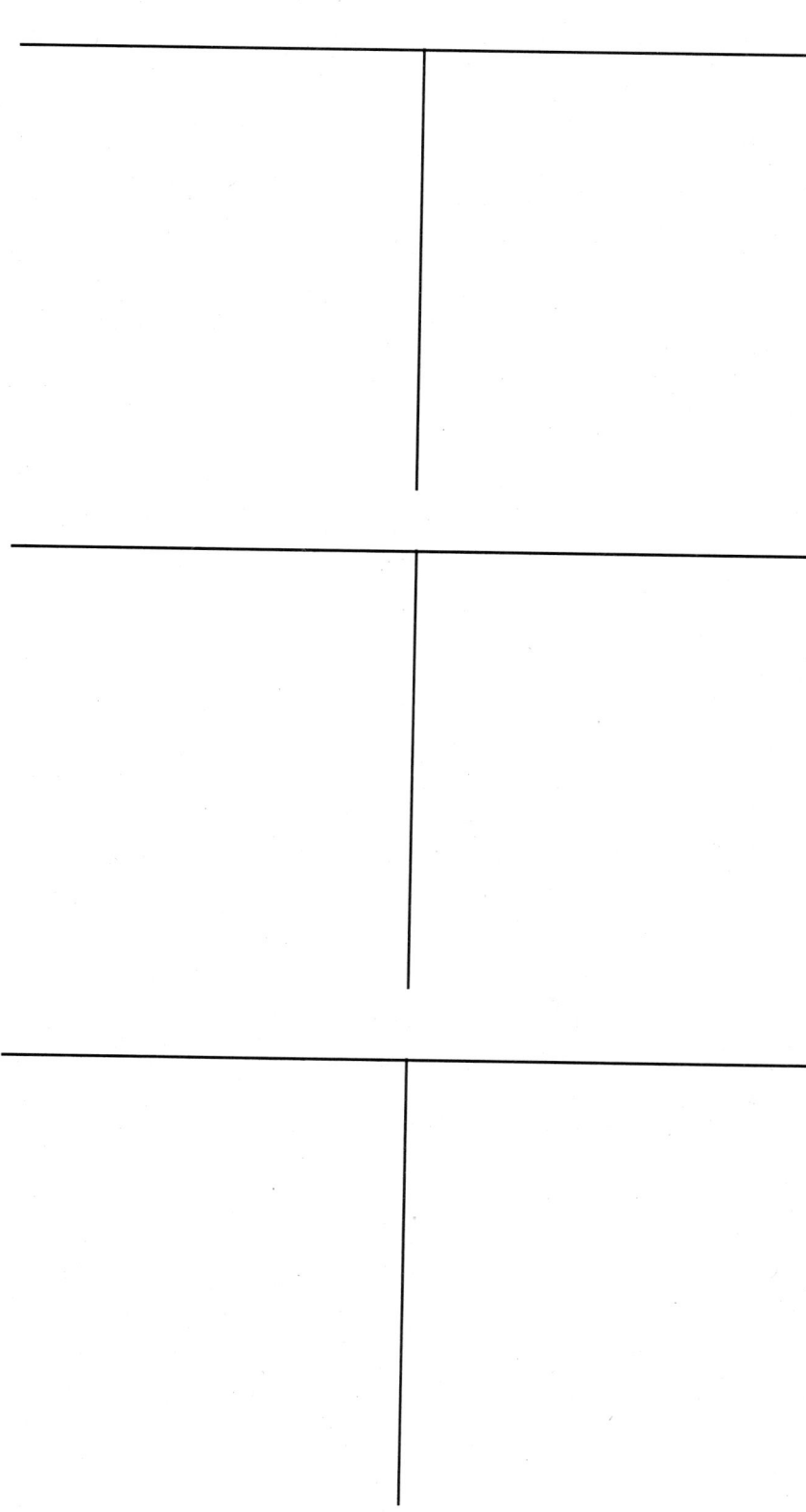

NAME
SECTION
DATE

**P12-7B** *(Continued)*

*Req. 3*

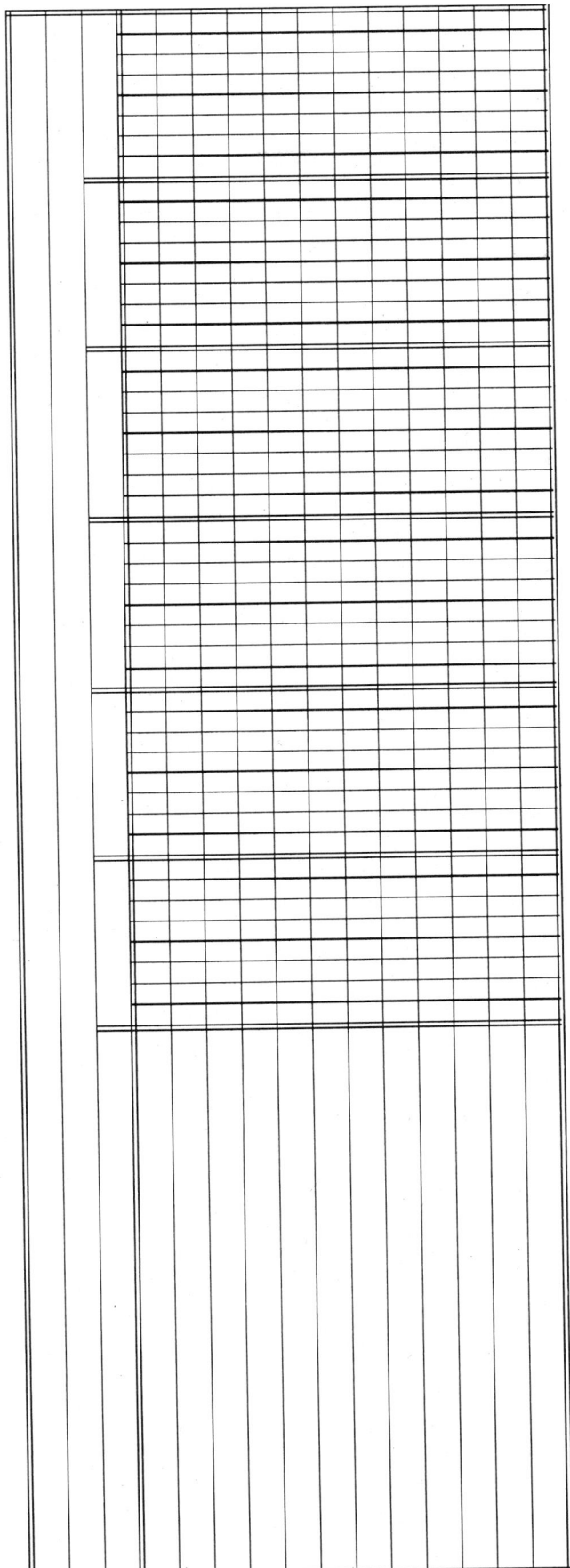

*Reqs. 1–4*

Reqs. 1–3

DE13-4

## Journal

| DATE | ACCOUNTS AND EXPLANATIONS | POST. REF. | DEBIT | CREDIT |
|------|---------------------------|-----------|-------|--------|
|  |  |  |  |  |
|  |  |  |  |  |
|  |  |  |  |  |
|  |  |  |  |  |
|  |  |  |  |  |
|  |  |  |  |  |
|  |  |  |  |  |
|  |  |  |  |  |
|  |  |  |  |  |
|  |  |  |  |  |
|  |  |  |  |  |
|  |  |  |  |  |
|  |  |  |  |  |
|  |  |  |  |  |
|  |  |  |  |  |
|  |  |  |  |  |
|  |  |  |  |  |

## Journal

| DATE | ACCOUNTS AND EXPLANATIONS | POST. REF. | DEBIT | CREDIT |
|------|---------------------------|------------|-------|--------|
|  |  |  |  |  |
|  |  |  |  |  |
|  |  |  |  |  |
|  |  |  |  |  |
|  |  |  |  |  |
|  |  |  |  |  |
|  |  |  |  |  |
|  |  |  |  |  |
|  |  |  |  |  |
|  |  |  |  |  |
|  |  |  |  |  |
|  |  |  |  |  |
|  |  |  |  |  |
|  |  |  |  |  |
|  |  |  |  |  |
|  |  |  |  |  |
|  |  |  |  |  |

1.

2.

| | | Journal | | | |
|---|---|---|---|---|---|
| DATE | | ACCOUNTS AND EXPLANATIONS | POST. REF. | DEBIT | CREDIT |
| | | | | | |
| | | | | | |
| | | | | | |
| | | | | | |
| | | | | | |
| | | | | | |
| | | | | | |
| | | | | | |

3.

## Journal

| DATE | ACCOUNTS AND EXPLANATIONS | POST. REF. | DEBIT | CREDIT |
|------|---------------------------|-----------|-------|--------|
|      |                           |           |       |        |
|      |                           |           |       |        |
|      |                           |           |       |        |
|      |                           |           |       |        |
|      |                           |           |       |        |
|      |                           |           |       |        |
|      |                           |           |       |        |
|      |                           |           |       |        |
|      |                           |           |       |        |
|      |                           |           |       |        |
|      |                           |           |       |        |
|      |                           |           |       |        |
|      |                           |           |       |        |
|      |                           |           |       |        |
|      |                           |           |       |        |
|      |                           |           |       |        |
|      |                           |           |       |        |
|      |                           |           |       |        |
|      |                           |           |       |        |
|      |                           |           |       |        |
|      |                           |           |       |        |
|      |                           |           |       |        |
|      |                           |           |       |        |
|      |                           |           |       |        |
|      |                           |           |       |        |
|      |                           |           |       |        |
|      |                           |           |       |        |
|      |                           |           |       |        |
|      |                           |           |       |        |

1.

| DATE | ACCOUNTS AND EXPLANATIONS | POST. REF. | DEBIT | CREDIT |
|------|---------------------------|------------|-------|--------|
| | **Journal** | | | |
| | | | | |
| | | | | |
| | | | | |
| | | | | |
| | | | | |
| | | | | |
| | | | | |
| | | | | |
| | | | | |

2.

*Req. 2*

## Journal

| DATE | ACCOUNTS AND EXPLANATIONS | POST. REF. | DEBIT | CREDIT |
|------|---------------------------|-----------|-------|--------|
|      |                           |           |       |        |
|      |                           |           |       |        |
|      |                           |           |       |        |
|      |                           |           |       |        |
|      |                           |           |       |        |
|      |                           |           |       |        |
|      |                           |           |       |        |
|      |                           |           |       |        |
|      |                           |           |       |        |
|      |                           |           |       |        |
|      |                           |           |       |        |
|      |                           |           |       |        |
|      |                           |           |       |        |
|      |                           |           |       |        |
|      |                           |           |       |        |
|      |                           |           |       |        |
|      |                           |           |       |        |
|      |                           |           |       |        |
|      |                           |           |       |        |
|      |                           |           |       |        |
|      |                           |           |       |        |
|      |                           |           |       |        |
|      |                           |           |       |        |
|      |                           |           |       |        |
|      |                           |           |       |        |
|      |                           |           |       |        |
|      |                           |           |       |        |
|      |                           |           |       |        |
|      |                           |           |       |        |

## Journal

| DATE | | ACCOUNTS AND EXPLANATIONS | POST. REF. | DEBIT | CREDIT |
|---|---|---|---|---|---|
| | | | | | |
| | | | | | |
| | | | | | |
| | | | | | |
| | | | | | |
| | | | | | |
| | | | | | |

Req. 1

| | | Journal | | | |
|---|---|---|---|---|---|
| DATE | | ACCOUNTS AND EXPLANATIONS | POST. REF. | DEBIT | CREDIT |
| | | | | | |
| | | | | | |
| | | | | | |
| | | | | | |
| | | | | | |
| | | | | | |
| | | | | | |
| | | | | | |
| | | | | | |
| | | | | | |
| | | | | | |
| | | | | | |
| | | | | | |
| | | | | | |
| | | | | | |
| | | | | | |
| | | | | | |
| | | | | | |
| | | | | | |
| | | | | | |
| | | | | | |
| | | | | | |
| | | | | | |
| | | | | | |
| | | | | | |
| | | | | | |
| | | | | | |
| | | | | | |
| | | | | | |
| | | | | | |
| | | | | | |
| | | | | | |
| | | | | | |
| | | | | | |
| | | | | | |

Req. 2

NAME
SECTION
DATE

*Req. 1*

## Journal

| DATE | ACCOUNTS AND EXPLANATIONS | POST. REF. | DEBIT | CREDIT |
|---|---|---|---|---|
| | | | | |
| | | | | |
| | | | | |
| | | | | |
| | | | | |
| | | | | |
| | | | | |
| | | | | |
| | | | | |
| | | | | |
| | | | | |
| | | | | |
| | | | | |
| | | | | |
| | | | | |
| | | | | |
| | | | | |
| | | | | |
| | | | | |
| | | | | |
| | | | | |
| | | | | |
| | | | | |
| | | | | |
| | | | | |
| | | | | |
| | | | | |
| | | | | |
| | | | | |
| | | | | |
| | | | | |

## Journal

| DATE | ACCOUNTS AND EXPLANATIONS | POST. REF. | DEBIT | CREDIT |
|------|---------------------------|------------|-------|--------|
|      |                           |            |       |        |
|      |                           |            |       |        |
|      |                           |            |       |        |
|      |                           |            |       |        |
|      |                           |            |       |        |
|      |                           |            |       |        |
|      |                           |            |       |        |
|      |                           |            |       |        |
|      |                           |            |       |        |
|      |                           |            |       |        |
|      |                           |            |       |        |
|      |                           |            |       |        |
|      |                           |            |       |        |
|      |                           |            |       |        |
|      |                           |            |       |        |
|      |                           |            |       |        |
|      |                           |            |       |        |
|      |                           |            |       |        |
|      |                           |            |       |        |
|      |                           |            |       |        |
|      |                           |            |       |        |
|      |                           |            |       |        |
|      |                           |            |       |        |
|      |                           |            |       |        |
|      |                           |            |       |        |

| | | Journal | | | |
|---|---|---|---|---|---|
| DATE | | ACCOUNTS AND EXPLANATIONS | POST. REF. | DEBIT | CREDIT |
| | | | | | |
| | | | | | |
| | | | | | |
| | | | | | |
| | | | | | |
| | | | | | |
| | | | | | |
| | | | | | |
| | | | | | |
| | | | | | |
| | | | | | |
| | | | | | |
| | | | | | |
| | | | | | |
| | | | | | |
| | | | | | |
| | | | | | |
| | | | | | |
| | | | | | |
| | | | | | |
| | | | | | |
| | | | | | |

|  |  |  |  |  |  |  |  |
|---|---|---|---|---|---|---|---|
| Stock Holders' Equity |  |  |  |  |  |  |  |
| Paid in Capital: |  |  |  |  |  |  |  |
| Preferred Stock | # |  | 1 | 0 | 0 | 0 | 0 | 0 |
| Paid in excess of par |  |  |  | 6 | 0 | 0 | 0 | 0 |
|  |  |  |  |  |  |  |  |
|  |  |  |  |  |  |  |  |
| Commonon Stock, No par |  |  | 4 | 3 | 0 | 0 | 0 | 0 |
| Donated Cap. |  |  | 4 | 4 | 0 | 0 | 0 | 0 |
| Total Paid in Cap. |  |  | 9 | 9 | 0 | 0 | 0 | 0 |
|  |  |  |  |  |  |  |  |
| Retained Earnings |  |  |  | 0 | 0 | 0 | 0 | 0 |
| Total Stock Equity : | # |  | 1 | 0 | 6 | 0 | 0 | 0 | 0 |

|  | 19 X 5 | | 19 X 6 | |
|---|---|---|---|---|
| Pref. stock | 10,000 | 48,000 | | |

| | | Journal | | | |
|---|---|---|---|---|---|
| DATE | | ACCOUNTS AND EXPLANATIONS | POST. REF. | DEBIT | CREDIT |
| | | | | | |
| | | | | | |
| | | | | | |
| | | | | | |
| | | | | | |

*Req. 1*

| | | Journal | | | |
|---|---|---|---|---|---|
| DATE | | ACCOUNTS AND EXPLANATIONS | POST. REF. | DEBIT | CREDIT |
| | | | | | |
| | | | | | |
| | | | | | |
| | | | | | |
| | | | | | |
| | | | | | |
| | | | | | |
| | | | | | |
| | | | | | |
| | | | | | |
| | | | | | |
| | | | | | |
| | | | | | |
| | | | | | |
| | | | | | |
| | | | | | |
| | | | | | |
| | | | | | |
| | | | | | |
| | | | | | |
| | | | | | |

*Req. 2*

| | | Journal | | | | |
|---|---|---|---|---|---|---|
| DATE | | ACCOUNTS AND EXPLANATIONS | POST. REF. | DEBIT | | CREDIT |
| | | | | | | |
| | | | | | | |
| | | | | | | |
| | | | | | | |
| | | | | | | |
| | | | | | | |
| | | | | | | |
| | | | | | | |
| | | | | | | |
| | | | | | | |
| | | | | | | |
| | | | | | | |
| | | | | | | |
| | | | | | | |
| | | | | | | |
| | | | | | | |
| | | | | | | |
| | | | | | | |
| | | | | | | |
| | | | | | | |

# Ethical Issue

**Computation:**

**Computation:**

Req. 1

_____

_____

_____

_____

Req. 2

| | | Journal | | | |
|---|---|---|---|---|---|
| DATE | | ACCOUNTS AND EXPLANATIONS | POST. REF. | DEBIT | CREDIT |
| | | | | | |
| | | | | | |
| | | | | | |
| | | | | | |
| | | | | | |
| | | | | | |
| | | | | | |
| | | | | | |
| | | | | | |
| | | | | | |
| | | | | | |
| | | | | | |
| | | | | | |
| | | | | | |
| | | | | | |
| | | | | | |
| | | | | | |
| | | | | | |
| | | | | | |
| | | | | | |
| | | | | | |

Req. 3a

*Req. 3b*

| | | Journal | | | | |
|---|---|---|---|---|---|---|
| DATE | | ACCOUNTS AND EXPLANATIONS | POST. REF. | DEBIT | CREDIT | |
| | | | | | | |
| | | | | | | |
| | | | | | | |
| | | | | | | |
| | | | | | | |
| | | | | | | |
| | | | | | | |
| | | | | | | |
| | | | | | | |
| | | | | | | |
| | | | | | | |
| | | | | | | |
| | | | | | | |
| | | | | | | |
| | | | | | | |
| | | | | | | |
| | | | | | | |
| | | | | | | |
| | | | | | | |
| | | | | | | |

Req. 1 & 2

Req. 3

*Req. 1a*

Req. 1b

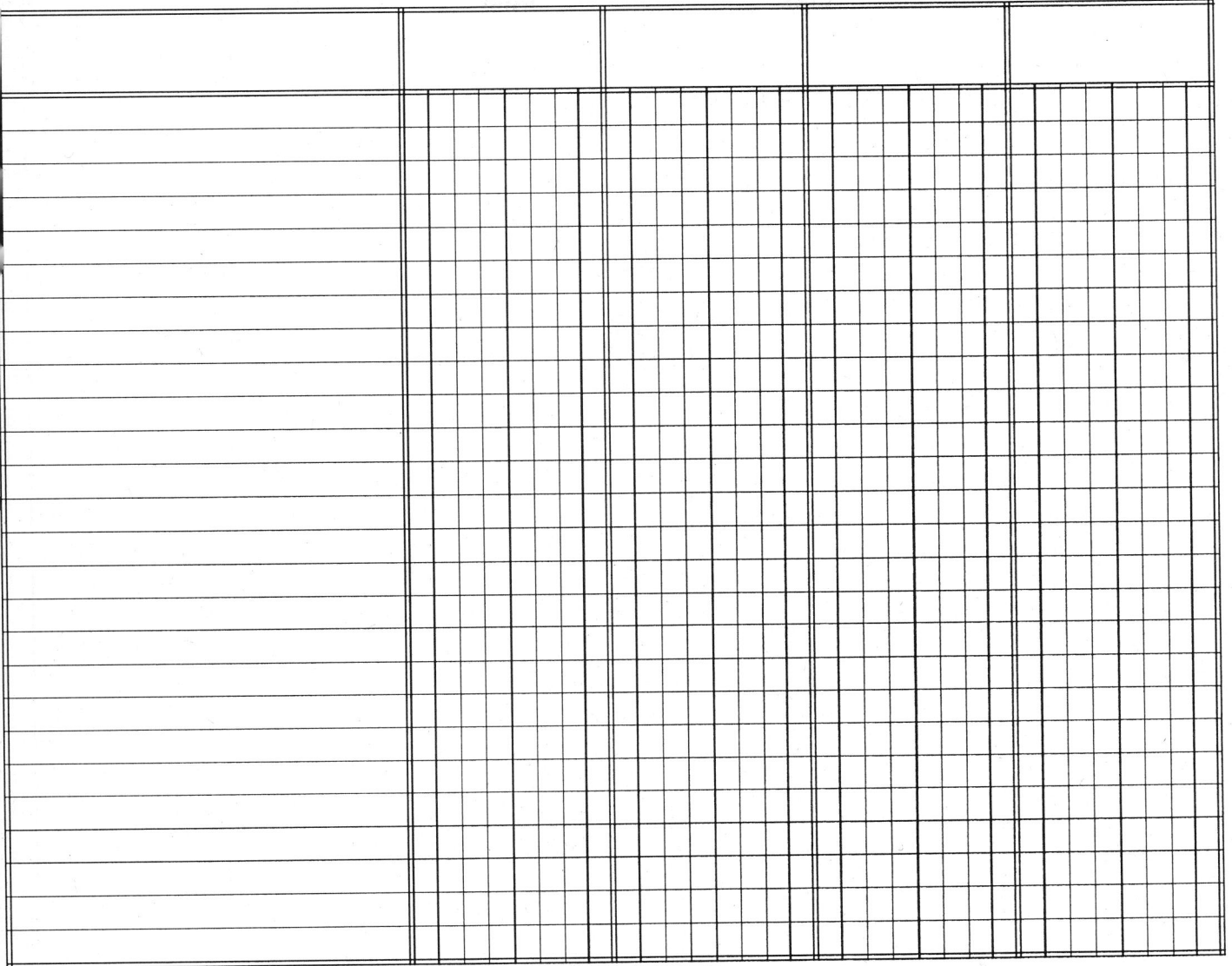

*Req. 2*

| | | Journal | | | |
|---|---|---|---|---|---|
| DATE | | ACCOUNTS AND EXPLANATIONS | POST. REF. | DEBIT | CREDIT |
| | | | | | |
| | | | | | |
| | | | | | |
| | | | | | |
| | | | | | |
| | | | | | |
| | | | | | |
| | | | | | |
| | | | | | |
| | | | | | |
| | | | | | |
| | | | | | |
| | | | | | |
| | | | | | |
| | | | | | |
| | | | | | |
| | | | | | |
| | | | | | |
| | | | | | |
| | | | | | |
| | | | | | |
| | | | | | |

Req. 1

| | | |
|---|---|---|
| | | |
| | | |
| | | |
| | | |
| | | |
| | | |
| | | |
| | | |
| | | |
| | | |

Req. 2

## Journal

| DATE | ACCOUNTS AND EXPLANATIONS | POST. REF. | DEBIT | CREDIT |
|---|---|---|---|---|
| | | | | |
| | | | | |
| | | | | |
| | | | | |
| | | | | |
| | | | | |
| | | | | |
| | | | | |
| | | | | |
| | | | | |
| | | | | |
| | | | | |
| | | | | |
| | | | | |
| | | | | |
| | | | | |
| | | | | |
| | | | | |
| | | | | |
| | | | | |
| | | | | |
| | | | | |

*Req. 3*

Req. 1

| | Journal | | | | | | | | | | | | | | | | | | | | | | | |
|---|---|---|---|---|---|---|---|---|---|---|---|---|---|---|---|---|---|---|---|---|---|---|---|---|
| DATE | | ACCOUNTS AND EXPLANATIONS | POST. REF. | | DEBIT | | | | | | | | CREDIT | | | | | | |
| | | | | | | | | | | | | | | | | | | | |
| | | | | | | | | | | | | | | | | | | | |
| | | | | | | | | | | | | | | | | | | | |
| | | | | | | | | | | | | | | | | | | | |
| | | | | | | | | | | | | | | | | | | | |
| | | | | | | | | | | | | | | | | | | | |
| | | | | | | | | | | | | | | | | | | | |
| | | | | | | | | | | | | | | | | | | | |
| | | | | | | | | | | | | | | | | | | | |
| | | | | | | | | | | | | | | | | | | | |
| | | | | | | | | | | | | | | | | | | | |
| | | | | | | | | | | | | | | | | | | | |
| | | | | | | | | | | | | | | | | | | | |
| | | | | | | | | | | | | | | | | | | | |
| | | | | | | | | | | | | | | | | | | | |
| | | | | | | | | | | | | | | | | | | | |
| | | | | | | | | | | | | | | | | | | | |
| | | | | | | | | | | | | | | | | | | | |
| | | | | | | | | | | | | | | | | | | | |
| | | | | | | | | | | | | | | | | | | | |

*Req. 2*

Req. 1-3

_____

_____

_____

_____

_____

_____

_____

_____

_____

_____

_____

_____

_____

_____

_____

_____

_____

_____

_____

_____

# Journal

| DATE | ACCOUNTS AND EXPLANATIONS | POST. REF. | DEBIT | CREDIT |
|------|---------------------------|------------|-------|--------|
|      |                           |            |       |        |
|      |                           |            |       |        |
|      |                           |            |       |        |
|      |                           |            |       |        |
|      |                           |            |       |        |
|      |                           |            |       |        |
|      |                           |            |       |        |
|      |                           |            |       |        |
|      |                           |            |       |        |
|      |                           |            |       |        |
|      |                           |            |       |        |
|      |                           |            |       |        |
|      |                           |            |       |        |
|      |                           |            |       |        |
|      |                           |            |       |        |
|      |                           |            |       |        |
|      |                           |            |       |        |
|      |                           |            |       |        |
|      |                           |            |       |        |
|      |                           |            |       |        |
|      |                           |            |       |        |

*Req. 5*

**Computation:**

**Computation:**

Req. 1

_____

_____

_____

_____

Req. 2

| DATE | ACCOUNTS AND EXPLANATIONS | POST. REF. | DEBIT | CREDIT |
|------|---------------------------|------------|-------|--------|
|      |                           |            |       |        |
|      |                           |            |       |        |
|      |                           |            |       |        |
|      |                           |            |       |        |
|      |                           |            |       |        |
|      |                           |            |       |        |
|      |                           |            |       |        |
|      |                           |            |       |        |
|      |                           |            |       |        |
|      |                           |            |       |        |
|      |                           |            |       |        |
|      |                           |            |       |        |
|      |                           |            |       |        |
|      |                           |            |       |        |
|      |                           |            |       |        |
|      |                           |            |       |        |
|      |                           |            |       |        |
|      |                           |            |       |        |
|      |                           |            |       |        |
|      |                           |            |       |        |
|      |                           |            |       |        |

**Journal**

*Req. 3a*

_____

_____

_____

_____

_____

_____

_____

_____

_____

_____

_____

_____

*Req. 3b*

| | | Journal | | | |
|---|---|---|---|---|---|
| DATE | | ACCOUNTS AND EXPLANATIONS | POST. REF. | DEBIT | CREDIT |
| | | | | | |
| | | | | | |
| | | | | | |
| | | | | | |
| | | | | | |
| | | | | | |
| | | | | | |
| | | | | | |
| | | | | | |
| | | | | | |
| | | | | | |
| | | | | | |
| | | | | | |
| | | | | | |
| | | | | | |
| | | | | | |
| | | | | | |
| | | | | | |
| | | | | | |
| | | | | | |
| | | | | | |
| | | | | | |
| | | | | | |
| | | | | | |

Req. 1 & 2

*Req. 3*

Req. 1a

*Req. 1b*

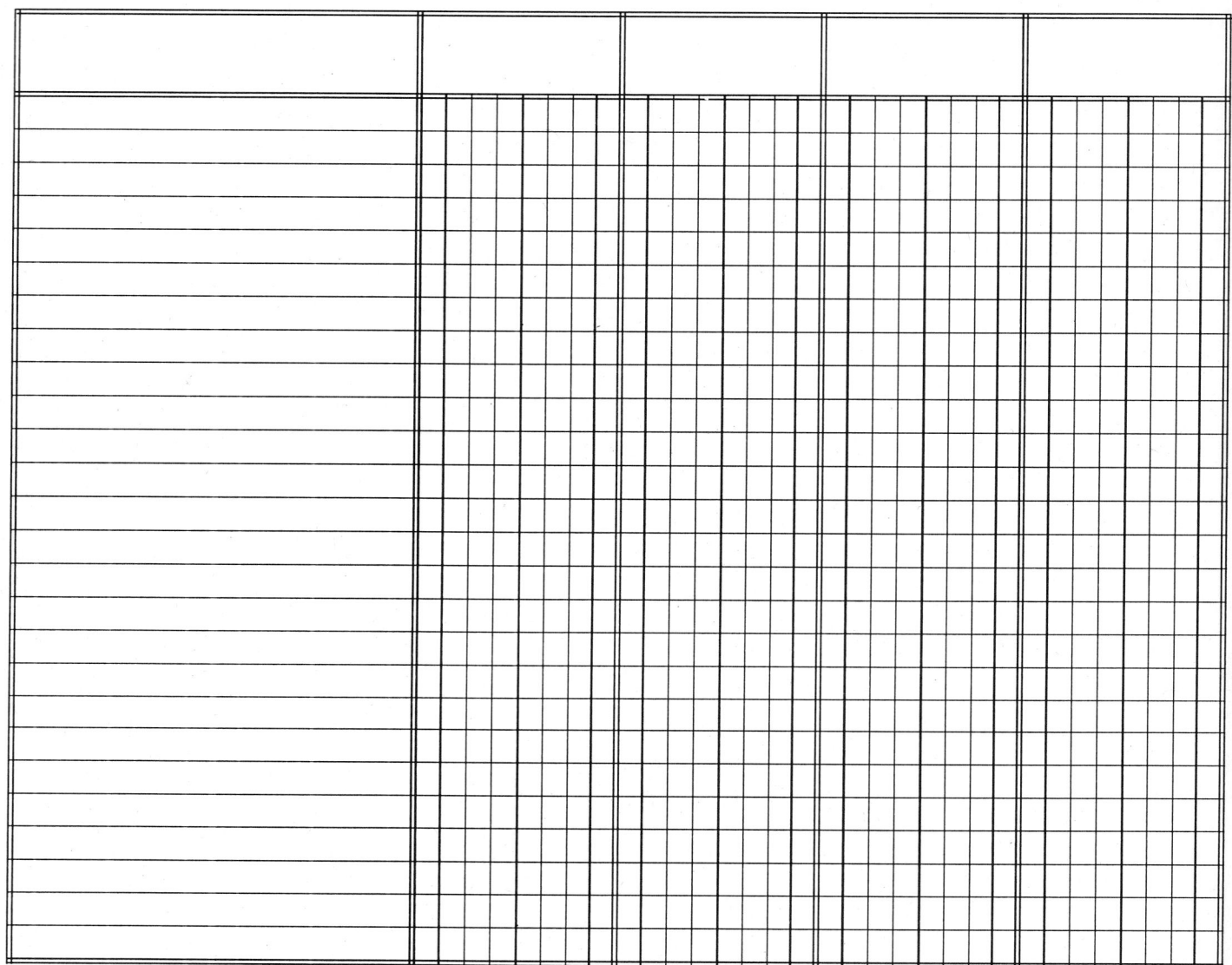

*Req. 2*

| | | Journal | | | |
|---|---|---|---|---|---|
| DATE | | ACCOUNTS AND EXPLANATIONS | POST. REF. | DEBIT | CREDIT |
| | | | | | |
| | | | | | |
| | | | | | |
| | | | | | |
| | | | | | |
| | | | | | |
| | | | | | |
| | | | | | |
| | | | | | |
| | | | | | |
| | | | | | |
| | | | | | |
| | | | | | |
| | | | | | |
| | | | | | |
| | | | | | |
| | | | | | |
| | | | | | |
| | | | | | |
| | | | | | |
| | | | | | |
| | | | | | |

Req. 1 - 5

Req. 6

*Req. 1*

| | |
|---|---|
| | |

*Req. 2*

| DATE | | ACCOUNTS AND EXPLANATIONS | POST. REF. | DEBIT | CREDIT |
|---|---|---|---|---|---|
| | | **Journal** | | | |
| | | | | | |
| | | | | | |
| | | | | | |
| | | | | | |
| | | | | | |
| | | | | | |
| | | | | | |
| | | | | | |
| | | | | | |
| | | | | | |
| | | | | | |
| | | | | | |
| | | | | | |
| | | | | | |
| | | | | | |
| | | | | | |
| | | | | | |
| | | | | | |
| | | | | | |
| | | | | | |

*Req. 3*

*Reqs. 1 & 2*

| | | Journal | | | | |
|---|---|---|---|---|---|---|
| DATE | | ACCOUNTS AND EXPLANATIONS | POST. REF. | DEBIT | CREDIT | |
| | | | | | | |
| | | | | | | |
| | | | | | | |
| | | | | | | |
| | | | | | | |
| | | | | | | |
| | | | | | | |
| | | | | | | |
| | | | | | | |
| | | | | | | |
| | | | | | | |
| | | | | | | |
| | | | | | | |
| | | | | | | |
| | | | | | | |
| | | | | | | |
| | | | | | | |
| | | | | | | |
| | | | | | | |
| | | | | | | |
| | | | | | | |
| | | | | | | |
| | | | | | | |
| | | | | | | |
| | | | | | | |
| | | | | | | |
| | | | | | | |
| | | | | | | |
| | | | | | | |
| | | | | | | |
| | | | | | | |

NAME
SECTION
DATE
*Req. 3*

Chapter 13

**Decision Case 1**
*(Continued)*

**Plan 1:**

**Plan 2:**

NAME
SECTION
DATE

Chapter 13

**Decision Case 1**
*(Continued)*

*Req. 4*

NAME

SECTION

DATE

Reqs. 1-4

Chapter 13

# Financial Statement
# Case 1

# Financial Statement
# Case 1

NAME
SECTION
DATE
Reqs. 1-4

Chapter 13

# Financial Statement
# Case 2

# Financial Statement Case 2